Introduction to

SEMICONDUCTOR
PHENOMENA AND DEVICES

LLOYD P. HUNTER
Professor of Electrical Engineering
University of Rochester

 ADDISON - WESLEY · READING, MASSACHUSETTS

ADDISON-WESLEY PUBLISHING COMPANY, INC.

READING, MASSACHUSETTS · Palo Alto · London

NEW YORK · DALLAS · ATLANTA · BARRINGTON, ILLINOIS

PREFACE

In approaching this subject it has become customary to introduce the main consideration of semiconductor devices with a relatively lengthy presentation of background material which often amounts to a short course in solid-state physics, complete with an introduction to modern physics. This book is in some ways an experiment in that an effort has been made to approach the main subject material by the shortest possible path which will allow an understanding of semiconductor phenomena and devices. The experimental approach consists in the fact that the necessary concepts of modern solid-state physics are presented in a very concise heuristic manner with almost no repetition or reinforcement. It is the experience of the author that such an approach does work well enough to allow considerably more time to be spent on the discussion and analysis of semiconductor devices.

In the main text, comprising Chapters 5 through 8, the point of view is still primarily heuristic, although there is more emphasis on quantitative results. An effort is made to approach problems by successive approximation in order to give the reader an appreciation of how to go about estimating the magnitude of an expected result and then how to refine this estimate to the desired degree of accuracy. Such a method often shows surprising accuracy with very short calculations. Several numerical examples are worked out in detail in the text to illustrate the method of attack on a variety of problems.

In the last two chapters a wide variety of device structures are discussed. Some of them, such as the "hook-collector" transistor are not widely used or known. The reason for including them in the discussion is because of their pedagogical value in illustrating and combining many of the phenomena involved in semiconductor device action.

There is no discussion of circuits or even of device-equivalent circuits, since it is felt that circuit applications are a separate subject and the admittance parameters, which are derived, allow the construction of whatever equivalent circuits the applications engineer desires. The emphasis is entirely on the physical understanding of the mechanisms of operation of the various devices developed in a reasonably short discussion of only the essentials.

Rochester, New York   L. P. H.
August 1965

CONTENTS

CHAPTER 1

THE ELECTRONIC STRUCTURE OF SOLIDS

In this chapter we will show the relation between the familiar electronic structure of atoms and the electronic structure of solids. We will first discuss briefly the electronic structure of the atom and review the concept of an energy level. The electronic structure of molecules and solids will then be shown to be a natural extension of the simpler atomic structure.

The treatment will be physical, with only as much mathematical development as is necessary to give an understanding. The approach will involve only the pseudoclassical application of some of the results of quantum mechanics. This approach is adequate for the understanding of the phenomena and devices involved.

1.1 The Energy-Level Concept

We will begin with the idea of a planetary electron in a circular orbit around a proton as shown in Fig. 1.1(a). Historically this is known as the *Bohr model* of the hydrogen atom. In such a structure the centripetal force of electrostatic attraction of the proton for the electron, q^2/r^2, is proportional (by Newton's second law) to the central acceleration of the electron traveling in the circular orbit, mv^2/r,

$$q^2/r^2 = mv^2/r = m\omega^2 r, \qquad (1.1)$$

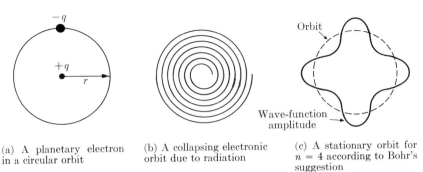

(a) A planetary electron in a circular orbit

(b) A collapsing electronic orbit due to radiation

(c) A stationary orbit for $n = 4$ according to Bohr's suggestion

FIG. 1.1. Electronic orbits.

where $\omega = 2\pi f$ and f is the frequency of revolution of the electron. (We are using the cgs-system of units.)

We will now calculate the total energy of this system under the convention that zero energy of the system is realized when the electron and proton are separated by an indefinitely large distance and both are at rest. If this condition is to represent zero total energy, it must also represent zero potential energy since there is no kinetic energy by definition of this state (both particles at rest). At a finite separation r we may calculate the potential energy from the familiar integral of force $\times$ distance, giving

$$\text{PE} = \int_{\infty}^{r} (q^2/r^2)\,dr = -q^2/r. \tag{1.2}$$

Here the negative sign represents the fact that as the electron moves toward the proton, radiant energy is lost so that the total energy of the system must now be negative.

From Eq. (1.1) and the definition of kinetic energy we find that at the distance r,

$$\text{KE} = \tfrac{1}{2}mv^2 = \tfrac{1}{2}q^2/r, \tag{1.3}$$

giving the total energy of the system as the sum of the kinetic and potential-energy terms:

$$E = \text{KE} + \text{PE} = \tfrac{1}{2}q^2/r - q^2/r = -\tfrac{1}{2}q^2/r. \tag{1.4}$$

In this discussion we have assumed that a planetary-electron configuration is stable. If we consider the implications of electromagnetic theory, we remember that an accelerated electric charge radiates. Since the electron is under centripetal acceleration at all times, it should radiate. It can be shown that this radiation has the same frequency as the revolution of the electron if the energy loss per revolution is small. This is not unreasonable since, edge on, a circulating charge looks like an oscillating charge. This frequency is

$$f = \frac{\omega}{2\pi} = \frac{(q^2/mr^3)^{1/2}}{2\pi}. \tag{1.5}$$

Since by radiating the system loses energy, the electron should slowly spiral into the center, radiating at an ever-increasing frequency as the atom collapses (see Fig. 1.1b).

Bohr's stationary orbit. The fact that atoms do not collapse and indeed exhibit a structure which may be thought of as consisting of "stationary" nonradiating electronic orbits led Bohr to make an ingenious suggestion which marks one of the early steps in the development of quantum theory. Bohr suggested that the orbital angular momentum of the electron was quantized so that any orbit which had an angular momentum equal to an integral number of units of Plank's constant $h/2\pi$ would be a "stationary" nonradiative orbit. This suggestion came more than ten years before the wave nature of the electron was postulated by DeBroglie and later observed by Davisson and Germer in a diffraction experiment using a beam of monoenergetic electrons.

It is easy to show that for a circular orbit quantization of angular momentum is equivalent to setting an integral number of electron wavelengths around the orbit as shown in Fig. 1.1(c). The angular momentum of the electron is given by $I\omega = mr^2\omega$, where $\omega = 2\pi f = v/r$. The quantization gives $n(h/2\pi) = m\omega r^2 = mvr$. Cross multiplying we find that

$$n(h/mv) = 2\pi r. \tag{1.6}$$

From Eq. (1.6) it is clear that if we define a wavelength

$$\lambda = h/mv \tag{1.7}$$

for the electron, we have set the condition that there be an integral number of such wavelengths around the orbit. The wavelength given by Eq. (1.7) is simply the wavelength that DeBroglie postulated would be exhibited by a particle of linear momentum mv. Modern electron and atomic beam diffraction establish this wavelength on a solid experimental basis so that indirectly it is verified that angular momentum must indeed be quantized in units of $h/2\pi$, usually designated $\hbar$.

We may calculate the radius of a stationary orbit by eliminating v between Eqs. (1.1) and (1.6) and solving for r:

$$r_n = \frac{n^2 h^2}{4\pi^2 m q^2}. \tag{1.8}$$

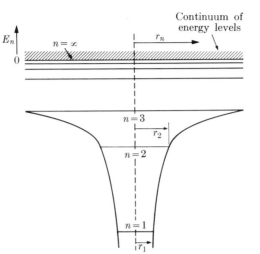

FIG. 1.2. Energy levels of a hydrogen atom.

By substituting $n = 1$ we may evaluate Eq. (1.8) for the radius of the first, or lowest, energy orbit of the hydrogen atom. Substituting the appropriate numerical values in Eq. (1.8), we find that $r_1 = 0.53$ angstrom units. This value is in good agreement with the size of the hydrogen atom deduced from experimental measurements of the moments of inertia of the hydrogen molecule. Another good experimental check is provided by the measured ionization energy of hydrogen. If the electron is completely removed from the nucleus, it must require at least the energy of this lowest state to accomplish the removal, since we have defined our zero of energy as the ionized state. The energy of the lowest state is given in Eq. (1.4) as

$$E_1 = -\tfrac{1}{2}q^2/r_1 = -13.6 \text{ ev.} \tag{1.9}$$

This agrees to three significant figures with the measured value of the threshold ionization voltage for hydrogen.

The general expression for the energy is

$$E_n = -\frac{q^2}{2r_n} = -\frac{2\pi^2 m q^4}{n^2 h^2}. \tag{1.10}$$

From Eq. (1.10) it is clear that the system can exist only in discrete energy levels determined by the stationary orbits of the electron. This is a direct result of applying the boundary condition that there be an integral number of electron wavelengths in each allowable orbit.

Figure 1.2 shows a plot of E_n vs. r_n as given in Eqs. (1.10) and (1.8). Here it is seen that as n increases, the energy interval between energy levels decreases until at the ionization level a continuous energy distribution is available to the system. This corresponds to the electron being infinitely removed from the proton and capable of existing at any value of kinetic energy. If the electron is infinitely removed, the boundary condition concerning an integral number of wavelengths in an orbit is also removed, with the direct result that any energy is available to the system.

The stationary states do not radiate. Radiation is given off only when an electron drops from a higher to a lower stationary state. When such an event occurs a single quantum of light (a photon) is emitted whose frequency ν is given by the expression

$$h\nu = E_n - E_{n-1}. \qquad (1.11)$$

Conversely the absorption of a light quantum of just the right energy (frequency) can boost an electron up in the energy scale. If the energy of the radiation is greater than the ionization energy of 13.6 ev, it can have any value, and will result in removing the electron completely (ionization) from the proton, and will give it a kinetic energy equal to the excess of the photon energy over the ionization energy.

We now see that for every allowed orbit there is an allowed energy. In more complicated systems, orbits are very hard to visualize; hence in most cases we will be primarily concerned with allowed energy levels.

Quantum-mechanical example. The treatment given so far makes plausible the existence of discrete energy levels by an argument which is a hybrid between classical physics and quantum physics. This is not too satisfactory, and at this point we will digress long enough to show how quantum physics arrives at the same result.

Since particles such as electrons and protons can be diffracted by crystal lattices, or even by ruled gratings, just as though they were waves, we must treat them as such, using the wave equation.

The classical differential equation having wave motion as a solution is

$$\nabla^2 \psi + \left(\frac{\omega}{c}\right)^2 \psi = 0, \qquad (1.12)$$

where c is the velocity of propagation, ψ is the wave amplitude, and $\omega = 2\pi f$. Using Eq. (1.7) for the wavelength and the relation $c = f\lambda$, we may transform Eq. (1.12) into

$$\nabla^2 \psi + \frac{4\pi^2 m^2 v^2}{h^2} \psi = 0. \qquad (1.13)$$

From the equations KE $= \frac{1}{2}mv^2$ and $P = mv$, we further modify (1.13) into

$$\nabla^2 \psi + \frac{4\pi^2}{h^2} 2m(E - \text{PE})\psi = 0,$$

or as it is usually written:

$$\nabla^2\psi + \frac{2m}{\hbar^2}(E - V)\psi = 0, \tag{1.14}$$

where total energy $= E$, PE $= V$, and $\hbar = h/2\pi$.

This is called the *Schrödinger form* of the classical wave equation or simply the *Schrödinger equation*. The wave amplitude ψ has no direct particle analog but the quantity $\bar{\psi}\psi(x, y, z)\, dv$ is proportional to the probability of finding the electron in the volume element dv at any given time. Since at any time the electron must be somewhere, the integral of $\bar{\psi}\psi$ over all space must be unity. If we were to take many instantaneous measurements of the positions of the electron in a given stationary state and if we recorded the number of times it was found in each volume element of space, we could make a plot of the $\bar{\psi}\psi$-function. The interpretation of the $\bar{\psi}\psi$-function as the probability of the presence of the particle is not unreasonable if we consider the analogy with light. We are quite used to the idea that the intensity of light is proportional to the square of the amplitude of its electromagnetic wave. Surely the square of a particle's wave function should be proportional to its "intensity" or presence.

The classical physical parameters of the state of a system can be found from the known wave function as mean expectation values. For example, the mean expectation value of the x-coordinate of the electron's position is the integral over all space of the function $(\bar{\psi}x\psi)$.

As a simple example we will solve the Schrödinger equation for the case of an electron in a potential-energy well of width w and infinite depth. Figure 1.3(a) shows the well under consideration. Here we have let $V = 0$ inside the well and $V = \infty$ outside the well. This means that the electron cannot escape from the well since an infinite amount of energy would be required to boost it out. Writing Eq. (1.14) in one dimension for the space inside the well gives

$$-\frac{d^2\psi}{dx^2} = \frac{2mE}{\hbar^2}\psi, \tag{1.15}$$

since $V = 0$. Assuming the solution

$$\psi(x) = \psi_0 \sin Bx, \tag{1.16a}$$

we find that

$$\psi''(x) = -B^2\psi_0 \sin Bx. \tag{1.16b}$$

Substituting (1.16) into Eq. (1.15) gives

$$B^2\psi_0 \sin Bx = \frac{2mE}{\hbar^2}\psi_0 \sin Bx \quad\text{or}\quad B^2 = \frac{2mE}{\hbar^2}. \tag{1.17}$$

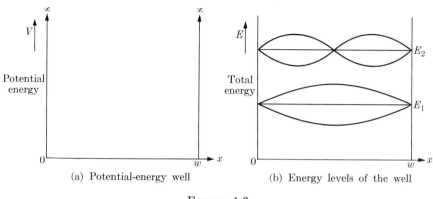

(a) Potential-energy well   (b) Energy levels of the well

FIGURE 1.3

To determine B we must apply the boundary conditions. Here we have confined the electron exclusively to the inside of the well by making it infinitely deep. This means that $\psi\bar{\psi}$ outside the well is zero. Therefore ψ must go to zero at the walls of the well.

The condition $\psi(x) = 0$ is automatically satisfied by the sine function. The condition $\psi(w) = 0$ can be met if

$$Bw = n\pi = w\left(\frac{2mE}{\hbar^2}\right)^{1/2}, \tag{1.18}$$

where n is an integer. This is analogous to the condition of the Bohr model that an orbit must have an integral number of wavelengths to be stable. Here the condition requires that we have standing waves between the walls of the well for all modes starting with a single half-wave for $n = 1$. The energy levels allowed by this condition are given by Eq. (1.18) solved for E:

$$E_n = \frac{\hbar^2\pi^2n^2}{2mw^2} = \frac{h^2}{8m}\left(\frac{n}{w}\right)^2. \tag{1.19}$$

It should be pointed out that it is the imposition of the boundary condition on the ψ-function that gives rise to the quantization of momentum and hence of the energy. This is generally true in quantum mechanics. The actual form of the potential-energy function is also of critical importance since it will determine the energy values of the stationary states.

Exactly the same procedure starting with the Schrödinger equation in polar coordinates and $V = -q^2/r$ will give the energy levels of the hydrogen atom. The only difference is that since the potential-energy function is finite and single-valued over all space outside the origin, we must apply a boundary condition of the ψ-function such that it must also be single-valued and finite over all space.

We now have a general procedure for all cases of arbitrary potential-energy variation, which will give allowed energy states of the system without arbitrary assumptions. Of course the mathematics usually requires some assumptions in order to render the equations soluble, but the assumptions are not of a fundamental physical nature.

1.2   The Multi-Electron Atom

The many-bodied problem as represented by the multi-electron atom has not been solved exactly in quantum mechanics any more than in classical mechanics. However, just as the astronomers have computed the motions of the members of the solar system to reasonable accuracy, so the energy levels of many multi-electron atoms have been computed to give a reasonable agreement with spectroscopic measurements.

The method used for this computation is called the *self-consistent field method*. In this method the electrons are added one at a time so that the contribution of each electron to the potential field of all the others can be computed and the ψ-functions adjusted accordingly. It is clear that whenever a ψ-function is modified, the overall potential function is changed. The problem then resolves into an iterative process in which the potential function is computed from an initial set of ψ-functions; this potential function is then used to solve for a new set of ψ-functions, which then determine a better potential function, etc. Finally the corrections to both the ψ-functions and the potential function become negligible, and the computation is said to have arrived at a self-consistent field of the potential function.

In any multi-electron atom each energy level can be occupied by only one electron at a time. This is a result of the application of the *Pauli exclusion principle*, which states that no two electrons of any system can have exactly the same set of quantum numbers. This means that the allowed energy levels of the system are filled from the lowest level up until the nuclear charge is balanced. If we consider an atom such as germanium, of atomic number 32, there will be 32 positive charges on the nucleus and 32 planetary electrons. In the absence of any excitation these electrons will occupy the 32 lowest energy levels of the system. The energy levels tend to be grouped and the group of levels which lie highest, but are still occupied by electrons, are called the *valence levels*. In the case of germanium there are four such levels, and their four electrons are called the *valence electrons*.

Allowed energy levels lying above the valence levels are called *excitation levels* and are used when the atom absorbs electronic energy (as opposed to translational energy). Transitions between these levels give rise to the emission and absorption spectra of the atom.

1.3   The Diatomic Molecule

When two like atoms are widely separated, they have identical systems of energy levels. When they are brought close together so that there is a coupling between them (chemical binding), each energy level of the separate systems is replaced by two closely spaced levels in the combined system. This is seen to be reasonable if it is remembered that the energy levels of the separate atoms were determined by fitting ψ-functions to the potential function, which is analogous to a resonance, and further that two resonant systems of the same frequency, when coupled, will show two new resonances at slightly different frequencies. In physical terms it is, of course, the application of the Pauli exclusion principle again. The

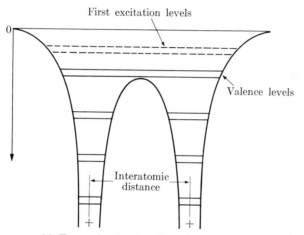

(a) Energy levels of a diatomic molecule

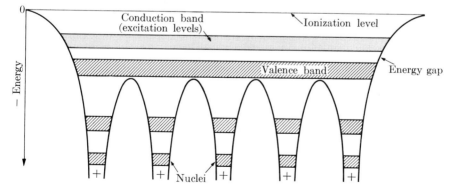

(b) Energy levels of a one-dimensional crystal

FIGURE 1.4

widely separated atoms are independent systems and two electrons, one in each atom, can have the same set of quantum numbers. However, once the atoms are brought together in a single system, no two electrons can have the same set of quantum numbers so that there must be a splitting of the energy levels.

Figure 1.4(a) shows a typical energy-level system for a diatomic molecule. Here it is seen that the valence-electron energy levels extend through both atoms and are terminated by the potential-energy well of the molecule as a whole. This means that the valence electrons are shared by the two atoms making up the molecule. It is this sharing of the valence electrons that serves to bind the atoms together chemically.

1.4   One-Dimensional Crystal

When many identical atoms are brought together to form a single system, the processes described above for the diatomic molecule are continued; around the energy values of the single energy levels of the atoms there are found a group of energy levels of the system equal in number to the total number of atoms in the system. The group of levels formed by the valence electrons of the atoms usually extends throughout the system and is called the *valence band*. Figure 1.4(b) illustrates such an assembly of atoms in a one-dimensional array. In this illustration the valence band of levels does not overlap the band of excitation levels, here called the *conduction band*. There exists an energy region between these two groups of levels which contains no allowed energy levels of the system. This region, when it exists free of allowed energy levels, is called the *energy gap*. Complex quantum-mechanical calculations have shown that real three-dimensional crystals have an electronic-band structure similar to that of the one-dimensional crystal shown in the figure. Such a structure will be the physical model used to explain many of the observations of the electrical properties of semiconductors.

1.5   Insulators, Conductors, and Semiconductors

In the preceding discussion of the one-dimensional crystal the various bands of energy levels were assumed not to overlap in energy. If this is the case in a real crystal and if the valence band of levels is completely filled with electrons so that no valence electron can change its energy when stimulated to do so by a moderate externally applied electric field, the crystal can carry no current and will be classed as an insulator. This is so because an electric current represents the motion of electrons in response to an applied field. Such responsive motion of electrons requires the changing of their previous state of random motion. Changing the state of motion of an electron requires that it be accelerated. The acceleration of an electron changes its kinetic energy and thus its total energy. In a crystal in which all neighboring allowed energy levels are already occupied, an electron cannot change its total energy without joining some other electron in its energy level. This is forbidden by the Pauli exclusion principle; therefore, a crystal with a filled valence band and a large energy gap cannot carry electronic current and is an insulator.

In a crystal in which the valence levels and the first excitation levels overlap in energy when enough atoms are brought together, there is a wide band of levels only some of which are occupied by the valence electrons. No energy gap exists in such a crystal. In this case the valence electrons can be accelerated into energy levels lying close by and therefore respond to an applied electric field. A conduction current can be carried by these electrons, and the crystal is an electrical conductor. Some crystals are so constituted that the valence band itself is only half-full of electrons so that the band overlap described above is not necessary for conduction. In either case, however, there is a high density of empty allowed energy levels immediately adjacent to those that are filled with electrons so that response to an accelerating field can take place.

In the case of a semiconductor there is an energy gap between a normally filled valence band and a conduction band of normally empty excitation levels. The difference between a semiconductor and an insulator is simply that the energy gap is smaller for a semiconductor so that at normal temperature, there will be a few electrons excited across the forbidden energy gap into levels in the conduction band by energy supplied by the thermal vibrations of the crystal lattice. These few electrons, finding themselves in a nearly empty conduction band, will be free to respond to a driving field and carry a small current.

In addition to the few electrons in the conduction band, there will be an equal number of electron vacancies in the energy-level system of the valence band (since the conduction electrons came from the valence band by thermal excitation). These vacant energy levels in the valence band will allow some shifting of energy among the valence electrons. Although it is not obvious, the net result of a vast number of valence electrons shifting energies with only a very small number of vacant energy levels available turns out to be equivalent to a situation where a small number of positive charges are moving freely in a nearly empty band of energy levels. Because of this equivalence, it is customary to think of valence-band conduction by positive charges rather than by electrons and the name assigned to such imaginary positive charges is "holes." This conduction is therefore usually referred to as *hole conduction*. The allusion of course is to the holes (vacancies) in the valence-band–energy-level system.

The conduction mechanism described above for a semiconductor obtains only for a pure semiconductor, and is called *intrinsic* conductivity.

Most real semiconductors are never pure enough to show intrinsic conductivity at room temperature, but rather exhibit a conductivity dependent on their impurity concentration, which is called *extrinsic* conductivity. Before considering the mechanism of extrinsic conductivity, we must consider in more detail the effect of electric fields on the energy-band scheme.

1.6   Fields and Energy Bands

We will employ a concept called the "free-electron model" for the present discussion. As we have seen above, it is relatively easy to calculate the energy levels in a rectangular potential well. Let us now imagine the entire crystal sample to constitute such a well with a uniform zero potential inside. In such a case it turns out that the kinetic energy will approach zero at the bottom of the well and will increase as one moves up in total energy. If we use this model for the distribution of energies in a single band with the bottom of the well representing the band edge, it is clear that the kinetic energy of an electron is zero at the band edge and increases as it ascends into the band.

Figure 1.5 shows three examples of the effect of an electric field on the boundaries of bands of energy levels. As their name implies, energy levels retain their discrete character in the presence of an electric field; however, the motion of an electron must certainly be affected in some way by the presence of the field. In Fig. 1.5(a) we illustrate the effect of a uniform electric field on a nearly empty conduction band. The boundaries of the conduction band are shown as tilted from left to right. Since the polarity of the field is indicated by the plus and minus signs at the ends of the figure, in this energy representation, we have adopted the convention that electrons tend to fall down. This means that an electron, when accelerated, must move up in the band. In the case of the tilted band an electron will tend, therefore, to remain at a given horizontal level as it is accelerated. In the conduction process an electron will not move very far under the influence of an electric field until it suffers a scattering collision with one of the atoms of the crystal. This collision will cause a reduction of the kinetic energy of the electron causing it to drop down toward the lower band edge in this diagram. A typical electron path is shown, where the small crosses represent scattering collisions.

With a constant accelerating field giving a constant tilt to the conduction band and with a given mean free time between scattering collisions, it should be clear that the electrons will tend to drift to the right at a constant average velocity. As the electric field is doubled, the acceleration between collisions will increase the average velocity so that it also will double. Such a situation means that the average velocity divided by the electric field will be constant. This constant is called the mobility of the

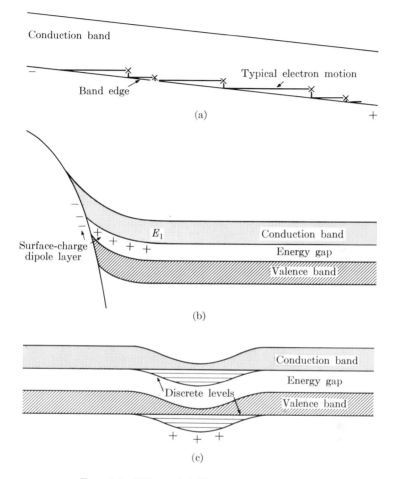

Fig. 1.5. Effect of fields on energy bands.

electrons in the semiconductor material, and is a temperature-sensitive material property.

Figure 1.5(b) shows the effect of a field due to a surface dipole layer of charges. If the polarity is as shown with the negative charges on the outer surface, the resulting field will bend the band edges up as they approach the surface of the crystal. Such a deflection of the band edges at the surface of the crystal results in the reflection of the electrons in the conduction band when they approach the crystal surface.

Figure 1.5(c) illustrates the effect of the field of a residual positive charge located in the interior of the crystal. The deflection of the bands in this case is of such a nature that it will tend to cause free moving electrons to collect in the neighborhood of the positive charge, as one would expect classically, and the potential well created by the positive charge will contain discrete energy levels of its own, which may be occupied by the electrons attracted to the charge. This effect is the essence of the effect of substitutional ionized chemical impurities in the semiconductor crystal lattice.

1.7   Numerical Example

In a multi-electron atom of atomic number 32 the innermost electron is removed by collision with an x-ray photon. Calculate the maximum wavelength the x-ray photon could have and still be capable of removing this electron. Also calculate the wavelength emitted when an electron from the second stationary orbit of the atom replaces the electron which has been removed.

In deriving Eq. (1.10) for the energy of the electron in a hydrogen atom we started with Eq. (1.1) for the force between an electron and a proton. Each of these particles has a single unit of charge. The atomic nucleus of this example has 32 units of positive charge so that the force becomes $32q^2/r^2$, and the energy equation analogous to Eq. (1.10) becomes

$$E_n = -Zq^2/2r_n, \tag{1.20}$$

where $r_n = n^2h^2/4\pi^2mZq^2$ and Z is the atomic number (32 in this example). The innermost level has the quantum number 1, and E_1 will be the energy required to remove this electron. Substituting r_n into E_n we get

$$E_n = -2\pi^2mZ^2q^4/n^2h^2. \tag{1.21}$$

Evaluating E_1 we use

$$m = 9 \times 10^{-28} \text{ gm}, \qquad h = 6.55 \times 10^{-27} \text{ erg/sec},$$
$$q = 4.77 \times 10^{-10} \text{ esu}, \qquad Z = 32.$$

Here we use q in electrostatic units because this unit is defined as the charge required to give a force of one dyne when two unit poles are separated by one centimeter, and force in dynes together with length in centimeters is consistent with mass in grams and h in ergs per second. With these substitutions, $E_1 = 21.9 \times 10^{-9}$ erg and $E_2 = 5.48 \times 10^{-9}$ erg.

In order to find the maximum wavelength of the x-ray photon capable of ejecting the innermost electron, we must convert E_1 to equivalent wavelength. From Eq. (1.11) we have $h\nu_1 = E_1$, and since $\lambda_1\nu_1 = c$, we find that

$$\nu_1 = 3.34 \times 10^{18} \text{ cps}$$

and

$$\lambda_1 = \frac{3 \times 10^{10}}{3.4 \times 10^{18}} = 0.90 \times 10^{-8} \text{ cm} \quad \text{or} \quad 0.9 \text{ A}.$$

This corresponds to the K x-ray absorption edge in germanium, which is atomic number 32. Actually this value is about 20% too short a wavelength, indicating that 20% too high a binding energy is given by this simple calculation.

The wavelength emitted when an electron in the E_2 level falls into the vacated E_1 level can be calculated from Eq. (1.11) also. Here $h\nu_{12} = E_1 - E_2$ giving $\nu_{12} = 2.50 \times 10^{18}$ cps and $\lambda_{12} = 1.20$ A. This agrees to within about 5% with the measured K_α x-ray emission of germanium.

Problems

1.1 If a potential well is 1 cm wide and is occupied by 10^{10} electrons, the lowest 10^{10} energy levels will be filled since there is a law that states that only one electron can occupy one energy level at one time (the Pauli exclusion principle). Calculate the wavelength of radiant energy absorbed if the uppermost electron is raised to the next higher energy level. (Formulas above use cgs units.)

1.2 Consider a square potential well of width w, with $V = 0$ inside the well and $V = A$ outside the well. Derive the expression for E_n analogous to Eq. (1.19).

Bibliography

1. R. T. WEIDNER and R. L. SELLS, *Elementary Modern Physics*, Allyn and Bacon, Boston, 1960.
2. A. J. DEKKER, *Solid State Physics*, Prentice-Hall, Englewood Cliffs, New Jersey, 1957.

CHAPTER 2

ELECTRONIC CONDUCTION
IN SOLIDS

2.1 The Density-of-States Function

The conductivity of a material is the product of the number of available charge carriers, their charge, and their mobility. The number of available carriers is determined by the number of available energy levels near the energy of the uppermost valence electrons. We will first calculate the density of energy levels as a function of electron energy for the case of free electrons in a metallic conductor. For this purpose we represent the conduction band of the metal as a single potential-energy well extending throughout the volume of the crystal. This assumes that the inner electrons of the atoms of the crystal effectively shield the nuclei so that the effect of the remaining nuclear charge can be represented as a uniform potential throughout the crystal.

We will assume a cubic potential-energy well of edge length L. The potential energy is assumed to be zero in the well and indefinitely large at the surfaces. Following the example of the one-dimensional well discussed in the first chapter, we must set up the conditions for standing electronic wave functions in the three principal directions between the sides of the cube. The conditions for such waves, given by Eq. (1.18), can be expressed as the quantization of the three components of momentum:

$$P_x = (h/2L)n_x, \qquad P_y = (h/2L)n_y, \qquad P_z = (h/2L)n_z. \qquad (2.1)$$

Here we have three quantum numbers n_x, n_y, and n_z, one for each component of momentum.

16

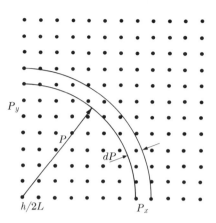

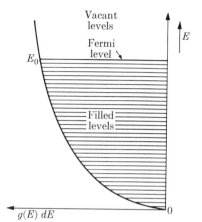

FIG. 2.1. States of a cubic potential well plotted in momentum space.

FIG. 2.2. Density-of-states function for free-electron model.

In Fig. 2.1 we have constructed a plot of momentum space using units of $(h/2L)$. Each dot represents an allowed value of momentum with integral values of n_x and n_y. It is easy to imagine this plot extended to three dimensions to include the P_z-component. To determine the number of allowed energy levels in a given momentum interval dP at momentum $|P|$, we need only count the dots in the lattice contained in dP.

Imagining this plot in three dimensions, we see that by calculating the volume of the positive octant of the spherical shell of radius P and thickness dP we will have the number of allowed energy levels in this particular momentum interval, $G(P)$:

$$G(P)\, dP = \tfrac{1}{8}(4\pi P^2\, dP)/(h/2L)^3. \qquad (2.2)$$

Now $L^3 = \mathcal{U}$, the volume of the crystal, and the total energy of the electron is its kinetic energy only (since we let PE $= 0$ inside the crystal). We will now convert this distribution of levels in momentum to a distribution in energy:

$$E = \tfrac{1}{2}mv^2 = P^2/2m, \qquad (2.3)$$

giving

$$P = \sqrt{2mE} \quad \text{and} \quad dP = \frac{m}{P}\, dE = \frac{m}{\sqrt{2mE}}\, dE. \qquad (2.4)$$

Equation (2.2) now becomes

$$g(E)\, dE = (4\pi \mathcal{U}m/h^3)\, \sqrt{2mE}\, dE, \qquad (2.5)$$

where $g(E)\, dE$ represents the number of energy levels of the system of volume $\mathcal{U}$, in the energy interval dE, at the energy E.

Figure 2.2 shows a plot of Eq. (2.5). The shaded area represents the energy levels filled with valence electrons at absolute zero. Here all the electrons have sought the lowest energy levels available. Since only one electron may occupy a given level at one time* because of the Pauli exclusion principle, N electrons will fill up the lowest N energy levels of the system at the zero of temperature. At elevated temperatures some of the electrons will be excited by thermal vibration to higher energy levels. The electrons capable of such excitation must be the electrons at the top of the energy distribution of Fig. 2.2, since only the top electrons are close enough to vacant allowed energy levels to be capable of interacting with the relatively low-energy phonons of the lattice vibration.

There is one very important parameter of a semiconductor which controls many of its electrical properties. This parameter is called the *Fermi level* and is defined as the energy at which the probability that an energy level will be occupied by an electron is one-half. At absolute zero this corresponds to the energy of the topmost electron in the system. Referring to Fig. 2.2, we see that the energy at the top of the shaded area is the Fermi level E_0. At an elevated temperature the Fermi level will be a bit lower for the $g(E)\ dE$ function illustrated because the density of levels increases monatomically with energy. To calculate the actual energy distribution of electrons in such a system, we must consider the effects of temperature on the occupancy of the allowed levels.

2.2   The Statistical Effect of Temperature

Without being rigorous we will attempt to sketch a line of reasoning that will render plausible the energy-distribution law for particles obeying the Pauli exclusion principle. A particularly simple approach to this question which we follow here is given in Reference 1.

We are familiar with the fact that the density of the atmosphere falls off exponentially with height. If we let the density at height h be $n(h)$, we may write the differential pressure as

$$dP = -nmg\ dh, \qquad (2.6)$$

where m is the mass of a gas molecule, g is the acceleration due to gravity, and n is the number of molecules per cubic centimeter at height h. Therefore $nm\ dh$ is the total mass of gas in a layer dh of area one square centimeter. The right-hand side of the equation is the weight of the gas in that layer. We may use the gas law to obtain another relation between P and n. In the relation $PV = RT$, we know that V is the volume of a mole of gas. If we scale the relation to include only one gas molecule at height h we know that the volume is $1/n$ cm^3, and R is replaced by Boltzmann's con-

---

* Here as elsewhere in this discussion the spin of the electron is ignored since its consideration has negligible bearing on the later discussions.

stant k, giving $P = nkT$. Differentiating with respect to h we get

$$\frac{dP}{dh} = kT\frac{dn}{dh}.$$ (2.7)

Eliminating dP/dh between (2.6) and (2.7) we get

$$-\frac{dn}{n} = \frac{mg}{kT}\,dh,$$ (2.8)

which integrates to

$$n = Ae^{-mgh/kT}.$$ (2.9)

It is recognized that mgh is the potential energy of a gas molecule at the height h so that we have the familiar Maxwell-Boltzmann distribution function

$$n(E) = Ae^{-E/kT},$$ (2.10)

which is interpreted as giving the density of particles in the energy interval dE at the energy E. We have considered the special case of the potential energy of molecules in the atmosphere but the relation holds for other kinds of energy as well.

The gas molecules in the atmosphere can take on a continuous range of energy values. In our solid-state considerations we have discrete allowed energy levels and we interpret (2.10) to give the number of particles occupying an energy level at the energy E. For electrons which obey the exclusion principle, we must see how (2.10) needs to be modified to include this principle.

If we let f_i be the probability that a state E_i is occupied, then $(1 - f_j)$ is the probability that state E_j is empty. Considering a transition from state E_i to state E_j, we may write the total transition probability as $P_{ij}f_i(1 - f_j)$, where P_{ij} is the probability per unit time that the transition of a particle takes place. Applying the principle of detailed balance we must write

$$P_{ij}f_i(1 - f_j) = P_{ji}f_j(1 - f_i).$$ (2.11)

If we have a distribution of particles that is in equilibrium, there must be just as many transitions per unit time in the direction $(j \rightarrow i)$ as there are in the direction $(i \rightarrow j)$. The rate of the transition $(j \rightarrow i)$ must be proportional to the product of the transition probability and the occupancy of the initial state E_j. Equating the rates of this transition and its inverse we have

$$P_{ij}e^{-E_i/kT} = P_{ij}e^{-E_j/kT}.$$ (2.12)

Here we must interpret the occupancy factor as less than unity (i.e., the probability of occupancy rather than the number of particles in state E_i).

Substituting (2.12) in (2.11) we find that

$$\left(\frac{f_i}{1-f_i}\right) e^{E_i/kT} = \left(\frac{f_j}{1-f_j}\right) e^{E_j/kT} = C. \qquad (2.13)$$

We note that all states are independent so that an expression like (2.13) can be written regardless of which states are considered. We are therefore justified in setting any such expression equal to a constant as shown. Solving for $f_i = f(E_i)$ we find that

$$f(E_i) = \frac{1}{e^{E_i/kT}/C + 1} = \frac{1}{e^{(E_i-E_0)/kT} + 1}, \qquad (2.14)$$

where we have let $C = e^{E_0/kT}$. The function $f(E_i)$ is called the *Fermi distribution function*, and the constant E_0 is the Fermi level. This function gives the probability that an energy level at E_i will be occupied by an electron. Examination of Eq. (2.14) shows that when $E_i = E_0$, the occupation probability is $\frac{1}{2}$. This is the proper definition of the Fermi level E_0 mentioned above. For energies far greater than E_0, the $+1$ in the denominator is negligible and (2.14) becomes identical with the better-known Boltzmann distribution function. The Boltzmann function is based on multiple occupancy of energy levels. The identity of these two distribution functions at high energies merely reflects the fact that when the occupation

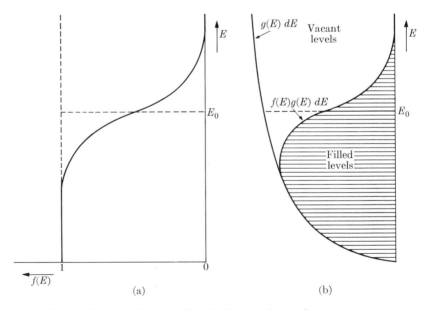

FIG. 2.3. Free-electron distribution at elevated temperature.

probability is low, the exclusion principle is irrelevant since there is a much lower probability of double occupancy anyway. For energies far below E_0, $f(E_i) \rightarrow 1$, showing that deep-lying energy levels are always filled. In Fig. 2.3(a), $f(E)$ is plotted on a vertical energy scale. A vertical energy scale is used to be consistent with our energy-level diagrams. (From here on we will drop the index subscript i.) It is seen that $f(E)$ is symmetrical about E_0 in the sense that the occupation probability at $E_0 + \Delta E$ is equal to the vacancy probability $(1 - f(E))$ at $E_0 - \Delta E$. This is reasonable if one notes that upon thermal excitation of the zero-temperature electron distribution of Fig. 2.2, any electrons found above E_0 must have come from levels below E_0, as illustrated in Fig. 2.3(b). In Fig. 2.3(b), $f(E)$ is shown to be the product of $f(E)$ and $g(E)$ which gives the number of electrons in an energy interval dE at the temperature T. This product will be used to determine the number of electrons and holes available for conduction in semiconductors and is fundamental in determining semiconductor properties.

2.3   The Effective-Mass Concept

It was mentioned earlier that the electrical conductivity was the product of the number of charged carriers, their charge, and their mobility. The mobility in turn depends upon the mass of the carrier. In a solid crystal the mass of an electron is not necessarily the same as its mass in free space. It usually has a smaller effective mass. To see how this comes about, we may consider the classical relation between energy and momentum:

$$E = \tfrac{1}{2}mv^2 = P^2/2m. \tag{2.15}$$

Taking the second derivative we find that

$$d^2E/dP^2 = 1/m. \tag{2.16}$$

In the classical relation (2.15) we find that the curvature of the function of energy in terms of momentum is the reciprocal of the mass of the particle. In this classical free-particle case the function is a parabola with a constant curvature. Therefore a free particle has a constant "effective" mass. If we generalize this concept to include any functional relation between energy and momentum, it is clear that the curvature may vary over a considerable range of momentum and therefore the "effective" mass of the particle may vary. In particular, if we consider the energy-momentum relationship typical of energy bands in crystals, we find that the curvature changes sign between the top and bottom of a band.

Figure 2.4 illustrates a typical energy-momentum curve for a crystal. Here the free-electron parabola of Eq. (2.15) is shown as a dashed line, and the actual E vs. P curve is shown as a solid line. It is to be noted that the

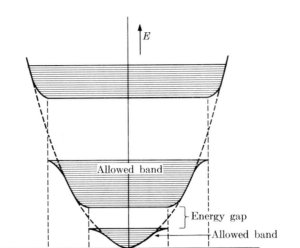

FIG. 2.4. Energy-momentum relation typical of electrons in crystals.

energy is discontinuous at momentum values of $P = \pm nh/2a$, where n is an integer and a is the spacing of atomic planes within the crystal. These discontinuities seem reasonable if we recall Fig. 2.1, where every time we moved from one standing-wave mode to another there was a discontinuous jump in energy. Here because of the same wave nature of the electron the effective DeBroglie wavelength corresponding to momenta of units of $h/2a$ will be just right for diffraction by the atomic planes of spacing a and will give rise to a similar energy discontinuity. This is another physical way of understanding the origin of energy gaps between bands of allowed energy levels. When we considered a single potential-energy well we found that the origin of the discrete energy levels in the boundary condition consisted of the reflection of the electron waves at the walls of the well. Now considering a crystal lattice with many planes of atoms, we find that the discontinuities in allowed energy occur due to the reflection of the electron waves by lattice planes. Combining the two concepts, we arrive at a pseudoclassical treatment of electrons in crystals by using the reflection of the electron waves at lattice planes to determine the distribution of allowed and forbidden energy bands, and when we are considering the distribution of energy levels within a band, we ignore the atom planes and represent the entire crystal volume as a single potential well. Detailed calculations showing the uses of atomic-plane reflections (Brillouin zones) are beyond the scope of this text and may be found in several standard texts on solid-state theory [2, 3]. If the detailed structure of energy bands is desired, of course one cannot use the simple potential-energy well concept, and the symmetry properties of the crystal lattice must be used at all times.

Inspection of Fig. 2.4 shows that the energy discontinuities force a variation in curvature in the E vs. P curve. The general form of the parabola must be followed since at very high energies the electron is again free and follows the parabola exactly. The curvature is seen to actually change sign between the top and bottom of an allowed band of energy levels. If we identify the mass of the electron with d^2P/dE^2, it follows that electrons must have negative mass near the top of allowed bands! This is at first very surprising but after reflection it can be seen to be consistent with the statement made earlier that electrons at the top of a nearly filled band behave like positive charges.

If an ordinary electron is brought into the field of a positive charge, it will be accelerated toward the charge. By Newton's second law, the acceleration is given by

$$a = \frac{F}{m} = \frac{q(-q)/r^2}{m} \tag{2.17}$$

(positive acceleration being defined to be in the r-direction which originates at the center of the positive charge). Now it is clear that the sign (or direction) of the acceleration can be changed either by changing the sign of m or the sign of the $(-q)$-charge. From this it follows that an electron with negative mass will be repelled by a positive charge in exactly the same way that an electron with positive charge would be repelled. It is an experimental fact that the charge carriers at the top of a band are accelerated by an electric field in a direction opposite to the one expected for free electrons.

Finally it is clear that the actual value of the effective mass of an electron depends upon the value of d^2P/dE^2. Again referring to Fig. 2.4, we see that the distortion imposed upon the E vs. P curve near the edges of a band is of such a nature that m is substantially smaller than it would be for a free electron at the same energy [4]. Experimentally most semiconductors show electronic mobilities which are an order of magnitude higher than most metals. This is due to the fact that the electrons involved in the conduction process in semiconductors are usually near band edges, whereas the comparable electrons in metals are usually near the center of a partly filled band system where the curvature of the E vs. P function is smaller.

The particular view of the electronic structure of solids which led to the negative effective-mass concept outlined here was the first real explanation of such well-known experimental facts as the positive Hall coefficient in bismuth, which indicated electrical conduction by positive charges rather than negative charges.

In the simple example described above we illustrated the effective-mass concept using a one-dimensional plot of energy vs. momentum. In a three-dimensional crystal there will be different spacings of atom planes in different crystallographic directions. Since diffraction of the electronic wave functions by sets of atom planes causes the energy-momentum discontinuities depicted in Fig. 2.4, we can see, for the simple case, that the curve of this figure would be different for different directions in the crystal. This in turn implies that the effective mass of an electron may be different for different directions in the crystal [4].

There are other complexities in the band structure of real three-dimensional crystals. For example, there may be overlapping bands which arise from different sets of atomic electronic states. In addition, it is possible that the energy minimum of a band does not necessarily occur at the zero momentum or wave number. In actual fact it turns out that the band structure of semiconductors furnishes examples of most of these complications. In the case of many of the semiconductor compounds made from the combination of third-group and fifth-group elements (for example, GaAs) the valence and conduction bands have the energy minima coincident with the zero of momentum. In silicon and germanium the energy minimum of the valence band is at the origin, but this is not so for the conduction band. In germanium the conduction band shows four energy minima lying out along the (111) crystallographic directions. For silicon there are three found along the (100) directions. In both cases the effective mass of conduction electrons is direction dependent. Also in both cases the valence band consists of overlapping bands with different effective masses for holes.

It is fortunate that the effect of all this on the general analysis of semiconductor devices can usually be adequately represented by using a single average effective mass for electrons and another average mass for holes.

2.4   Electronic Conduction in Semiconductors

Intrinsic conductivity [5]. A typical semiconductor material in the ideal pure state has a substantial forbidden energy gap between a valence band, which at absolute zero is completely filled with electrons, and a conduction band, which is completely empty. From the previous discussion we see that the material will behave like an insulator at absolute zero. As the temperature is raised, a few electrons will be thermally excited across the energy gap leaving vacant energy levels (holes) in the valence band and providing essentially free electrons in the conduction band. We will now consider this situation quantitatively.

Figure 2.5 graphically shows the product $g_c(E)f(E)$ for the conduction band and $g_v(E)f(E)$ for the valence band. At the left of the figure we have illustrated the two density-of-states distributions $g_c(E)$ and $g_v(E)$. At ab-

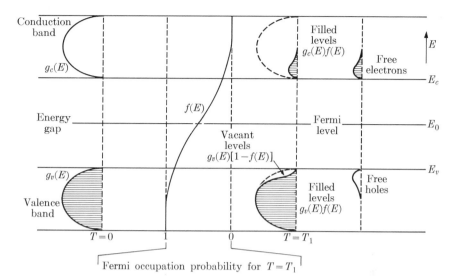

Fig. 2.5. Graphical representation of the origin of free carriers in an intrinsic semiconductor.

solute zero, $g_v(E)$ is completely full of electrons and $g_c(E)$ is completely empty. Next, to the right is shown the Fermi occupation probability $f(E)$ for the temperature T. The product of $g_c(E)$ and $f(E)$ and that of $g_v(E)$ and $f(E)$ appear next. Here it can be seen that the product (solid line) gives the distribution of filled levels in each band. Finally the so-called free-electron and free-hole distributions are shown, the free electrons being the filled levels of the conduction band, and the free holes, the vacant levels of the valence band.

We have already noted that the density-of-states function $g(E)$ for the free-electron approximation is given by

$$g(E) = \frac{4\pi\mathbb{U}m}{h^3} \sqrt{2mE}. \tag{2.18}$$

This function starts at the bottom of a band and increases indefinitely. Here we are dealing with a valence and a conduction band both of which are finite in width. Obviously Eq. (2.18) cannot represent the density-of-states function throughout a finite band. Therefore we must consider that (2.18) represents this function only at the band edge. In other words, as we start at the bottom of a band we are assuming that the density of states increases as $E^{1/2}$ for an energy interval of several times kT. At the top of a band we invoke the effective-mass principle and turn the function (2.18) upside down, letting the density of states increase as $E^{1/2}$ as we descend

in energy several times kT from the top edge of the band. This last strat-
agem amounts to assuming that the electrons at the top of the band behave
like positive charges with zero kinetic energy at the top of the band. This
is reasonable if we think of the actual charge carrier at the top of the valence band as a "hole" or electron vacancy. In this case since the actual
electrons of the band are seeking their lowest level, the vacancies will rise
to the top and tend to remain there. A vacancy at the very top will tend
to remain there suggesting that a "hole" at the top band edge should have
little or no motion or kinetic energy.

To determine the electronic occupation of the energy levels of the band,
we must multiply the density-of-states function (2.18) by the Fermi occupation probability, Eq. (2.14), obtaining

$$g(E)f(E) = \left(\frac{2^{5/2}\pi\mathcal{V}m^{3/2}}{h^3}\right)\left(\frac{(E - E_c)^{1/2}}{\exp\,[(E - E_0)/kT] + 1}\right). \qquad (2.19)$$

Here we have used $(E - E_c)$ as the energy term in the $g_c(E)$-function
since the allowed states only start at the energy E_c. In using Eq. (2.18) for
the $g_c(E)$-function, we are assuming that whatever detailed structure the
band may have, it can be approximated at the band edge by a single half-
power term. The total number of electrons thermally excited to the conduction band at temperature T is given by the integral of $g(E)f(E)$ over
the band. Since this product decreases two orders of magnitude in each
energy interval of $4.6kT$, and since we will assume the $g_c(E)$ to be represented by Eq. (2.18) over at least this energy range from the band edges,
we will integrate from E_c to infinity to approximate the integral over the
band:

$$\int_{E_c}^{\infty} g_c(E)f(E)\,dE = \frac{2^{5/2}m^{3/2}\pi\mathcal{V}}{h^3}\int_{E_c}^{\infty}\frac{(E - E_c)^{1/2}\,dE}{\exp\,[(E - E_0)/kT] + 1}. \qquad (2.20)$$

If $(E_c - E_0)$ is large compared with kT, we may neglect the 1 in the denominator, and the integral becomes

$$\frac{2^{5/2}m^{3/2}\pi\mathcal{V}}{h^3}\,e^{E_0/kT}\int_{E_c}^{\infty}(E - E_c)^{1/2}\,e^{-E/kT}\,dE$$

$$= \left(\frac{2\pi m_n kT}{h^2}\right)^{3/2}\mathcal{V}e^{-(E_c-E_0)/kT} = \mathfrak{N}, \qquad (2.21)$$

where $\mathfrak{N}$ is the total number of free electrons in the conduction band of a
crystal of volume $\mathcal{V}$, m_n is the effective mass of the electrons at the bottom
of the band, and E_c is the energy at the bottom of the conduction band.
From here on we will work with the density of electrons $n = \mathfrak{N}/\mathcal{V}$, instead of always computing the volume of the crystal.

In an exactly similar manner we find the density of vacancies or holes in the valence band to be

$$p = \left(\frac{2\pi m_p kT}{h^2}\right)^{3/2} e^{(E_v - E_0)/kT}. \tag{2.22}$$

One additional fact should be pointed out. Because of the symmetry of the Fermi function and the assumed symmetry of $g_c(E)$ and $g_v(E)$, the Fermi level, E_0 [the $\frac{1}{2}$ probability point of $f(E)$], is located exactly at the center of the energy gap so that the number of free electrons would exactly equal the number of free holes (vacancies) from which they came. If $g_v(E)$ should be substantially greater than $g_c(E)$ near the band edge, the Fermi function would have to be raised somewhat in order to give equal electrons and vacancies. This would put the Fermi level, E_0, somewhat above the center of the energy gap. From Eqs. (2.21) and (2.22) it follows that

$$np = \left(\frac{2\pi kT}{h^2}\right)^3 (m_n m_p)^{3/2} e^{-\Delta E/kT}. \tag{2.23}$$

This can be recognized as a form of the mass action law of chemistry. Here n and p are the concentrations of electrons and holes respectively, and $\Delta E = E_c - E_v$ (the width of the forbidden energy gap) is the activation energy for the reaction

Electron + Hole $\rightleftarrows$ Filled valence-band level.

In a pure semiconductor n and p are equal and are designated n_i so that by taking the square root of Eq. (2.23) we may write

$$n_i = (\text{const}) \, e^{\Delta E/2kT}. \tag{2.24}$$

We are now in a position to calculate the conductivity of a bar of intrinsic semiconductor material.

If a bar of semiconductor material of cross-sectional area A and length L carries a current I with an applied voltage V, we can write

$I =$ (The number of charge carriers) $\times$ (The charge/carrier)
$\times$ (The average velocity/carrier).

With only electrons present, $I = nAq\bar{v}_n$, and with only holes, $I = pAq\bar{v}_p$; with both, $I = (nq\bar{v}_n + pq\bar{v}_p)A$. If we express the average velocities in terms of a mobility μ defined as

(The average velocity per unit field)
$\times$ (The applied electric field, $V/L = \varepsilon$),

we can write

$$I = (nq\mu_n + pq\mu_p)A\mathcal{E}. \tag{2.25}$$

Now the definition of conductivity σ is $\sigma = J/\mathcal{E}$, where J is current density, I/A. From (2.25) we then obtain

$$\sigma = nq\mu_n + pq\mu_p. \tag{2.26}$$

This is a general relation. For our particular case of intrinsic conductivity of a semiconductor, we have found that $n = p = n_i$, so that the intrinsic conductivity σ_i becomes

$$\sigma_i = n_i q(\mu_n + \mu_p). \tag{2.27}$$

Extrinsic conductivity in semiconductors [5]. When the free current carriers are supplied by the thermal ionization of impurity atoms rather than thermal excitation across the energy gap, the resulting electrical conductivity is called extrinsic. Figure 2.6(a) shows the energy system associated with a single impurity atom of the "donor" type. The name is meant to suggest that this type of impurity "donates" an electron to the conduction band when it is ionized. Typically such an impurity has one or two more valence electrons than the atoms of the host semiconductor lattice. When this impurity enters the lattice substitutionally (in the normal position of a lattice atom), it does not need all its valence electrons to satisfy the bonding arrangement of the lattice and retains the extra valence electron or electrons in rather large orbits of low binding energy. The example shown is for arsenic in a crystal of germanium. Here arsenic has a valence of five and germanium has a valence of four. The fifth arsenic electron is therefore not needed in the chemical bonding and is available for easy donation to the conduction process.

To get an idea of the separation of such a donor level from the conduction band we may consider the arsenic impurity (after four of its valence electrons are occupied in bonding) as a hydrogenlike atom embedded in the environment of a germanium crystal. We may then consider the loss of the remaining electron to the conduction band as ionization of this hydrogenlike atom. The calculation of the ionization energy then resolves itself into the evaluation of Eq. (1.10), corrected for the dielectric constant of germanium. Since the dielectric constant should appear as the square in the denominator of (1.10), and has the value 16 in germanium, it is seen that the ionization energy of the impurity should be $\frac{1}{256}$ of the hydrogen ionization energy, or about 0.05 ev. In fact the ionization of arsenic in germanium is measured to be 0.013 ev. Such a qualitative agreement is all that can be expected of such a simple model. Using the effective-mass concept, we may suggest that this discrepancy might be a result of

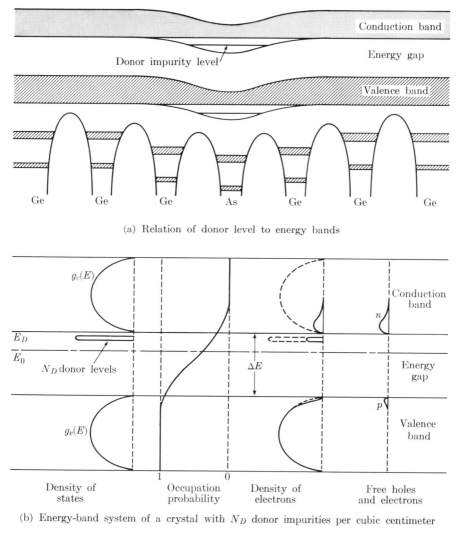

(a) Relation of donor level to energy bands

(b) Energy-band system of a crystal with N_D donor impurities per cubic centimeter

FIGURE 2.6

the fact that the electron in the conduction band shows a low effective mass. Since the electronic mobility of germanium is quite high, this seems reasonable. Actually the effective mass of the electron in the conduction band of germanium is a very complicated question [3], and we cannot push this simple model any further. It is hoped, however, that the above discussion does serve to give an idea of the factors involved in the origin of the low ionization energy of the donor and acceptor impurities in semiconductors.

Figure 2.6(b) shows the energy-band system of a crystal with a density of N_D donor impurities per cubic centimeter. The presence of these impurities adds a new set of allowed energy levels to the system. If the impurities are present in concentrations so low that they are physically separated far beyond the diameter of the effective orbit of the state, then all can exist at essentially the same energy since there is no coupling between them. Unless N_D is of the order of $10^{18}/cm^3$, the band of donor levels shown will be very narrow (~ 0.001 ev) and will lie about 0.01 ev below the bottom edge of the conduction band. Since the Fermi function has an appreciable variation only over the range where $(E - E_0)/kT \sim 1$, and since N_D is very much less than the density of levels in the conduction band, the donor levels will be almost completely ionized by thermal excitation at room temperature when $kT \sim 0.025$ ev. This fact can be appreciated by reference to Fig. 2.6(b). Here the Fermi level is shown slightly above the center of the gap since most of the conduction electrons come from the donor levels, and there will be very few vacancies in the valence band. A small displacement of the Fermi function does not change the percentage of ionized (vacant) donor levels much because it is nearly zero at the energy of the donor levels. A small displacement does, however, radically change the balance between the vacant valence-band levels and the filled conduction-band levels since these bands are wide and have an energy-level density that is several orders of magnitude higher. The process of finding equilibrium, therefore, is to shift the position of the Fermi function until the number of vacant donor levels and valence-band levels (holes) combined equals the number of free electrons in the conduction band. The detailed charge balance may be written

$$N_D \left\{ 1 - \frac{1}{\exp\left[(E_D - E_0)/kT\right] + 1} \right\} + p = n. \qquad (2.28)$$

In most real cases, p and the Fermi function are negligible, giving $N_D = n$. For relatively high values of N_D, the Fermi function ceases to be negligible, and only p may be dropped from (2.28).

In the impure semiconductor material described above, the conduction of electricity takes place primarily by the movement of the free electrons, n; this type of impure semiconductor is called N-type. (The N stands for negative particle conduction.)

If the semiconductor material has an impurity of valence less than that of the atoms of the host lattice which enter the lattice substitutionally it will tend to borrow electrons from the valence band to satisfy its bonding requirements. This will create electronic vacancies or holes in the valence band of the crystal, and the electrical conduction will be predominantly by holes. Such a semiconductor is said to be P-type. The impurity centers are called *acceptor* centers since they "accept" electrons from the valence band. In this case the Fermi level is lowered from its intrinsic position until the number of vacant valence-band levels is equal to the number of ionized acceptor centers plus the number of electrons in the conduction band. With appreciable acceptor doping the number of free electrons is negligible.

For many problems it is necessary to find the position of the Fermi level [6]. Here we will develop an approximation which is easy to use under the assumption that the Fermi level is more than $2kT$ away from the band edge and that the position of the Fermi level for intrinsic material is located at the center of the energy gap.

Letting the amplitude constants of Eqs. (2.21) and (2.22) be N_c and N_v, respectively, and assuming that $N_D \simeq n$, we may write Eq. (2.21) as

$$N_D \simeq n = N_c e^{(-E_c + E_0)/kT}. \tag{2.29}$$

The same equation for the intrinsic case with E_0 at the gap center is

$$n_i = N_c e^{-\Delta E/2kT}. \tag{2.30}$$

If we define the zero of energy to be the gap center, we find that $E_c = \Delta E/2$ and $E_v = -\Delta E/2$. Substituting in Eq. (2.29) we obtain

$$N_D = N_c e^{(-\Delta E/2 + E_0)/kT} = n_i e^{E_0/kT}. \tag{2.31}$$

Solving for E_0 for an N-type sample gives

$$E_0 = kT \ln (N_D/n_i). \tag{2.32}$$

The equality of N_v and N_c in the intrinsic equation is implied by the assumption that E_0 is at the gap center for the intrinsic case. If the density-of-states functions for the two bands are not symmetrical about the gap center or if the effective masses are different, this is no longer true, and the procedure must be modified accordingly. Following Moll [7], we can still use the amplitude constants N_v and N_c and approach the problem graphically on the basis of Eq. (2.29) and its P-type counterpart. This is shown in Fig. 2.7. Plotting the $\ln n$ to the right above and the $\ln p$ to the right below, a point N_c is marked on the upper scale (at $E = E_c$), and a point N_v is marked on the lower scale (at $E = E_v$). Straight lines with slopes of $(E_c - E)/kT$, are now drawn through these points. The intersection point of these lines is E_0 for intrinsic material, and its projection on either the $\ln n$- or $\ln p$-scale is the intrinsic carrier density, n_i. The position of the Fermi level for any value of N_A or N_D can be found by projecting the appropriate value on the proper curve, as shown.

When N_D or N_A is very large, a direct projection will not work because the Fermi level will be too near E_A or E_D, and more detailed calculations,

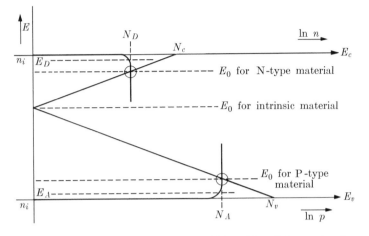

FIG. 2.7. Graphical representation of Fermi-level determination.

which do not neglect the unit term in the denominator of the Fermi function, will be necessary. The curves near the band edge illustrate this effect
graphically.

In either case the number of current carriers (either holes for P-type or
electrons for N-type) is essentially constant over a wide temperature range,
the *extrinsic conductivity* range. The conductivity is then

$$\text{For N-type,} \qquad \sigma_n = N_D q \mu_n, \qquad\qquad (2.33)$$
$$\text{For P-type,} \qquad \sigma_p = N_A q \mu_p.$$

In reality there are always some of both types of impurity present in a
semiconductor since the levels of doping usually used are of the order of
one part in 10^{-6} or 10^{-7}, and it is very difficult to purify the original
material (before doping) to better than 10^{-9}. Because of this, equations
(2.33) are usually written as

$$\sigma_n = (N_D - N_A) q \mu_n, \qquad \sigma_p = (N_A - N_D) q \mu_p. \qquad (2.34)$$

If N_D and N_A are comparable in magnitude, the material is said to be com-
pensated.

Figure 2.8 shows the general behavior of the resistivity of an N-type
semiconductor material over a wide range of temperature. At the top of
the figure is shown the position of the Fermi level plotted on the same
temperature scale. It should be noted that for the intrinsic range it lies
between the donor levels and the center of the gap, and in the very low
temperature range it lies between the donor levels and the conduction
band edge.

In the intrinsic range the number of electrons thermally excited across the energy gap greatly exceeds the number of ionized donor or acceptor levels. The rapid drop of the resistivity with increasing temperature in this range is due to the exponentially increasing number of current carriers [see Eq. (2.23)]. This is characteristic of a semiconductor, and the pressure of negative temperature coefficient of resistance is one of the experimental tests used to distinguish a semiconductor material from a metallic material. In the latter case there is no energy gap and, therefore, no way of increasing the number of free carriers by increasing the temperature.

In the extrinsic range the number of electrons (or holes in a P-type material) remains substantially constant and equal to the number of donor centers. The positive temperature coefficient of resistance in this region is a mobility effect and has the same basic origin as the positive temperature coefficient of resistance in a metal.

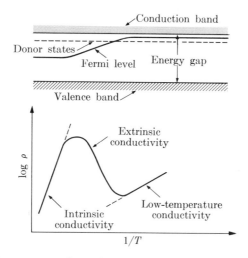

Fig. 2.8. Temperature dependence of resistivity in a semiconductor.

In the low-temperature conductivity range the rising resistivity is primarily due to a rapidly decreasing mobility caused by the scattering of charge carriers by ionized impurity centers. This and other mobility effects will be discussed in the next section. At very low temperatures the rising resistivity is partly due to the condensation of the extrinsic carriers back into their donor or acceptor levels, and the carriers thereby remove themselves from circulation. Both N-type and P-type materials show the resistivity behavior of Fig. 2.8. In the P-type material the Fermi level moves down instead of up as the temperature is lowered, stopping between the acceptor levels and the top of the valence band at very low temperatures.

Mobility effects. We have stated that mobility is a temperature-sensitive material property. Here we will describe roughly the origin of the temperature and impurity behavior of such materials.

In a perfectly pure semiconductor material the scattering collisions that give rise to the electronic or hole mobility occur with lattice atoms (the electron-electron or hole-hole collisions are negligible). At very low temperatures the lattice atoms are nearly at rest in lattice positions so that they have low scattering cross sections for current carriers. As the temperature is increased the lattice atoms acquire thermal vibrations of greater amplitude and thus increase their scattering cross section. To understand this, one should remember that the allowed energy states of the system are derived from boundary conditions which "fit" electronic "orbits" to a perfectly periodic array of atoms. So long as this array remains perfectly periodic, there can be no collisions between electrons and lattice atoms any more than the orbital electron of hydrogen can collide with its nucleus. However, when this perfect array is disturbed by thermal lattice vibration, the possibility of collision is introduced, and as temperature is increased, the increased amplitude of the lattice vibrations gives an increased probability of electron-phonon collision.

To compute the mobility of an electron in a crystal lattice, one must consider the effect of two competing processes on the momentum distribution of the free electrons. The two processes are the acceleration of the electrons by an electric field and the scattering of moving electrons by phonons. Figure 2.9 shows a schematic diagram of momentum space. Remembering that in equilibrium the electrons fill up the lowest levels of the band except for thermal excitation, we represent the case of thermodynamic equilibrium by the inner dashed circle. Here the symmetry of the circle indicates that there are equal numbers of electrons moving in each direction. When an electric field is applied which tends to accelerate electrons in the x-direction, it will move the equilibrium distribution to the position of the solid circle in a time Δt. If there are no collisions in time Δt, the circle will retain its original form since each electron receives the same ΔP_x. Let the field be removed at the end of Δt. As time goes on, the scattering of electrons by phonons will first spread the shifted distribution of

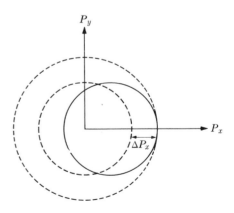

Fig. 2.9. Effects of electric field and scattering on the electronic momentum distribution.

the solid circle out into the large dashed circle. This represents the randomization of the velocities of all the electrons without loss of energy. Since the electron mass is small compared to the atomic mass, the energy loss at each scattering collision will indeed be quite small. After the passage of an extended period of time, however, the small losses of energy in each collision will cause the larger dashed distribution to shrink to the equilibrium one. This last process transfers the electrical energy to lattice energy and represents the I^2R-loss.

From the above description it should be clear that if all three processes are continuously active, the electronic-momentum distribution will reach a dynamic-equilibrium position to the right of the origin and at a size somewhat larger than the equilibrium size, when the scattering process just balances the field acceleration. If the velocity of the center of the shifted distribution is divided by the field producing the shift, we find the mobility of the electrons in the material. The result of such a calculation gives

$$\mu = \frac{\langle v \rangle}{\mathcal{E}} = \frac{q\ell}{\sqrt{2mkT}}, \qquad (2.35)$$

where $\langle v \rangle$ is the velocity of the center of gravity of the momentum distribution in the dynamic equilibrium case, ℓ is the mean free path between collisions, and $\mathcal{E}$ is the electric field applied. It turns out that ℓ varies as $1/T$ since it decreases as lattice vibration amplitude increases. The first-order temperature variation of μ is then $1/T^{3/2}$. Experimentally most semiconductor materials show a temperature dependence of mobility of $1/T^m$, where m ranges from 1.5 to 2.5. This variation of mobility with temperature accounts for the temperature coefficient of resistance in the extrinsic temperature range for semiconductors and in the entire temperature range for metals.

If the semiconductor is impure, the ionized donors and acceptors are very efficient for scattering the charged current carriers. Their efficiency (large scattering cross section) results from the Coulomb electrostatic force between them and the current carriers. Since there are only about 10^{-7} as many impurity atoms as there are lattice atoms, the effect of the impurity atoms is usually not noticed until the temperature is lowered. At low temperatures, of the order of 50°K, the impurity scattering effect takes over in limiting the mean free path and hence the mobility, and as the temperature drops further, the impurity scattering mean free path decreases, since the more slowly moving electrons and holes spend more time in the neighborhood of an ion and are therefore deflected by its field from greater distances. This effect contributes significantly to the rise of resistivity at low temperatures shown in Fig. 2.8.

2.5 Numerical Example

Given a potential-energy well of dimensions $1 \times 2 \times 3$ cm^3. Assume that the potential energy is zero inside the well and goes to an indefinitely large value on the surfaces. Regarding all degenerate states of the system with a single energy as a single state, calculate the difference in energy between the eighth and ninth energy levels of an electron in this potential well.

For this example we must count the standing electron wave patterns that give the nine lowest energy levels of the system. Letting the x-dimension be 3 cm, the y-dimension, 2 cm, and the z-dimension, 1 cm, we may write the three components of momentum as in Eq. (2.1):

$$P_x = hn_x/2x = hn_x/6, \qquad P_y = hn_y/2y = hn_y/4,$$
$$P_z = hn_z/2z = hn_z/2. \tag{2.36}$$

The energy of any state is $P^2/2m$, from Eq. (2.3), and $P^2 = P_x^2 + P_y^2 + P_z^2$. We can evaluate the first nine states of the system by finding the combinations of quantum numbers n_x, n_y, and n_z which give the nine lowest values of the sum:

$$P^2 = h^2(n_x^2/36 + n_y^2/16 + n_z^2/4). \tag{2.37}$$

To carry out this evaluation, we construct Table 2.1 for various possible combinations of quantum numbers. By inspection it is clear that further

TABLE 2.1

n_x	n_y	n_z	P^2/h^2	State number
1	0	0	$\frac{1}{36} + 0 + 0 = 0.0278$	1
0	1	0	$0 + \frac{1}{16} + 0 = 0.0625$	2
0	0	1	$0 + 0 + \frac{1}{4} = 0.2500$	6
1	1	0	$\frac{1}{36} + \frac{1}{16} + 0 = 0.0903$	3
1	0	1	$\frac{1}{36} + 0 + \frac{1}{4} = 0.2778$	7
0	1	1	$0 + \frac{1}{16} + \frac{1}{4} = 0.3125$	8
1	1	1	$\frac{1}{36} + \frac{1}{16} + \frac{1}{4} = 0.3403$	9
2	0	0	$\frac{1}{9} + 0 + 0 = 0.1111$	4
0	2	0	$0 + \frac{1}{4} + 0 = 0.2500$	6
2	2	0	$\frac{1}{9} + \frac{1}{4} + 0 = 0.3611$	10
2	1	0	$\frac{1}{9} + \frac{1}{16} + 0 = 0.1736$	5
2	0	1	$\frac{1}{9} + 0 + \frac{1}{4} = 0.3611$	10
1	2	0	$\frac{1}{36} + \frac{1}{4} + 0 = 0.2778$	7
3	0	0	$\frac{1}{4} + 0 + 0 = 0.2500$	6
3	1	0	$\frac{1}{4} + \frac{1}{16} + 0 = 0.3125$	8

combinations of quantum numbers will give even larger sums and therefore higher energies. Here it is seen that state 6 is threefold degenerate, since the quantum numbers (001), (020), and (300) all give the same energy. State 7 is twofold degenerate with the quantum numbers (101) and (120). The two states of interest in this problem are state 8, (011) and (310), and state 9, (111). The energy difference is given by

$$\Delta E_{89} = (h^2/2m)(0.3403 - 0.3125) = 6.6 \times 10^{-28} \text{ erg.} \tag{2.38}$$

This corresponds to 4.2×10^{-16} ev.

The ninth state is at an energy of $0.3403h^2/2m = 0.81 \times 10^{-26}$ erg from the bottom of the band. We see from Eq. (2.5) that as we move up in energy the number of states in an interval dE increases as $E^{1/2}$. This means that the states get closer together. For example, at an energy of 1 ev (1.6×10^{-12} erg) above the bottom of the band, we would find about 8.5×10^6 energy levels in an energy interval of 4.2×10^{-16} ev equal to ΔE_{89}.

Problems

2.1 Given that there are 10^{22} electrons in 1 cm^3 of a metal. Using the free electron model, calculate:
(a) the value of E_0 in electron volts;
(b) the number of electrons in the energy interval 2.795 ev and 2.805 ev at $T = 300°K$ ($kT = 39$ reciprocal ev).

2.2 In a real case the amplitude constant in Eq. (2.23) must be determined experimentally because m_n, m_p, and $g(E)$ are unknown. Given a semiconductor material where Eq. (2.23) is $np = Ae^{-\Delta E/kT}$, with $A = 10^{40}$ (at 300°K), $\Delta E = 1.0$ ev, and a donor density of $N_D = 10^{15}$ centers/cm^3. Calculate the position of the Fermi level in electron volts above the center of the energy gap for $T = 100$, 300, and 600°K. Also, give the fraction of the N_D-levels filled at each temperature; $E_D = 0.48$ ev above the center of the energy gap. [*Hint:* Remember that for an N-type material $n = p + N_D$ and neglect the 1 in the denominator of Eq. (2.28).]

2.3 If 3×10^{15} acceptors/cm^3 are added to the material of Problem 2.2 at an energy $E_A = 0.48$ ev below the center of the gap, find the position of the Fermi level at 200°K.

2.4 Using the hydrogen atom model of a substitutional impurity, estimate the upper concentration limit of the impurity which could be used without experiencing broadening of the impurity band of allowed states in germanium (interatomic distance about 4 angstroms).

2.5 Given that at every level of energy (as measured from the band edge) $g_v(E) = 3g_c(E)$. Calculate the position of the Fermi level at 300°K for a pure material.

Bibliography

1. R. B. ADLER, A. C. SMITH, and R. L. LONGINI, *Introduction to Semiconductor Physics*, SEEC Vol. I, John Wiley and Sons, New York, 1964.
2. A. J. DEKKER, *Solid State Physics*, Prentice-Hall, Englewood Cliffs, New Jersey, 1957.
3. C. KITTEL, *Quantum Theory of Solids*, John Wiley and Sons, New York, 1963.
4. B. LAX, H. J. ZEIGLER, R. N. DEXTER, and E. S. ROSENBLUM, "Directional Properties of the Cyclotron Resonance in Germanium," *Phys. Rev.* **93,** 1418 (1954).
5. R. SEITZ, *Modern Theory of Solids*, McGraw-Hill, New York, 1940.
6. W. SHOCKLEY, *Electrons and Holes in Semiconductors*, D. Van Nostrand, Princeton, New Jersey, 1950.
7. J. L. MOLL, *Physics of Semiconductors*, McGraw-Hill, New York, 1964.

CHAPTER 3

RADIATION AND IMPURITY EFFECTS

3.1 The Concept of Lifetime

All previous considerations have involved the state of thermodynamic equilibrium. We will now consider nonequilibrium conditions. Suppose that by some means a number of electrons are taken from the valence band and placed in the conduction band. This requires an investment of energy sufficient to raise the energy of these electrons an amount at least equal to the width of the energy gap. After the excitation of these electrons, there will be an excess of both holes and electrons above the thermodynamic equilibrium number. Equilibrium must be restored by some sort of recombination process through which the excess electrons fall back into the excess vacant energy levels of the valence band. We refer to the dropping down of a free electron into a vacant valence-band level as the "recombination" of an electron and a hole. The process of recombination proceeds at a rate which is proportional to the excess density of the electrons and holes. This then means that the excess density of carriers dies away exponentially with time. The time constant of this decay of the excess carrier density is called the lifetime of the material.

The process of recombination of holes and electrons must conserve momentum. Because of this the probability of a direct recombination between an electron near the bottom of the conduction band and a hole near the top of the valence band is very remote, since to conserve momentum the two carriers would have to have equal and opposite momentum before recombination. A much more probable event is to have one or the other carrier "trapped" in a deep energy level of an impurity atom so that when recombination occurs the excess momentum can be transferred to the crystal lattice. The excess momentum in this case will be found in lattice vibrations. For this reason lifetime can be controlled by controlling the density of deep level traps in the semiconductor material or on its surface. The major difficulty lies in the fact that there is a great variety of crystal imperfections and impurities which are capable of providing trapping centers (often called recombination centers). In practice the crystal perfection and purity of the bulk material under the best conditions give a lifetime of the order of one millisecond. For device use this is deliberately degraded by doping or surface treatment to something less than one microsecond.

We have defined lifetime in terms of the time constant of the decay of an excess density of carriers. It is equally, however, the time constant of the restoration of a deficient density of carriers. This can be understood by considering the nature of an equilibrium. A constant density means that the thermal-generation rate and the recombination rate are equal. In an exponential process the initial rate extrapolated linearly in time gives a time for zero concentration equal to the time constant of the exponential. Therefore the fact that the initial rates of recombination and regeneration must be equal to maintain a constant density means that their time constants are also equal. The material lifetime is therefore the time constant for the restoration of equilibrium from either an excess or a deficient density of carriers.

Trap recombination [1].

As noted above, momentum is most easily conserved if recombination occurs via a relatively deep trap. We will proceed to consider the statistics of such a trap recombination.

Let us assume that we have a density N_T of deep trapping levels situated in the energy gap of the semiconductor at the energy E_T. We shall first consider the case where the Fermi level E_0 coincides with the trapping level E_T. In this case the traps will be half-full of electrons by definition of the Fermi level. If n_1 is the density of electrons in the conduction band when $E_0 = E_T$ and C_n is the probability per unit time that an electron will be captured if all traps are empty of electrons, we can write the trapping rate as $\frac{1}{2}n_1C_n$. To maintain equilibrium this must also be the regeneration rate. In general, then, we may write the regeneration rate for any trap occupancy fraction f_T as $g = f_T n_1 C_n$. Similarly, the general capture rate is $(1 - f_T)nC_n$, where n is any given density of conduction-band electrons. The net rate of capture can now be written for electrons as

$$U_{cn} = (1 - f_T)nC_n - f_T n_1 C_n. \tag{3.1}$$

Here it must be understood that the trap occupancy fraction f_T is simply the Fermi probability function, $[e^{(E_T-E_0)/kT} + 1]^{-1}$. For trapping of holes we may write a similar expression,

$$U_{cp} = f_T p C_p - (1 - f_T) p_1 C_p, \qquad (3.2)$$

where C_p is the probability of hole capture when the trapping levels are completely filled with electrons and p_1 is the density of holes in the valence band when $E_0 = E_T$. Equating (3.1) and (3.2) gives a solution for f_T under the equilibrium condition that equal numbers of holes and electrons must be trapped per unit time to give steady recombination:

$$f_T = \frac{C_n n + C_p p_1}{C_n(n + n_1) + C_p(p + p_1)}. \qquad (3.3)$$

Similarly we find that

$$1 - f_T = \frac{C_n n_1 + C_p p}{C_n(n + n_1) + C_p(p + p_1)}. \qquad (3.4)$$

Now substituting Eqs. (3.3) and (3.4) into (3.1) and remembering that $U_{cn} = U_{cp} = U$ for steady recombination, we get

$$U = \frac{C_n C_p(pn - p_1 n_1)}{C_n(n + n_1) + C_p(p + p_1)}, \qquad (3.5)$$

where the product $p_1 n_1 = n_i^2$ since both densities are for the same position of the Fermi level.

Now we let n_0 and p_0 be the equilibrium electron and hole densities for a general position of the Fermi level. We may now write

$$n = n_0 + \Delta n$$

and   (3.6)

$$p = p_0 + \Delta n,$$

where Δn is the excess density of either electrons or holes created by some excitation process. Lifetime has been defined above as the constant of proportionality between the rate of recombination and the excess density of carriers. We then write

$$U\tau = \Delta n, \qquad (3.7)$$

where τ is the excess carrier lifetime. From Eq. (3.5) and the above definitions we find that

$$\tau = \frac{(n_0 + n_1 + \Delta n)/C_p + (p_0 + p_1 + \Delta n)/C_n}{n_0 + p_0 + \Delta n}. \qquad (3.8)$$

In an N-type semiconductor we have $n_0 \gg p_0$; also if we assume that $n_0 \gg \Delta n$ and if n_0 and n_1 are $\gg p_1$, Eq. (3.8) reduces to

$$\tau = \frac{1 + n_1/n_0}{C_p}. \tag{3.9}$$

The above assumptions interpreted physically mean that the Fermi level E_0 is well above both the E_T-level and the center of the energy gap, and that the excess density is not due to a massive excitation.

In a P-type sample we may have the analogous conditions, $p_0 \gg n_0$, p_0 and $p_1 \gg n_1$, and $p_0 \gg \Delta n$. In this case, Eq. (3.8) reduces to

$$\tau = \frac{1 + p_1/p_0}{C_n}. \tag{3.10}$$

From Eqs. (3.9) and (3.10) it is clear that the limiting lifetime in an N-type sample is $\tau = 1/C_p = \tau_p$, the lifetime of the minority holes, and in a P-type sample, $\tau = 1/C_n = \tau_n$, the lifetime of the minority electrons. For this reason lifetime is often called "minority-carrier" lifetime.

Since there is no *a priori* reason for C_p and C_n to be equal, it is clear that as one moves the position of the Fermi level relative to the band edges, one should expect the lifetime to change. An example of a typical semiconductor is shown in Fig. 3.1.

We can cast Eqs. (3.9) and (3.10) in a more usable form by noting that

$$n_1 = N_c e^{-(E_c - E_T)/kT}, \qquad n_0 = N_c e^{-(E_c - E_0)/kT},$$
$$p_1 = N_v e^{(E_v - E_T)/kT}, \qquad p_0 = N_v e^{(E_v - E_0)/kT}, \tag{3.11}$$

where N_c and N_v are the amplitude constants in Eqs. (2.21) and (2.22), respectively. Now the ratios can be written:

$$n_1/n_0 = e^{(E_T - E_0)/kT},$$
$$p_1/p_0 = e^{(E_0 - E_T)/kT}, \tag{3.12}$$

giving for N-type material:

$$\tau = \tau_p(1 + e^{(E_T - E_0)/kT}), \tag{3.13}$$

and for P-type material:

$$\tau = \tau_n(1 + e^{(E_0 - E_T)/kT}). \tag{3.14}$$

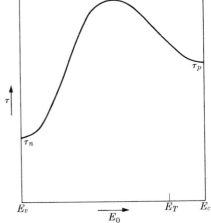

Under the assumptions stated for Eqs. (3.9) and (3.10), we can deter-

FIG. 3.1.   Variation of lifetime with Fermi-level position.

mine the range of validity of their counterparts, Eqs. (3.13) and (3.14). The conditions $n_0 \gg p_0$ for N-type material and $p_0 \gg n_0$ for P-type material require E_0 to be several kT away from the center of the energy gap toward the appropriate band edge. The conditions $n_1 \gg p_1$ for N-type and $p_1 \gg n_1$ for P-type material place the same requirement on E_T. From this it can be seen that Eqs. (3.13) and (3.14) are not valid for E_0, or E_T, or both near the center of the energy gap. Also these equations are not valid for E_0 on one side of center and E_T on the other side of center.

When E_0 and E_T are on opposite sides of the energy-gap center we have the conditions $n_0 \gg p_0$ and $p_1 \gg n_1$ or vice versa. For the N-type case we find that Eq. (3.8) reduces to

$$\begin{aligned} \tau &= \tau_p + \tau_n(p_1/n_0) \\ &= \tau_p + \tau_n(m_p/m_n)^{3/2} \exp\left[(E_c - E_0) - (E_T - E_v)\right]/kT. \end{aligned} \quad (3.15)$$

For the P-type case we find that

$$\begin{aligned} \tau &= \tau_n + \tau_p(n_1/p_0) \\ &= \tau_n + \tau_p(m_n/m_p)^{3/2} \exp\left[(E_0 - E_v) - (E_c - E_T)\right]/kT. \end{aligned} \quad (3.16)$$

Here m_p and m_n are the effective masses of the holes and electrons respectively. Again Eqs. (3.15) and (3.16) are not valid near the center of the energy gap. In terms of Fig. 3.1, Eq. (3.13) would govern the right-hand side, Eq. (3.16) would govern the left-hand side, and Eq. (3.8) would govern the center section.

In effect, the ratio of effective masses is equal to the inverse of the square of the mobility ratio according to Eq. (2.28). We can accordingly substitute $(m_n/m_p)^{3/2} = (\mu_p/\mu_n)^3$ in Eqs. (3.16) and (3.15).

3.2 Photoconductivity

One of the ways of obtaining excess current carriers is by optical excitation. The absorption of a photon of energy $h\nu$ which is greater than the energy-gap width ΔE will elevate an electron from the valence band to the conduction band. This process is illustrated in Fig. 3.2. The excess carriers produced in this way will lower the electrical conductivity of the material. The threshold wavelength for this effect is given by

$$\lambda_0 = \frac{c}{\nu} = \frac{hc}{\Delta E}, \quad (3.17)$$

where c is the velocity of light. Numerically $hc = 1.234$ to give λ_0 in microns if ΔE is in electron volts. Below the threshold energy, the light is largely transmitted through the material or reflected from its surface. Since the dielectric constant of many semiconductors is high, the resulting high index of refraction causes considerable surface reflection unless the light is incident normally.

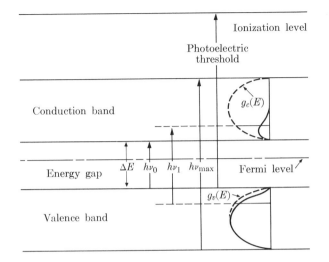

FIG. 3.2. Key frequencies in the photoelectric excitation of a semiconductor.

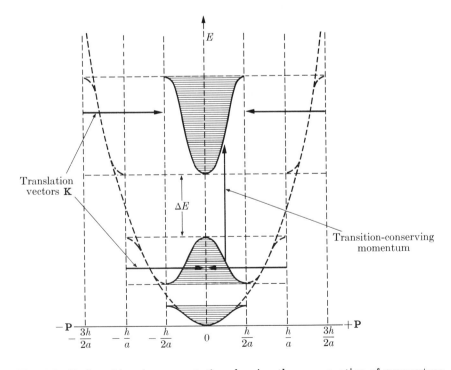

FIG. 3.3. Reduced band representation showing the conservation of momentum.

Spectral response. As the threshold energy $h\nu_0$ is exceeded, the photoconductive response rapidly increases for a constant photon flux. This increase is due to the fact that an increase in photon energy allows transitions, such as $h\nu_1$ in Fig. 3.2, between pairs of energy levels nearer the center of the bands where the density of levels is higher. Momentum must also be conserved in the excitation process.

To see how energy levels in different bands are related in momentum, we will illustrate a reduced energy-momentum plot based on that of Fig. 2.4. In Fig. 2.4 discontinuities in energy are found for $\mathbf{P} = \pm nh/2a$, where n is an integer. Inside $\pm h/2a$ we have the central zone of the figure. It can be shown [2] that all outer zones can be mapped into the central zone by translating along a vector $\mathbf{K}$ which in our one-dimensional case is simply $\pm h/a$.

Consider now the second zone of Fig. 2.4 found between $\pm h/2a$ and $\pm h/a$. If we take the right-hand side and translate it a distance $-h/a$ along the $\mathbf{P}$-axis, we see that it forms the left-hand side of the second band in Fig. 3.3. Similarly, if we translate the left-hand side of the second band of Fig. 2.4 a distance $+h/a$ along the $\mathbf{P}$-axis, we see that it forms the right-hand side of the second band of Fig. 3.3. The second band of Fig. 2.4 has now been reduced to the smaller second band of Fig. 3.3, which lies within the same momentum range as the first band. The translations described above leave unchanged the actual electronic wave functions associated with the individual energy levels within a band.

When the same two vectors are applied to the third allowed band, the result is as shown at the top of Fig. 3.3. If we now consider these upper two reduced bands as representing the valence and conduction bands of a semiconductor, we see that conservation of momentum implies a vertical transition in this energy-momentum plot. Such a transition connects energy levels which are symmetrically spaced relative to the energy gap if the bands are symmetric. It is for this reason that the transition $h\nu_1$ of Fig. 3.2 is shown to be essentially symmetric with respect to the energy gap.

Continuing the discussion of spectral response, we see that as the photon energy is further increased, the photoconductive response begins to drop off as the maximum density of levels is passed. Actually it drops off faster and sooner than might be expected from such a fundamental consideration, because of other competing processes. For one thing, the effects of the surface become much more important as the absorption coefficient increases, since the hole-electron pairs are created much nearer the surface. If, for example, the surface recombination rate greatly exceeds the recombination rate in the bulk material, there will be greater loss of photoelectrically produced carriers when the absorption coefficient increases, and the overall photoconductive effect may decrease.

When the energy of the light increases to the photoelectric threshold, as shown in Fig. 3.2, the emission of photoelectrons from the surface begins. By this time the photoconducting process is usually rather inefficient.

***Sensitization of photoconductors* [3].** It is a well-known fact that in many semiconductor materials the photoconductive sensitivity is greatly increased by the addition of trace impurities of the proper kind. In the preceding discussion it was noted that the recombination rate was proportional to the number of excess minority carriers. In an N-type sample, holes are the minority carriers and we find [see Eq. (3.7)] that

$$U = -\frac{dp}{dt} = \frac{\Delta p}{\tau_p}, \tag{3.18}$$

where the constant of proportionality is the reciprocal of the hole lifetime τ_p. For a given light flux there will be a generation rate g which will determine the dynamic equilibrium density of holes:

$$g = \frac{dp}{dt} \qquad \text{or} \qquad \Delta p = g\tau_p. \tag{3.19}$$

The dark conductivity is electronic and is given by $nq\mu_n$. Under illumination equal numbers of electrons and holes are created so that $\Delta n = \Delta p$, and the illuminated conductivity is

$$\sigma = (n + \Delta p)q\mu_n + \Delta pq\mu_p. \tag{3.20}$$

To increase sensitivity it is clear that we must increase Δp for a given light flux. By Eq. (3.19) this is seen to require an increase in τ_p.

Since this lifetime is controlled by trap recombination, it follows that we must either reduce the number of recombination centers present either by purification or by increasing the crystalline perfection of the sample, or we must render these recombination centers less effective in some way. Sensitization by the addition of trace impurities is believed to achieve the latter effect. If the added impurity has a recombination cross section which is smaller than that of the original impurity or crystal imperfection, if it introduces an energy level at a somewhat higher energy than that of the original center, and if this energy level is usually filled with an electron, it is possible that electrons from these trace impurities can fill the original recombination centers, thus rendering them ineffective for recombination and increasing the effective lifetime of the sample. It should be noted that regardless of the mechanism, the higher photoconductive sensitivity is associated with a longer lifetime and hence a slower device response time.

Considering a more specific example of this mechanism, we will assume that the crystal defect or impurity originally causing the poor lifetime (higher recombination rate) captures holes and then assumes a single plus charge which is attractive to an electron from the conduction band for recombination. This represents a relatively large electronic capture cross section, or a large C_n and a low τ_p. In N-type germanium, it is found that nickel shows two deep-lying energy levels in the forbidden energy gap. If E_0 is above these levels and E_T is below them, the energy levels will be essentially filled with electrons at equilibrium and so will the trapping levels at E_T. The nickel levels will now have a double negative charge, and the trapping levels will be neutral. Then if we inject equal numbers of holes and electrons photoelectrically, we will find that a certain number of holes will be captured by the $Ni^=$-centers either directly, or indirectly by way of the trapping levels. A nickel center having trapped one hole will still be negatively charged, Ni^-. If an E_T-center traps a hole, and if the density of nickel centers is great enough, one of the nickel electrons will drop down to fill the trap and return it to electrical neutrality without involving a conduction-band electron. Furthermore, an $Ni^=$-center should have a much greater capture cross section for holes than a neutral trap does. Now the important point is that having trapped a hole, the nickel center is still negatively charged and represents a low capture cross section for an excess electron in the conduction band. Thus by adding nickel we have greatly decreased the effective C_n and increased the τ_p, since the capture hole may live a long time in the nickel center, allowing excess electrons to make many transits between the device electrodes. It should be noted that even though the excess holes are trapped, they continue to neutralize the space charge of the excess electrons which are still free to carry current. By this means we have greatly increased the device sensitivity.

There are two necessary conditions implied in the above model of sensitization. First, the naturally occurring recombination centers must lie below the nickel levels so that holes normally captured by them will now be captured in the nickel centers, and second, the light excitation level involved must be low enough that the nickel centers are not saturated with holes.

3.3 Effects of Nuclear Radiation

When a high-energy particle of appreciable mass strikes the nucleus of a lattice atom, it knocks it out of its lattice position and sends it careening through the lattice displacing many other atoms. The net result of this action is to produce many lattice defects which can act either as trapping centers or in some cases as donors and acceptors.

In germanium of average resistivity, it seems that the net result of high-energy particle irradiation is to drastically reduce the lifetime of the material and also to produce acceptor centers. This means that N-type material tends to become P-type, and P-type material tends to increase its conductivity. In silicon, irradiation does not convert one conductivity type into the other, but seems to decrease the conductivity of both types so that any sample tends toward a degraded intrinsic behavior (degraded because lifetime and mobility are much lower than normal). In both cases, the active centers are thought to be lattice vacancies and interstitial atoms. The energy levels created in the energy gap by these defects are assumed to be near the center of the gap for silicon and nearer the valence band for germanium, accounting roughly for the behavior described above.

In germanium, the interstitial atoms have two widely separated levels both filled with electrons for electrical neutrality. The lattice vacancies also have two levels, but both are below the center of the gap and are empty for electrical neutrality. At normal temperatures the electron from the upper interstitial atomic level will drop down into one of the vacancy levels, and the other vacancy level will accept an electron from the valence band, thus creating a hole. This tends to move the conductivity in the P-type direction.

Radiation detection [4]. Up to this point we have considered only thermal and photoelectric excitation of valence-band electrons to the conduction band. It is, of course, possible to excite these electrons by impact ionization. In this process a high-energy particle collides with a valence-band electron and transfers sufficient energy to it to lift it across the energy gap into the conduction band. It turns out that all high-energy radiations give the same ionization rate. That is, a 1-Mev particle, when absorbed, will yield about 3×10^5 ion pairs in silicon regardless of whether the particle is an electron, a proton, an alpha particle, or a gamma ray. Of course, the absorption coefficient for gamma rays in silicon is quite low compared to that of the other particles, but once a gamma photon is absorbed it gives the same yield.

The reason for the uniform yield for a given energy regardless of particle type can be understood if one considers the mechanism of particle absorption. For light particles (protons, beta rays, and gamma rays) the initial collision in the semiconductor produces a high-energy recoil electron. From this point on, the degradation of the energy is identical, and we may expect identical results. For heavy particles, we may have a portion of the initial particle energy go into recoiling atomic nuclei. These nuclei in turn will primarily cause electronic ionization, and so again most of the energy rather quickly turns up in high-energy electrons.

It is an interesting fact that the average energy required for the collision excitation of an electron-hole pair in a semiconductor material is between three and four times the energy-gap width. For example, in silicon the average energy absorption per pair is 3.5 ev and $3\,\Delta E = 3.36$ ev; in germanium the average energy per pair is 2.8 ev and $4\,\Delta E = 2.88$ ev. Again this can be understood by considering the absorption mechanism in more detail. Since the absorption of all high-energy particles results in the production of a number of high-energy recoil electrons, we will consider the career of one of these recoil electrons. First, we note that such an electron will transfer a substantial portion of its energy to a second electron upon collision, since they are of equal mass. As the electron avalanche proceeds, the average electronic energy drops off as the number of energetic electrons increases. Finally, one by one, the participating electrons reach an energy approximately four times the energy of the band gap, ΔE. Each such electron will now create an electron-hole pair with an excess kinetic energy of about 3 ΔE. Since it is very improbable that any one of the three particles involved in an ionizing collision process will be at rest following the collision, we will estimate the limits we might expect. First, any particle with 1 ΔE or less of excess kinetic energy after the collision will not make another ionizing collision, but rather will lose its energy by phonon collision. If each of the three particles involved (the impinging electron or hole and the product electron-hole pair) has 1 ΔE of excess energy, the final ionizing collision in the upper limit will involve an electron or hole with an energy of 4 ΔE. If the impinging particle has an energy of 3 ΔE and we consider equipartition of the excess energy after collision as the most probable result, one has to calculate the probability that one particle will deviate enough to possess energy of about 1.5 ΔE in order to produce yet another ionizing event. Since 1 ΔE is lost in the process of exciting the pair, this leaves only 0.25 ΔE for each of the remaining particles. Anything less than this turns out to be relatively improbable so that we may expect that the average energy per pair produced will be between 3 and 4 ΔE, as observed.

It must be kept in mind that a semiconductor detector used to detect massive high-energy particles will have a finite life due to the radiation damage suffered by the material. It also should be kept in mind that particles such as gamma rays and neutrons have a much lower absorption coefficient in a semiconductor than do the charged particles so that they will be detected only with a low efficiency even though, once absorbed, they will give an equal amount of ionization per unit of energy.

3.4 Stimulated Emission [5]

The energy gap of a semiconductor lends itself to use in light amplification by stimulated emission of radiation. Figure 3.4 shows a schematic diagram of the conduction and valence bands of a semiconductor, illustrating this phenomenon. If we take a semiconductor as shown and irradiate it from a high-intensity source with a pumping frequency ν_p so that the energy $h\nu_p$ is significantly greater than the energy gap ΔE, we increase the electron density at the bottom of the conduction band and, by an equal amount, the hole density at the top of the valence band.

In order to get gain in a stimulated emission (by recombination), we must "invert" the electron population at the band edges. Inversion means that the density of electrons at the bottom of the conduction band times the density of holes at the top of the valence band must be greater than the density of electrons at the top of the valence band times the density of vacant levels at the bottom of the conduction band, ensuring that when the crystal is stimulated by light of energy equal to the energy gap, radiative recombination is a more probable event than is pair production. This requires very strong "pumping," that is, a very high rate of electron-hole pair formation and a relatively long minority-carrier lifetime. (Other methods of pumping, such as electrical injection, will be discussed later.)

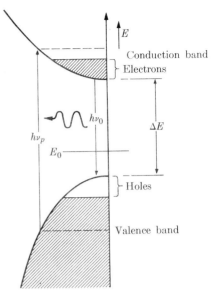

Fig. 3.4.   Stimulated emission in a semiconductor.

If the crystal is now stimulated with light of energy $h\nu_0 = \Delta E$, we may stimulate the transition of these excess electrons back to the valence band. A coherent burst of light of frequency ν_0 can be expected, since each emitted photon can trigger another conduction electron to recombine. As these photons traverse the crystal, an avalanching photon emission takes place. The process can be further enhanced by fabricating the crystal with plane parallel sides so that the effective path length can be increased through multiple internal reflections. Because of the electron population inversion, there will be little loss of photons by the excitation of electrons back into the conduction band at the beginning of the process. As the light burst builds up, it tends to return large numbers of electrons to the valence band so that photons begin to be lost by reexciting electrons. The avalanche then dies out, and a pumping period is required before another avalanche can be started. Continuous wave operation would only be possible if the pumping rate could keep up with the avalanching process.

Some semiconductors seem to involve trapping levels (within the energy gap) in laser action because the stimulated emission frequency measures more than that corresponding to the energy gap. The basic principle, however, is the same as that illustrated above. Traps may help efficiency by aiding in momentum conservation as well as increasing the lifetime of the inverted population. It should be noted that a long lifetime is necessary to achieve a large population inversion without excessive pumping.

3.5 Degenerate Doping

So far we have not considered the effect of very heavy doping. If enough donor impurities are introduced into a semiconductor crystal, the donor energy levels will tend to merge with the energy levels at the bottom of the conduction band. This is brought about by the fact that the high density of donor centers causes the orbits of the donor electrons in neighboring centers to overlap resulting in a splitting of the levels, which were originally discrete and isolated. This is analogous to the splitting of the levels of the individual atoms when a diatomic molecule is formed. In addition to this effect, the high density of donors will cause the Fermi level to move up to a position inside the conduction-band level. All of this has the effect of destroying the semiconductor properties of the material (there is no longer an energy gap between filled and empty levels), and the material exhibits metallic conductivity. A semiconductor material doped to such a level is said to be degenerate. Often such doping can be achieved only by approaching the limits of solid solubility of the doping impurity which is usually in the 0.1 to 1.0% impurity concentration range. This effect also accounts for the fact that many semiconductor materials (including silicon) were originally thought to be metal, since at 99% purity they indeed behave electrically like metals. The same effect can be obtained with acceptor impurities when their density becomes great enough to cause the Fermi level to move inside the top of the valence band.

3.6 Numerical Example

Given a 20-ohm-cm N-type germanium bar 1 cm long and having a cross section of 1 mm^2, with a 100-μsec minority-carrier lifetime. Calculate the intensity in foot-candles of a light falling on a 1 mm by 1 cm side of the bar, which is necessary to decrease its resistance by a factor of two. Assume that the light has a wavelength of 0.54μ and that all of the light striking the bar is absorbed in electron-hole pair production.

First we must calculate the density of current carriers present in the dark so that we will know how many light-produced carriers must be added to double the conductivity of the bar. For 20-ohm-cm material, $\sigma = 0.05$, and we may write the conductivity from Eq. (2.26) and $n_i^2 = np$ as

$$\sigma = 0.05 = q(n\mu_n + p\mu_p) = q[n\mu_n + (n_i^2/n)\mu_p]. \tag{3.21}$$

For germanium at room temperature we find from the Appendix that $n_i^2 = 6.3 \times 10^{26}$. Also $\mu_n = 3900$ cm/sec per unit field and $\mu_p = 1900$ cm/sec per unit field. Substituting these values and solving Eq. (3.21) for n we find that

$$n = 7.6 \times 10^{13}/\text{cm}^3$$

and

$$p = n_i^2/n = 0.83 \times 10^{13}/\text{cm}^3.$$

In the photoelectric electron-hole pair production we create equal numbers of electrons and holes. The problem is then to add equal increments to n and p in Eq. (3.21) to give $\sigma = 0.10$. We write

$$\sigma = 0.10 = q(\Delta n + 7.6 \times 10^{13})\mu_n + (\Delta n + 0.83 \times 10^{13})\mu_p. \quad (3.22)$$

Solving for Δn (using the same values of μ_n and μ_p as before) gives $\Delta n = 5.4 \times 10^{13}/\text{cm}^3$. This value of Δn is a dynamic equilibrium value under continuous light excitation. In the 10^{-2}-cm^3 volume of our bar we need 5.4×10^{11} excess holes and electrons. These excess carriers are decaying at a rate of $5.4 \times 10^{11}/\tau = 5.4 \times 10^{15}/\text{sec}$. Therefore we must have a total of 5.4×10^{15} photons/sec striking the lateral surface of the bar in order to maintain the required dynamic equilibrium.

At a wavelength of 0.54μ, one lumen represents 0.00161 watt (*Handbook of Chemistry and Physics*). This can be converted to quanta per second using $h\nu$ in ergs per quantum and one watt = 10^7 ergs/sec. This gives one lumen of $0.54\text{-}\mu$ light to be equal to 3.8×10^{15} quanta/sec. Therefore we need 1.4 lumens falling on the lateral surface of the bar to maintain a reduction of a factor of two in the resistance of the bar. Since a foot-candle is defined as 1 lumen/ft^2 we find, using the lateral surface area of our bar, that 1.3×10^4 foot-candles of illumination are required.

Problems

3.1 It is possible to estimate the position of the Fermi level by calculating an imaginary half-gap width which would give $n_i = N_D$ at the temperature in question. Using the same approach, estimate the N_D needed to render the material degenerate at 300°K, given $np = Ae^{-\Delta E/kT}$, where $A = 10^{40}$ and $\Delta E = 1.0$ ev.

3.2 Given a 20-ohm-cm P-type germanium bar, having a cross section of 1 mm^2 and length of 1 cm. If the lifetime of the material is 100 μsec and ohmic contacts are made to the end surfaces of the bar, calculate the current one would expect to flow in the bar for 20 v applied across the bar, first with an area of 1 mm^2 illuminated by 10^{15} photons/sec adjacent to the positive end of the bar, and second, with the same area illuminated adjacent to the negative end of the bar. Assume that all incident photons are effective in electron-hole pair production with a unit quantum efficiency.

3.3 Given an N-type silicon crystal of 10 ohm-cm resistivity at room temperature. If the crystal contains a set of recombination centers at an energy $E_T = 0.40$ ev above the center of the energy gap, what would be the hole lifetime at $-100°C$, given a room temperature value of 3.2×10^{-6} sec.

3.4 The room temperature ΔE of germanium is 0.72 ev, $n_i^2 = 6.25 \times 10^{26}$, and $\mu_n/\mu_p = 2.0$. Calculate m_n/m_0 and m_p/m_0, where m_0 is the free-electron mass. Assume the free-electron model for both bands.

Bibliography

1. W. SHOCKLEY and W. T. READ, JR., "Statistics of the Recombination of Holes and Electrons," *Phys. Rev.* **87**, 835–842 (1952).
2. A. ROSE, "Lifetime of Free Electrons and Holes in Solids," *Progress in Semiconductors*, Vol. 2, John Wiley and Sons, New York, 1957.
3. F. SEITZ, *The Modern Theory of Solids*, McGraw-Hill, New York, 1940, Chapter VIII.
4. G. DEARNALEY, "Semiconductor Nuclear Radiation Detectors," *J. Brit. Inst. Radio Engrs.*, 153–169 (August, 1962).
5. G. J. LASHER, "Threshold Relations and Diffraction Loss for Injection Lasers," *IBM J. Res. Develop.* **7**, 58–62 (1963).

CHAPTER 4

SEMICONDUCTOR CONTACTS AND JUNCTIONS

4.1   The Metal-Semiconductor Contact

In a metal there is no forbidden gap between the semicontinuous energy-state distributions of the valence and the conduction bands. The allowed energy levels are filled up to the Fermi level at absolute zero, and at an elevated temperature the state occupancy drops from nearly 100% to nearly zero in an energy range of a few kT on either side of the Fermi level. Figure 4.1 illustrates this situation.

When two systems are placed in electrical contact and allowed to seek an equilibrium, their Fermi levels must be the same, since the energy re-

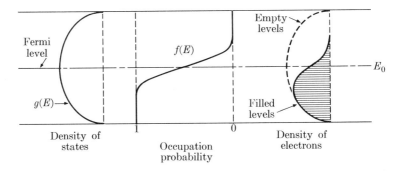

Fig. 4.1.   The conduction band of a metal.

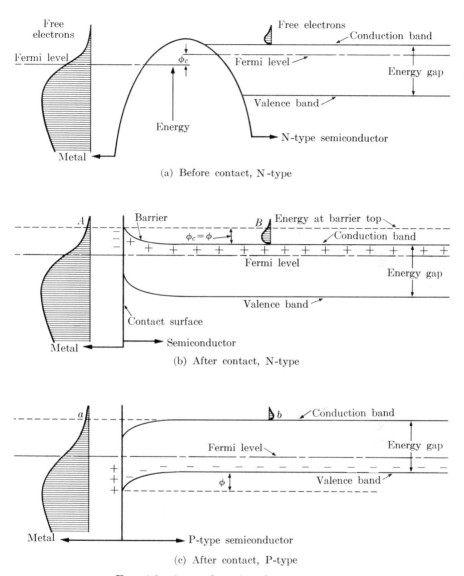

(a) Before contact, N-type

(b) After contact, N-type

(c) After contact, P-type

Fig. 4.2. A metal-semiconductor contact.

quired to remove an electron from the composite system must not be different for different parts of the system. If the Fermi levels of the two component parts of the system are not originally at the same energy, electrons will flow from the one with the higher level to the one with the lower level until they are both charged electrostatically an amount sufficient to bring their Fermi levels to the same energy. This process is illustrated in Fig. 4.2.

In part (a) of the figure the two systems are shown before contact. The Fermi level of the N-type semiconductor is shown higher than that of the metal. While still separate, the electrons of the two materials are retained by the potential barriers of the surfaces. When electrical contact is made (Fig. 4.2b), the surface barriers of both are modified, and electrons can flow from the semiconductor to the metal until the Fermi levels are equal. These electrons form a negative charge layer on the surface of the metal which repels other electrons in the semiconductor until it is neutralized by a matching positive charge layer consisting of ionized donor atoms inside the semiconductor surface. This field effect is represented by the bending up of the band edges of the semiconductor at its surface. Such a bend keeps the normal electron density in the N-type semiconductor conduction band away from the surface.

The similar case for a metal-P-type semiconductor contact is shown in Fig. 4.2(c). Here the electronic flow is from the metal to the semiconductor, creating a dipole charge layer of polarity opposite to that of an N-type contact. In both cases, net charge ceases to flow when the potential barrier is large enough to match the top of the majority-carrier distribution on one side of the barrier to the minority-carrier distribution on the other side.

At equilibrium the electrons above the top of the barrier [shown at A and B in Figure 4.2(b)] are free to flow either way. We will now show that there is no net flow when the two Fermi levels have the same energy. If x_m is the fraction of filled levels in the metal in a small energy interval above the barrier ϕ, and x_s the same fraction in the semiconductor, then the number of electrons above the barrier is

$$\text{In the metal,} \qquad g_m(\phi)x_m,$$
$$\text{In the semiconductor,} \qquad g_s(\phi)x_s.$$

The number of vacant energy levels is

$$\text{In the metal,} \qquad g_m(\phi)(1 - x_m),$$
$$\text{In the semiconductor,} \qquad g_s(\phi)(1 - x_s),$$

where $g_m(\phi)$ and $g_s(\phi)$ are the density of states in the metal and semiconductor at the top of the barrier.

If P_{ms} and P_{sm} are the probabilities of transition from the metal to the semiconductor and vice versa, we may write the opposing currents as

$$\text{Metal} \rightarrow \text{semiconductor} \rightarrow P_{ms}g_m x_m(1 - x_s)g_s,$$
$$\text{Semiconductor} \rightarrow \text{metal} \rightarrow P_{sm}g_s x_s(1 - x_m)g_m.$$

Each of these currents depends on the product $g_s g_m$, and will be equal for

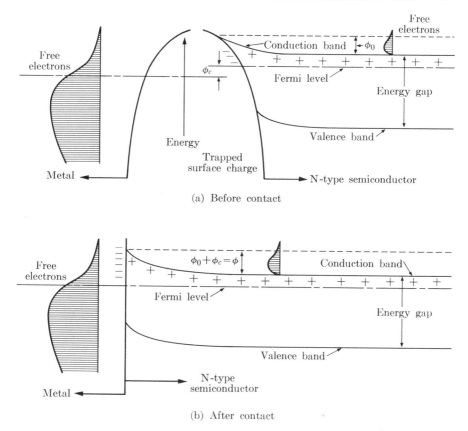

FIG. 4.3. Effect of trapped surface charge on barrier height.

no net flow. In order for these currents to be equal, P_{ms} must equal P_{sm} and x_m must equal x_s. The first is true by symmetry and the second is true by definition of a common Fermi level. From this it can be seen that there is no net flow when the two sides have a common Fermi level, regardless of the size of the density of states functions $g_m(\phi)$ and $g_s(\phi)$.

The difference in the Fermi levels before contact is known as the contact potential difference. In the example given here, this difference in connection with the energy-gap width of the semiconductor determined the height of the final barrier between the two materials. In actual practice, metal-semiconductor contacts show very little correlation between this difference and measured barrier heights. This is usually explained by assuming that the semiconductor carries a permanent dipole layer of trapped charge on its surface which creates a barrier different from that which would be expected from a contact potential difference. Figure 4.3 shows such a barrier before and after contact with a metal. Here the

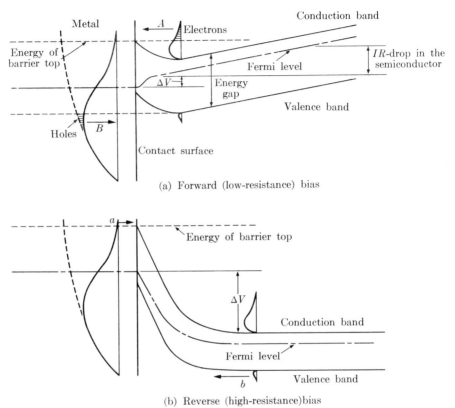

FIG. 4.4. A biased metal-semiconductor contact.

trapped surface charge is shown as negative, and it can be seen that the final barrier height ϕ is the sum of the height of the barrier due to the surface charge ϕ_0 and contact difference of potential, ϕ_c. If the surface charge had been positive, the band edges would have bent down at the surface, and ϕ_0 would have been of the opposite sign, giving a final $\phi < \phi_c$. From this it can be seen that the actual value of ϕ is not to be correlated directly with ϕ_c.

If we apply an electrical bias across the metal-semiconductor contact, as shown in Fig. 4.4, we will shift the Fermi levels relative to each other, and charge will again flow. This time the power supply will maintain the difference in the Fermi levels and a steady current will flow.

In Fig. 4.4(a) is shown the case of "forward" or low-resistance bias. Here the majority electron distribution in the N-type semiconductor is raised relative to the top of the barrier and a portion (A in the figure) flows freely over into the metal. It is opposed only by the much smaller number of free electrons in the metal which are also above the top of the barrier. When the Fermi level of the semiconductor is raised in this manner, the top of the valence band is also raised so that there are more vacant energy levels in the metal (B in the figure) opposite the valence band of the semiconductor than are normally found in the valence band at these energies. This distribution of holes will flow from the metal to the semiconductor, thus increasing the number of charge carriers capable of contributing to the conduction process in the semiconductor near the metal surface. This phenomenon is known as *minority-carrier injection* and is most important in the operation of diodes and transistors.

When minority carriers (holes in N-type material or electrons in P-type material) are injected into a semiconductor, their charge must be neutralized by an increase in the majority-carrier density in their neighborhood. These excess majority carriers come from the electrical contacts. In the case considered here there are injected holes just inside the semiconductor near the metal, and there must therefore be an increase in the electron density to neutralize the hole charge at the same place.

In the forward-bias example shown in Fig. 4.4(a), there is a slope to the band edges and Fermi level remote from the junction at the right of the diagram. This slope represents the electric field required in the body of the semiconductor to maintain the relatively large forward current by the drift of the majority electron distribution. The voltage drop across the contact itself is designated ΔV and shown as a step in the Fermi level in the barrier region.

We have learned that an excess of holes and electrons above the equilibrium number will decay away by recombination with a time constant, known as the lifetime of the material. Also, since these excess carriers are in random thermal motion, they will tend to diffuse into the semiconductor away from the metal contact, where the excess density is maintained. The distance they diffuse on the average during their lifetime is known as their *diffusion length* and is designated L_p for the holes in question. In a region of the semiconductor within a distance L_p of the metal contact, there is therefore a significant reduction of the electrical conductivity when the contact is forward-biased. Historically it was the careful measurement and interpretation of this phenomenon which led to the invention of the transistor.

Figure 4.4(b) shows the case for "reverse" or high-resistance bias of the metal-semiconductor contact. Here the Fermi level of the semiconductor is lowered relative to that of the metal, thus presenting a higher barrier to the majority electron distribution in the semiconductor. The current which flows in this case consists only of the small electron density in the metal a above the barrier flowing into the semiconductor and an equally small minority distribution of holes in the valence band of the semiconductor b flowing into the metal. Increasing this bias to higher values cannot make any more carriers available to the conduction process, nor can it speed up the motion of the carriers appreciably. The reverse current therefore saturates at a low value at a low reverse bias and remains low. Nearly all of the voltage drop in this case is across the contact since the leakage current is small, and hence the IR-drop in the semiconductor is small.

For large reverse biases, the saturation current increases due to the impact ionization of excess holes and electrons in the high field region of the barrier. Eventually this effect leads to electrical breakdown when the impact ionization becomes an avalanche.

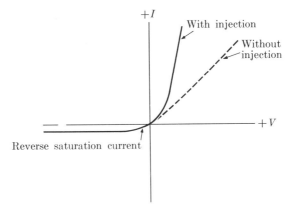

FIG. 4.5. Characteristic curve for a metal–N-type semiconductor contact.

A typical volt-ampere characteristic is shown in Fig. 4.5 with and without the effect of minority-carrier injection. As can be seen, the injection phenomenon significantly reduces the forward resistance of the contact. This is particularly true if the contact is a point contact and the spreading resistance in the semiconductor, which constitutes the major factor in the total resistance, is subject to carrier injection modulation.

4.2 Semiconductor PN-Junctions; the Diode Equation

If we take a semiconductor crystal with donor impurities in one end and acceptor impurities in the other end and with a sharp boundary between the N- and P-regions, we have what is known as a PN-junction. The energy-level diagram of such a system is shown in Fig. 4.6. In Fig. 4.6(a), it is seen that the Fermi level exists at a single energy value throughout the crystal. This is the case for no applied bias voltage. At the junction, the bands are warped in such a way that the two majority-carrier distributions are confined to their own areas (electrons on the N-type side and holes on the P-type side). The warping is just sufficient to establish that no net current flows across the junction. This means that the minority

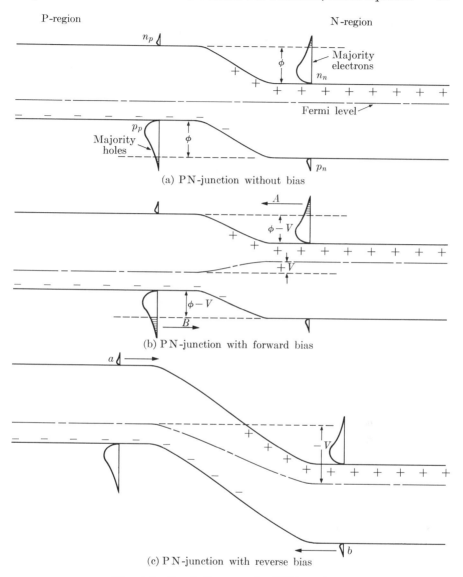

(a) PN-junction without bias

(b) PN-junction with forward bias

(c) PN-junction with reverse bias

Fig. 4.6. Band diagram of a PN-junction.

hole current from N to P is just balanced by the hole current from P to N over the barrier and involving the tip of the majority hole distribution on the P-side. The minority holes are designated p_n and the majority holes p_p in the figure. At the same time the current of the minority electron distribution n_p is balanced by the current of the tip of the majority electron distribution n_n coming from the N-region. The barrier height is designated ϕ.

Minority-carrier injection. Figure 4.6(b) shows the case of a PN-junction with forward bias. The Fermi levels are different on the two sides by the amount of the applied bias voltage V. Here it should be pointed out that the energy scale of all our energy-level diagrams will be given in terms of the electron volt, which is the kinetic energy an electron receives when falling through the potential difference of one volt. Therefore the effect of a bias voltage will be to shift the energy of one side of the diagram by an amount numerically equal to the voltage. The barrier to the flow of the majority-carrier distributions is thus lowered so that more carriers are above the top of the barrier, and a current can flow which increases rapidly as the voltage is increased. A bias equal to ϕ is finally reached, where both majority-carrier distributions in their entirety are free to cross the junction. Having crossed the junction, each now becomes an excess minority-carrier distribution dying out in the P-region at a distance L_n and in the N-region at a distance L_p from the junction. These excess minority-carrier distributions, however, require space-charge neutralization, and hence the majority distributions must be augmented in the region of the junction. Obviously this is a positive feedback process since now the larger n_n- and p_p-distributions can increase the density of injected carriers and so require even larger distributions for neutralization.

In Fig. 4.6(c) is shown the case for reverse bias of the junction. Here the barrier is raised with respect to the majority-carrier distributions so that the minority distributions flow under the barrier. This current soon depletes the minority carriers on both sides of the junction within a diffusion length. The reverse current then saturates at a low value. A rectifier V vs. I curve results and is very similar to that of Fig. 4.5.

We have found previously that the density of electrons in the conduction band of an N-type material is given by Eq. (2.13) as

$$n_n = \left(\frac{2\pi m_n kT}{h^2}\right)^{3/2} e^{-(E_c-E_0)/kT} = N_c e^{-(E_c-E_0)/kT}. \tag{4.1}$$

The density above the barrier ϕ is similarly given as an approximation by

$$n_\phi = N_c e^{-(E_c+q\phi-E_0)/kT}, \tag{4.2}$$

(where ϕ is given in volts, not energy). From Eqs. (4.1) and (4.2) we see that

$$n_\phi = n_n e^{-q\phi/kT}. \tag{4.3}$$

This is a reasonable approximation so long as $q\phi \gg kT$. With no bias, the minority electrons in the P-region must balance n_ϕ, so that we have

$$n_p = n_n e^{-q\phi/kT}. \tag{4.4}$$

If a voltage V is applied, the effective barrier height is changed, as shown in Fig. 4.6. We may now write

$$n(V) = n_n e^{-q(\phi-V)/kT} \tag{4.5}$$

for the density of electrons above the barrier on the N-type side when a bias V is applied. Assuming that the net current of electrons across the junction is determined by diffusion of electrons from the region of higher electron density to the region of lower density, we must find the excess of $n(V)$ over n_p:

$$n(V) - n_p = n_n e^{-q(\phi-V)/kT} - n_n e^{-q\phi/kT} = n_n e^{-q\phi/kT}(e^{qV/kT} - 1)$$
$$= n_p(e^{qV/kT} - 1). \tag{4.6}$$

This excess electron density diffusing across the junction will give the electron current.

Minority-carrier diffusion. In simple diffusion, where the diffusing particles are in random motion, it can be seen that if their average speed is independent of their density, the particles in a region of high density will tend to move away in all directions into regions of low density. Of course, the particles in regions of low density are also moving out in all directions, but since there are fewer particles in regions of low density than there are in regions of high density, the net flow will be away from the regions of high particle density. In such a process the particle current density is directly proportional to the gradient of the particle density. In our one-dimensional case we may write the electronic current density as

$$J_n = qD_n \frac{dn}{dx}, \tag{4.7}$$

where D_n is a constant of proportionality, called the *diffusion constant* for electrons, and (dn/dx) is the *gradient* of the electron density n. Here the conventional current flows in the direction of (dn/dx), since we are dealing with electrons moving in the negative (dn/dx)-direction.

It has been pointed out that excess current carriers disappear by recombination and that the rate of recombination is directly proportional to the density of excess carriers; that is, a given percentage recombines in a given time interval. This gives an exponential law of the decay of excess density. In a steady-state situation, where a constant excess is maintained at the surface of the junction, the excess density must drop off exponentially with distance from the junction, as shown in Fig. 4.9. We will now designate the excess density at the surface of the junction as $n(0)$. Here the zero stands for zero distance from the junction. As one proceeds into the P-region, the excess density can be represented as $n(x) = n(0)e^{-x/L_p}$, where $n(0) = n(V) - n_p$. The initial slope (dn/dx) of this excess density distribution is then $(-n(0)/L_n)$, where L_n (the diffusion length) is the average distance an electron will diffuse in its lifetime τ_n. Substituting this initial slope for (dn/dx) in Eq. (4.7) we have

$$J_n = qD_n(n(V) - n_p)/L_n = qD_n(n_p/L_n)(e^{qV/kT} - 1). \qquad (4.8)$$

Here the distance variable into the P-region is in the negative x-direction (Fig. 4.6) so that (dn/dx) is positive. In a similar manner we may write the diffusion current for holes as

$$J_p = qD_p(p_n/L_p)(e^{qV/kT} - 1), \qquad (4.9)$$

and the total current density across the PN-junction is

$$J = J_p + J_n = q\left(\frac{D_n n_p}{L_n} + \frac{D_p p_n}{L_p}\right)(e^{qV/kT} - 1). \qquad (4.10)$$

This equation is applicable under certain limitations. The condition that $q(\phi - V) \gg kT$ is a limitation because this development was based on Eqs. (2.13) and (2.14), which represent the free carrier distributions at barrier height as

$$N_c \exp\left[-(E_c + q\phi - E_0)/kT\right] \qquad \text{and} \qquad N_v \exp\left[(E_v - q\phi - E_0)/kT\right].$$

Such a representation is inaccurate for effective energy $q(\phi - V)$ within a few kT of the band edge, since at the band edge the carrier density really goes to zero and does not continue to increase exponentially. In terms of Fig. 4.6, this limitation can be expressed as follows. So long as the shaded portions of the electron distribution A and the hole distribution B include only the high-energy exponential tails of the total electron and hole distributions, Eq. (4.10) is valid. The maximum of these distributions occurs at the thermal energy kT from the band edge, and so $q(\phi - V)$ must remain greater than kT if the density is to be expressed as an exponential. This limitation means that for positive voltage bias, V must remain at least 50 mv less than ϕ, if Eq. (4.10) is to be valid at room temperature. For negative V this equation is good up to the physical breakdown voltage of the junction.

In addition to the above limitation, we note that Eqs. (2.13) and (2.14) neglected the unit term in the denominator of the Fermi function so that results based on these equations are valid only for doping levels low enough to keep E_0 several kT from the band edge. This is not a very restrictive limitation, since it allows most practical doping levels. We also note that as V approaches ϕ, the neglect of the effects of space-charge neutrality in injection is no longer valid and the diffusion process becomes much more complex and is superseded by a combination of conduction and diffusion involving the entire majority-carrier distributions. For negative values of V, however, the simple diffusion process is good to quite high values of voltage.

As V becomes negative, Eq. (4.10) reduces to the saturation current

$$J = -q\left(\frac{D_n n_p}{L_n} + \frac{D_p p_n}{L_p}\right) = -J_0. \tag{4.11}$$

The diffusion length $L = \sqrt{D\tau}$ so that Eq. (4.11) can be written

$$J_0 = q(n_p\sqrt{D_n/\tau_n} + p_n\sqrt{D_p/\tau_p}). \tag{4.12}$$

This shows explicitly the dependence of the reverse saturation current of a PN-junction diode on the minority-carrier lifetimes.

The saturation current given in Eqs. (4.11) and (4.12) consists entirely of minority-carrier distributions a and b of Fig. 4.6 leaking across the reverse-biased junction. In large-gap semiconductors such as silicon, this diffusion leakage is small compared with the current generated in the depletion region of the junction due to thermal carrier regeneration. Since the depletion region is by definition "depleted" of current carriers, there is a thermal regeneration process which attempts to restore the thermo-dynamic-equilibrium intrinsic density of holes and electrons. The current so produced may dominate the leakage current density of the junction. The magnitude of this regeneration current will be calculated in Section 5.1.

Depletion capacitance. The steady-state operation of a PN-junction is determined by the injection and diffusion of minority-charge carriers as described above. The transient or ac-operation of a junction must also take into account the capacitance of the junction. From Fig. 4.6, it can be seen that in the region of band-edge curvature, the ionized donors and acceptors will be incompletely neutralized by their respective free-electron and hole distributions. The ionized donors on the N-type side are repre-sented by the plus signs just below the edge of the conduction band, and the ionized acceptors of the P-type side are represented by the minus signs just above the valence band. At the top of the figure, two plus and two minus signs are shown within the region of curvature between the P- and N-type sides. These signs symbolize a dipole layer of charge at the junction which is just sufficient to create the built-in voltage step designated by ϕ. The region of the junction occupied by the neutralized donor and acceptor charge is called the depletion region.

If an external bias is applied, the total voltage step across the depletion region changes, and the dipole layer of charge must also change. This is accomplished by a flow of the majority free-carrier distributions either toward (forward bias) or away (reverse bias) from the junction, thus leaving a different number of unneutralized donors and acceptors. We now

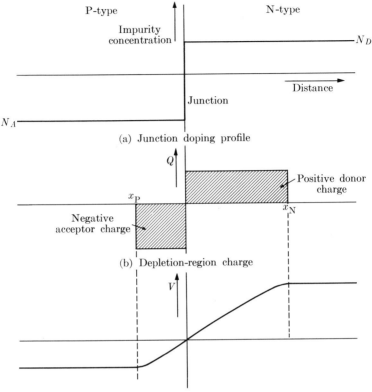

FIG. 4.7. Depletion region of an abrupt junction.

see that to change the voltage across the junction, charge must flow above and beyond the charge flow constituting the diffusion current. This implies a junction capacitance. Since this charge flows into or out of the depletion region, it is called a depletion capacitance.

Proceeding more quantitatively, we will consider an abrupt PN-junction in which the donor and acceptor impurities maintain a uniform concentration right up to the metallurgical junction, as shown in Fig. 4.7(a). Figure 4.7(b) shows the uncompensated space-charge regions on both sides of the junction. These two depletion-region space charges must balance to give a dipole charge layer.

On the N-type side we have a donor impurity density N_D so that the donor charge density is qN_D. From the Poisson equation we have

$$\frac{d^2\phi}{dx^2} = -\frac{\rho}{\epsilon} = -\frac{qN_D}{\epsilon}. \tag{4.13}$$

Integrating to obtain the field in this region, we get

$$\frac{d\phi}{dx} = -\frac{qN_Dx}{\epsilon} + C_1. \tag{4.14}$$

But we know that $(d\phi/dx) = 0$ at $x = x_N$ where space-charge neutralization takes over (see Fig. 4.7c). This allows evaluation of C_1:

$$C_1 = \frac{qN_Dx_N}{\epsilon}. \tag{4.15}$$

Integrating a second time to get the barrier voltage step on the N-type side of the junction, we find that

$$\phi = -\frac{qN_Dx^2}{2\epsilon} + \frac{qN_Dx_Nx}{\epsilon} + C_2. \tag{4.16}$$

If we choose both the origin of voltage and the origin of x at the center of the junction, we have $C_2 = 0$, since $\phi = 0$ when $x = 0$. The voltage drop ϕ_N in the N-type material is

$$\phi_N = \frac{-qN_Dx_N^2}{2\epsilon} + \frac{qN_Dx_N^2}{\epsilon} = \frac{qN_Dx_N^2}{2\epsilon}. \tag{4.17}$$

Similarly, on the P-type side we have

$$\phi_P = \frac{qN_Ax_P^2}{2\epsilon} \tag{4.18}$$

so that the total voltage drop across the junction in the absence of bias is

$$\phi = \phi_P + \phi_N = \frac{q}{2\epsilon}(N_Ax_P^2 + N_Dx_N^2). \tag{4.19}$$

Now the charge of the dipole layer must balance, giving

$$N_Ax_P = N_Dx_N. \tag{4.20}$$

Substituting in (4.19) we get

$$x_N = \left[\frac{2\epsilon\phi N_A}{qN_D(N_D + N_A)}\right]^{1/2} \quad \text{and} \quad x_P = \left[\frac{2\epsilon\phi N_D}{qN_A(N_A + N_D)}\right]^{1/2}. \tag{4.21}$$

By definition the capacity per unit area is

$$C = \left[\frac{\epsilon}{x_N + x_P}\right] = \left[\frac{\epsilon qN_AN_D}{2\phi(N_A + N_D)}\right]^{1/2} = \left[\frac{\epsilon qN_AN_D}{2(\phi - V)(N_A + N_D)}\right]^{1/2}. \tag{4.22}$$

Here we have substituted $(\phi - V)$ for ϕ to include the effect of external voltage bias on the barrier height, ϕ being the unbiased barrier height. The same result is obtained if C is calculated as $C = dQ/d\phi$. It should be noted that as the reverse-bias voltage is increased, the capacity of the junction decreases. This is due to the fact that the depletion region widens with increasing reverse-bias voltage in order to increase the charge in the dipole layer.

4.3   The Photovoltaic Effect

In discussing photoconductivity in Section 3.2, we saw that the excess current carriers injected by the absorption of photons can enhance the electrical conductivity of a piece of semiconductor material. If a PN-junction is present, the excess photo-injected carriers will increase the free-carrier densities on either side of the junction, thus requiring a new adjustment of the relative levels of the two sides for zero net current flow. This results in a photovoltage across the junction.

Let us consider the junction of Fig. 4.8. The light produces excess minority carriers Δn and Δp on the two sides of the junction. Let us assume conditions of low-level optical excitation of minority carriers, which can be expressed as

$$n_p \ll \Delta n \ll n_n, \qquad p_n \ll \Delta p \ll p_p. \tag{4.23}$$

Further, assuming uniform illumination and uniform optical absorption in the bulk material on either side of the junction, we may conclude from the definition of minority-carrier lifetime that

$$\frac{\Delta n}{\tau_n} = \frac{\Delta p}{\tau_p} = g = cI_L, \tag{4.24}$$

where I_L is the light intensity and the carrier generation rate g is proportional to it. If we imagine the junction of Fig. 4.8 to be forward-biased

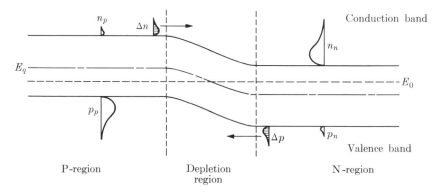

FIG. 4.8. Photovoltaic cell junction under optical excitation.

by an amount ΔV so that there is no net current across the junction, we may write the total electron current moving to the right in the conduction band as

$$i_n = (qAD_n/L_n)(\Delta n - n_p e^{q\Delta V/kT}). \tag{4.25}$$

Here the first term represents the diffusion of the excess density Δn to the right, and the second term represents the portion of the n_n electron distribution raised above the top of the barrier by the application of ΔV and diffusing to the left [compare Eq. (4.8)].

In a similar manner we can write the net current of holes moving to the right in the valence band as

$$i_p = (qAD_p/L_p)(p_n e^{q\Delta V/kT} - \Delta p). \tag{4.26}$$

For the open-circuit condition these currents must be equal and therefore cancel each other. The forward-bias voltage ΔV required to achieve this cancellation then represents the photoelectric voltage desired. Equating (4.25) and (4.26) and solving for ΔV, we obtain the open-circuit photovoltage

$$\Delta V = \frac{kT}{q} \ln\left[\frac{D_n \Delta n L_p + D_p \Delta p L_n}{D_n n_p L_p + D_p p_n L_n}\right]. \tag{4.27}$$

We may eliminate Δn and Δp by use of Eq. (4.24) and we may substitute resistivities for n_p and p_n, since $n_p = q\mu_p\rho_p n_i^2$ and $p_n = q\mu_n\rho_n n_i^2$ when $n_p \ll p_p$ and $p_n \ll n_n$. Also defining a mobility ratio $\mu_n/\mu_p = b = D_n/D_p$ we may write

$$\Delta V = \frac{kT}{q} \ln\left[\frac{(b\tau_n L_p + \tau_p L_n)cI_L}{(\rho_p L_p + \rho_n L_n)q\mu_n n_i^2}\right]. \tag{4.28}$$

Equation (4.28) expresses the open-circuit photovoltage in terms of the junction material parameters and the light intensity.

We may express the short-circuit photocurrent in a similar manner. Letting $\Delta V = 0$ in Eqs. (4.25) and (4.26), we may write the total current $i = i_n - i_p$, obtaining

$$i = qA[D_n(\Delta n - n_p)/L_n + D_p(\Delta p - p_n)/L_p]. \tag{4.29}$$

Here again Δn and Δp may be eliminated by using Eq. (4.24).

Referring to Figure 4.8, we may now interpret the photovoltage graphically. The dashed line labeled E_q is called a *quasi-Fermi* level and is placed at a level on each side such that the one-half probability point of the Fermi function must be located at that level in order to obtain Δn and Δp as the product of the Fermi function and the density-of-states functions $g_c(E)$ and $g_v(E)$, respectively. This level then represents the one to which the majority-carrier distribution on the other side of the junction must have its true Fermi level raised in order to cancel out any net electron or hole flow. In the special case of $\tau_n = \tau_p$ and equal doping, the separation of the quasi-Fermi level and the true Fermi level on either side is equal to ΔV, the photovoltage. In other more general cases this is not quite true, since only the overall net current is zero, and the electron and hole currents are not necessarily zero individually.

4.4   The Linvill Lumped Model [3]

In the use of passive circuit components, such as resistors and capacitors, a lumped resistance and capacitance are used in circuit analysis. For example, no one would think of using the physical dimensions of the resistor, together with the resistivity of its material, in order to analyze its effect in a circuit. In an analogous manner, Linvill has lumped the physical dimensions and intrinsic material behavior in his analysis of the characteristics of diodes and transistors. To do this he has coined new words for the material behavior characteristics. Just as the material characteristic impeding the flow of electric current is called *resistance*, so the material characteristic which allows current carriers to move by a diffusion process is called *diffusance*, and the material characteristic which causes current carriers to recombine is called *combinance*.

The definition of these lumped parameters is as follows. Let us consider a planar PN-junction of area A. From Eq. (4.10) we find the current through this junction to be given by

$$I = qA\left(\frac{D_n n_p}{L_n} + \frac{D_p p_n}{L_p}\right)(e^{qV/kT} - 1). \tag{4.30}$$

The terms $n_p(e^{qV/kT} - 1)$ and $p_n(e^{qV/kT} - 1)$ represent the concentrations of excess minority electrons and holes at the junction surface. Designating these as $n(0)$ and $p(0)$, respectively, since we are letting $x = 0$ at the junction surface, we may write

$$I = qA[D_n n(0)/L_n + D_p p(0)/L_p], \tag{4.31}$$

where $n(0)/L_n$ and $p(0)/L_p$ are the initial gradients of the electron and hole concentrations as they diffuse away from the junction surface. Figure 4.9 shows these injected minority-carrier concentrations. At the top of the figure is shown the familiar band representation of the carrier distributions, with holes diffusing to the right and electrons to the left. At the bottom of the figure is shown a simplified plot of only the minority-carrier distributions corresponding to the ones above. At the bottom both carrier concentrations are plotted. It can be seen that both hole and electron currents add to give a conventional current (4.31) flowing to the right.

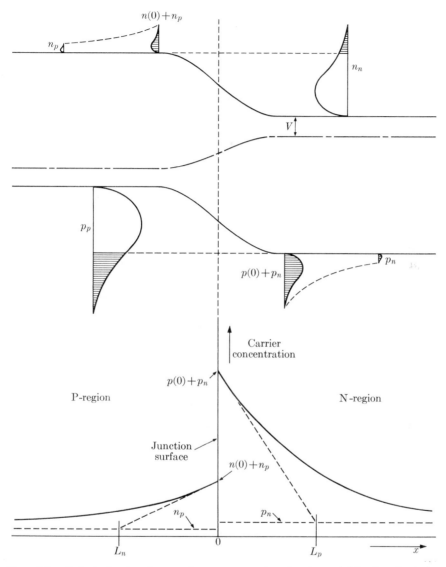

FIG. 4.9. Injected minority-carrier concentration in the neighborhood of the junction.

By analogy with Ohm's law, we may write Eq. (4.31) in the form

$$I_d = H_{dn}n(0) + H_{dp}p(0), \tag{4.32}$$

where $n(0)$ and $p(0)$ are analogous to voltages and H_{dn} and H_{dp}, called the *electron diffusance* and the *hole diffusance*, respectively, are analogous to conductances. It should be noted that H_{dn} and H_{dp} represent opposite sides of the junction. It can be seen that $H_{dn} = qAD_n/L_n$ and $H_{dp} = qAD_p/L_p$. The diffusion length represents the effective distance over which the initial concentration gradient is maintained. In general, then

$$H_d = qAD/w, \qquad (4.33)$$

where w is the length of material in which the diffusion current is flowing.

Let us now consider the hole-diffusion current shown in Fig. 4.9. It is understood that there is also an electron current, which may not be negligible, and which can be treated in a completely analogous manner. From this figure it is clear that the gradient (dp/dx) steadily diminishes as one leaves the junction. At each point of x the diffusion current is dying away with distance. Since the junction is a two-terminal device, the total current is constant through every cross-sectional plane, and as the minority-carrier diffusion current diminishes, the majority-carrier drift current increases. The mechanism by which minority-carrier diffusion is replaced by majority-carrier drift is the recombination of the minority carriers. Therefore there is a recombination current operating in parallel with the diffusion current.

In Eq. (4.24) the recombination rate of excess minority carriers is given by $\Delta p/\tau_p$. In terms of the symbolism of Eq. (4.31) the recombination current of the holes is given by

$$I_c = q(A\,dx)p(x)/\tau_p, \qquad (4.34)$$

or by lumping constants,

$$I_c = H_{cp}p(x), \qquad (4.35)$$

where $p(x)$ is the density of excess holes at a distance x from the junction surface, and the recombination occurs in the volume $(A\,dx)$ around the point x, and H_{cp} is called the *hole combinance*. For electrons, H_{cn} is analogous to H_{cp}, and in general, we may write

$$H_c = qAw/\tau, \qquad (4.36)$$

where the volume in which the recombination occurs is Aw. Both H_d and H_c have the dimensions of ql^3t^{-1}. At any point x in Fig. 4.9 the total current is given by $I = I_d + I_c$. At $x = 0$, $I_c = 0$, and $I = I_d$, at a large value of x, where $p(x) = 0$, $I_d = 0$ and $I = I_c$ integrated from zero to x. At this large x, the actual current is carried by the drift of the majority electrons in the N-region, and thus the drift current equals the total recombination current of the junction region.

The area under the curve of Fig. 4.9 represents stored minority carriers in transit. Therefore it is also proportional to stored charge. In all of the preceding discussion, we were considering only dc-current. If we are to consider ac-current, we must also consider this stored charge. The total charge stored under the curve of Fig. 4.9 at the bottom is given by $qA[L_p p(0) + L_n n(0)]$. For the hole diffusion current, we would find the same terminal current, for example, for the same terminal gradient $(p(0)/L_p)$, which, in the absence of recombination, would require only the charge stored under the line from $p(0) + p_n$ to L_p. Such a stored charge distribution implies a sink for holes at $x = L_p$. If we now consider the recombination process as a mechanism for producing such an effective sink leading to the same initial hole concentration gradient, we may consider the effective stored charge required to give the observed terminal diffusion current as

$$Q = qAL_p p(0)/2. \tag{4.37}$$

Differentiating with respect to time, we find the storage current to be

$$I_s = \frac{dQ}{dt} = \frac{qAL_p}{2} \frac{dp(0)}{dt}, \tag{4.38}$$

and in lumped form,

$$I_s = S_p \frac{dp(0)}{dt}. \tag{4.39}$$

A similar S_n is operative on the P-side of the junction for the electronic diffusion current. These S-constants are called *storances*, and they are analogous to capacitances. In general, then,

$$S = qAL/2. \tag{4.40}$$

There are other lumped quantities suggested by Linvill for other charge transport mechanisms but we will confine ourselves to the use of diffusance, combinance, and storance for most examples.

4.5 Numerical Example

Calculate and compare the diffusion-current densities in reverse-bias saturation at 300°K for a germanium and a silicon PN-junction diode, given the properties of the materials listed in Table 4.1. The diffusion

TABLE 4.1

Property		Germanium	Silicon
Diffusion constant for electrons,	D_n	80 cm^2/sec	20 cm^2/sec
Diffusion constant for holes,	D_p	47 cm^2/sec	12 cm^2/sec
Lifetime for electrons in P-region,	τ_n	10^{-6} sec	10^{-6} sec
Lifetime for holes in N-region,	τ_p	10^{-5} sec	10^{-5} sec
Donor density in N-region,	N_D	10^{14}/cc	10^{14}/cc
Acceptor density in P-region,	N_A	2×10^{16}/cc	2×10^{16}/cc
Intrinsic resistivity at 300°K,	ρ_i	45 ohm-cm	2×10^5 ohm-cm

leakage-current densities required are given by Eq. (4.11). The problem will be to calculate the values of n_p, p_n, L_n, and L_p from the data given.

We will first find n_p and p_n for the two regions of the two materials. We know that $np = n_i^2$ so that the first task is to find n_i^2 from the given intrinsic resistivities. From Eq. (2.19) we have

$$1/\rho_i = \sigma_i = n_i q(\mu_n + \mu_p). \tag{4.41}$$

The mobilities for pure material and the value of q are given in the Appendix at the back of the book. Solving Eq. (4.41) for n_i and evaluating for the two materials we have,

For germanium,	For silicon,
$n_i = (1/\rho_i)q(\mu_n + \mu_p)$	$n_i = (1/\rho_i)q(\mu_n + \mu_p)$
$\quad = (1/45)\ 1.6 \times 10^{-19}$	$\quad = (1/2 \times 10^5)\ 1.6 \times 10^{-19}$
$\quad\quad \times (3900 + 1900)$	$\quad\quad \times (1500 + 480)$
$\quad = 2.4 \times 10^{13}/\text{cc};$	$\quad = 1.6 \times 10^{10}/\text{cc}.$

Using the relation $np = n_i^2$, we may now calculate the required p_n and n_p for the two materials. From the requirement for the detailed balance of charge to yield space-charge neutrality, we know that $n_n = N_D + p_n$ and $p_p = N_A + n_p$, so that the np-products for the N-region may be written as:

$n_n p_n = p_n(N_D + p_n) = n_i^2$	$n_n p_n = p_n(N_D + p_n) = n_i^2$
$\quad = p_n(10^{14} + p_n)$	$\quad = p_n(10^{14} + p_n)$
$\quad = 5.8 \times 10^{26},$	$\quad = 2.5 \times 10^{20},$
giving $\ p_n = 5.5 \times 10^{12}/\text{cm}^3;$	giving $\ p_n = 2.5 \times 10^6/\text{cm}^3.$

The similar calculation in the P-region gives

$n_p p_p = n_p(2 \times 10^{16} + n_p)$	$n_p p_p = n_p(2 \times 10^{16} + n_p)$
$\quad = 5.8 \times 10^{26},$	$\quad = 2.5 \times 10^{20},$
giving $\ n_p = 2.6 \times 10^{10}/\text{cm}^3;$	giving $\ n_p = 1.3 \times 10^4/\text{cm}^3.$

We are now ready to calculate the L_n- and L_p-values. This is accomplished by using the relation $L = (D\tau)^{1/2}$ given in Eq. (4.11). In the N-region, we have

$$L_p = (D_p\tau_p)^{1/2} = 2.2 \times 10^{-2}\ \text{cm}, \qquad L_p = (D_p\tau_p)^{1/2} = 1.1 \times 10^{-2}\ \text{cm},$$

and in the P-region

$$L_n = (D_n\tau_n)^{1/2} = 8.9 \times 10^{-3}\ \text{cm}, \qquad L_n = (D_n\tau_n)^{1/2} = 4.5 \times 10^{-3}\ \text{cm}.$$

Finally, we may calculate the two diffusion-leakage currents from Eq. (4.11):

$$J = q\left(\frac{D_n n_p}{L_n} + \frac{D_p p_n}{L_p}\right)$$
$$= 1.6 \times 10^{-19}(2.3 + 118)10^{14}$$
$$= 1.9 \text{ ma/cm}^2,$$

$$J = q\left(\frac{D_n n_p}{L_n} + \frac{D_p p_n}{L_p}\right)$$
$$= 1.6 \times 10^{-19}(0.58 + 27)10^{8}$$
$$= 0.46 \text{ nanoamp/cm}^2.$$

From this result it can be seen that the diffusion-leakage current of a silicon diode is about six orders of magnitude smaller than that of a germanium diode (other parameters being equal). In actual practice it is observed that the leakage of a silicon diode is larger than this predicted diffusion leakage, being only about three orders of magnitude less than that of a germanium diode. Surface leakage at large reverse-bias voltages may play some part in the silicon-diode leakage current, but in general, the major part of this current is due to carrier regeneration in the depletion layer of the junction. This subject is discussed in Section 5.1.

Problems

4.1 By balancing field current ($qn\mu_n \, dv/dx$) against diffusion current ($qD_n \, dn/dx$) in the region of a barrier, derive the Einstein relation $\mu_n = qD_n/kT$.

4.2 A germanium diode has a very heavily doped N-region and a P-region in which the density of acceptors is $6 \times 10^{13}/\text{cm}^3$. Calculate the lifetime of the minority electrons in the P-region, given that a current density of 1 amp/cm^2 is measured at a forward voltage of 100 mv. (The measurement is made at 300°K.)

4.3 In a silicon PN-junction of equal doping on both sides of 10^{17} impurity atoms/cm^3, compare the open-circuit photovoltage for $\tau_n = \tau_p$ and for $\tau_n = 10\tau_p$. Indicate the polarity of the voltage. Assume that the entire device (including regions remote from the junction) is illuminated by a light of sufficient intensity to produce 10^{13} excess minority carriers per cubic centimeter in the P-region.

4.4 Derive an expression for the depletion capacitance of a linearly graded PN-junction, where $N_D - N_A = ax$ (for $x = 0$ at the center of the junction) analogous to Eq. (4.22).

Bibliography

1. D. LeCroissette, *Transistors*, Prentice-Hall, Englewood Cliffs, New Jersey, 1963.
2. J. Moll, *Physics of Semiconductors*, McGraw-Hill, New York, 1964.
3. J. G. Linvill and J. F. Gibbons, *Transistors and Active Circuits*, McGraw-Hill, New York, 1961.

CHAPTER 5

DIODES

Semiconductor material is used in a wide variety of electrical components, but by far the most important devices using semiconductors are diodes and transistors. Historically, both of these components have been made with metal-semiconductor point contacts, but present PN-junction technology has advanced to the point where only devices made with junctions seem to be of major significance. Accordingly, we will confine our discussion to junction devices.

5.1 Diffusion Analysis of the Diode

At the outset we will establish a continuity equation for excess current carriers. We will begin by considering electronic current as an example. It has been previously noted that the electron diffusion-current density is given by

$$J_n = -(-q)D_n \frac{dn}{dx}. \tag{5.1}$$

Here, the first minus sign means that the particle current flows in the direction of a negative (dn/dx); that is, from a region of high electron concentration to a region of low electron concentration. If n increases with x to the right, Eq. (5.1) shows that the electrons move to the left and conventional current flows to the right.

From the definition of mobility (average velocity per unit field), we may write the drift-current density as

$$\mathcal{J}_n = -qn\mu_n \frac{dV}{dx}. \tag{5.2}$$

Here, V increasing with x to the right will cause electrons to drift to the right, and conventional current to flow to the left. It should be noted that q itself always represents a positive number. The total conventional current due to electrons is

$$J = J_n + \mathcal{J}_n = q\left(D_n \frac{dn}{dx} - n\mu_n \frac{dV}{dn}\right). \tag{5.3}$$

If we now consider an element of unit area and thickness dx (therefore the volume of the element is dx), we may compute the rate of change of particle density in the element, due to current flow, as

$$\frac{\partial n}{\partial t} = \frac{1}{q}\frac{\partial J}{\partial x}. \tag{5.4}$$

If we consider particles (electrons) flowing to the left, we see from Eq. (5.4) that with J increasing across dx to the right, the density n in the element will be increasing with time.

Finally, we must consider the effect of recombination. The rate is given by Eq. (4.24) to be $\Delta n/\tau_n$. The balance for electrons may now be written

$$\frac{\partial n}{\partial t} = -\frac{n - n_p}{\tau_n} + \frac{1}{q}\frac{\partial J}{\partial x}. \tag{5.5}$$

Substituting (5.3) we have

$$\frac{\partial n}{\partial t} = -\frac{n - n_p}{\tau_n} + D_n \frac{\partial^2 n}{\partial x^2} + \mu_n \frac{\partial(n\mathcal{E})}{\partial x}, \tag{5.6}$$

where the electric field $\mathcal{E} = -(dv/dx)$. In most cases which we will consider, the drift-current term is negligible, and the one-dimensional electron continuity equation (5.6) for excess electrons in P-type material reduces to

$$\frac{\partial n}{\partial t} = -\frac{n - n_p}{\tau_n} + D_n \frac{\partial^2 n}{\partial x^2}. \tag{5.7}$$

There is a similar excess hole continuity equation applying to N-type material:

$$\frac{\partial p}{\partial t} = -\frac{p - p_n}{\tau_p} + D_p \frac{\partial^2 p}{\partial x^2}. \tag{5.8}$$

To solve these equations, we will use the following expressions for the minority-carrier charge densities:

$$p(x, t) = p_n + p_1(x) + p_2(x)e^{j\omega t}, \tag{5.9}$$

$$n(x, t) = n_p + n_1(x) + n_2(x)e^{j\omega t}. \tag{5.10}$$

Substituting (5.9) into (5.8) gives two differential equations: a time-independent (dc) equation,

$$0 = -\frac{p_1}{\tau_p} + D_p \frac{d^2 p_1}{dx^2}, \tag{5.11}$$

and a time-dependent (ac) equation,

$$j\omega p_2 = -\frac{p_2}{\tau_p} + D_p \frac{d^2 p_2}{dx^2}. \tag{5.12}$$

Since p_1 must be finite at $x = \infty$, the solution of (5.11) is

$$p_1 = P_1 e^{-x/L_p}, \tag{5.13}$$

where

$$L_p = \sqrt{D_p \tau_p}.$$

Equation (5.13) represents the space distribution of minority carriers under steady-state conditions, as represented in Fig. 4.9.

The solution of (5.12), which is finite at $x = \infty$, is also found to be

$$p_2 = P_2 \exp\left[-x(1 + j\omega\tau_p)^{1/2}/L_p\right]. \tag{5.14}$$

Substituting in Eq. (5.9) we find that

$$\begin{aligned}
p(x, t) = p_n &+ P_1 \exp\left(-x/L_p\right) \\
&+ P_2 \exp\left[-x(1 + j\omega\tau_p)^{1/2}/L_p\right] \exp\left(j\omega t\right),
\end{aligned} \tag{5.15}$$

and in a similar manner Eq. (5.10) becomes

$$\begin{aligned}
n(x, t) = n_p &+ N_1 \exp\left(-x/L_n\right) \\
&+ N_2 \exp\left[-x(1 + j\omega\tau_n)^{1/2}/L_n\right] \exp\left(j\omega t\right).
\end{aligned} \tag{5.16}$$

Now converting to the diode current-density, we use the simple diffusion equation (4.7):

$$j = j_n + j_p$$
$$= -q\left(D_n \frac{\partial n}{\partial x} + D_p \frac{\partial p}{\partial x}\right). \tag{5.17}$$

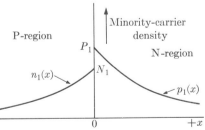

Here, positive current is assumed to flow to the right, and the disposition of the P- and N-regions and the associated minority-carrier density gradients are shown in Fig. 5.1. It can be seen that positive holes are

FIG. 5.1. Excess minority-carrier distributions illustrating Eq. (5.13) and its electronic counterpart.

flowing to the right but that dp/dx is negative. Similarly, negative electrons are flowing to the left and dn/dx is positive. Therefore we must put a negative sign before the entire expression to satisfy the arbitrary assumption of positive current to the right.

Differentiating (5.15) and (5.16), evaluating at $x = 0$, and substituting into (5.17), we get the terminal current density of the diode. Since the diffusion current is only equal to the total current of the diode at the surface of the junction, we must evaluate both dn/dx and dp/dx at $x = 0$. It should also be noted that both Eqs. (5.17) and (5.16) give the carrier density as a function of positive x. From Fig. 5.1 it is clear that $n_1(x)$ and $p_1(x)$ drop off in opposite directions from the junction surface. For this reason we must change the sign of the derivative dn/dx when substituting in Eq. (5.17). The negative sign in front of (5.17) accomplishes this so that the dn/dx from Eq. (5.16) can be substituted directly:

$$j = \frac{qD_n}{L_n}[N_1 + N_2(1 + j\omega\tau_n)^{1/2}e^{j\omega t}] + \frac{qD_p}{L_p}[P_1 + P_2(1 + j\omega\tau_p)^{1/2}e^{j\omega t}].$$
$$(5.18)$$

In order to interpret Eq. (5.18), we may refer to Fig. 4.6(b). Here it is seen that the initial concentration or density of electrons flowing into the P-region under forward bias is the distribution labeled A, which is here identified with N_1. Similarly, the distribution of holes flowing into the N-region is labeled B and is here identified with P_1; N_2 and P_2 are the amplitudes of the ac component not shown in Fig. 4.6.

If we now refer to the reverse-bias condition illustrated in Fig. 4.6(c), we see that all diffusion current is determined by the minority distributions a and b, here identified with n_p and p_n. The reverse saturation-current density given in Eq. (4.11) can be written as:

$$I_0 = qA\left(\frac{D_n n_p}{L_n} + \frac{D_p p_n}{L_p}\right) = I_{n0} + I_{p0},\qquad(5.19)$$

where A is the area of the junction. We can now write the total diode current in terms of I_{n0} and I_{p0} as follows:

$$i = \frac{I_{n0}}{n_p}[N_1 + N_2(1 + j\omega\tau_n)^{1/2}e^{j\omega t}] + \frac{I_{p0}}{p_n}[P_1 + P_2(1 + j\omega\tau_p)^{1/2}e^{j\omega t}].$$
$$(5.20)$$

It should be pointed out that there is no small-signal limitation in Eq. (5.20); i is linear in N and P regardless of the size of N or P.

In addition to this diffusion component of the dc saturation current, given by Eq. (5.19), there is the regeneration component mentioned in Chapter 4. By adding x_N and x_P, we obtain the full depletion width of the diode junction. From Eq. (4.21) this width is

$$x(V) = x_N + x_P = \left[\frac{2\epsilon(\phi - V)(N_A + N_D)}{qN_AN_D}\right]^{1/2}. \quad (5.21)$$

By definition, this depletion region is void of current carriers. The regeneration current is given by the intrinsic density of carriers, n_i, divided by the effective lifetime, τ, and multiplied by the volume of the region (this is a first-order approximation and assumes traps at the center of the energy gap):

$$I_r = \frac{qAx(V)n_i}{\tau} = \frac{Aqn_i}{\tau}\left[\frac{2\epsilon(\phi - V)(N_A + N_D)}{qN_AN_D}\right]^{1/2}. \quad (5.22)$$

Since each electron-hole pair is generated at the same point in the depletion region, together they carry the current of only one carrier crossing the entire depletion region. The effective lifetime τ will be at least as long as the longer lifetime on either side of the junction (see Fig. 3.1).

From Eq. (5.22) it is clear that the larger the reverse bias V and the shorter the lifetime τ, the larger will be this regeneration component of the reverse saturation current. To combine Eqs. (5.19) and (5.22), we first transform (5.19) by the substitution of $n_p = n_i^2/N_A$ and $p_n = n_i^2/N_D$, and let τ represent the lifetime throughout the diode. The total reverse saturation current then becomes:

$$I_0 = \frac{qAn_i}{\tau}\left\{n_i\left[\frac{N_DL_n + N_AL_p}{N_AN_D}\right] + \left[\frac{2\epsilon(\phi - V)(N_A + N_D)}{qN_AN_D}\right]^{1/2}\right\}, \quad (5.23)$$

where the first term, originating from the diffusion leakage-current, is seen to decrease rapidly as n_i decreases. From this we can conclude that at room temperature, wide-gap semiconductor diodes will exhibit a leakage current dominated by the regeneration term, and narrow-gap diodes will show diffusion leakage. As the temperature is lowered in a low-gap material, the n_i drops exponentially so that a transition from diffusion to regeneration leakage may occur in the same device. At room temperature a germanium diode shows diffusion leakage, while a silicon diode shows primarily regeneration leakage.

Small-signal analysis. To introduce voltage in place of the electron and hole densities we define

$$v = V_1 + V_2e^{j\omega t}. \quad (5.24)$$

From Eq. (4.6) we may write the excess minority-carrier density at the junction surface as

$$p(0, t) = p_n + P_1 + P_2e^{j\omega t} = p_ne^{qv/kT}. \quad (5.25)$$

Substituting (5.24) we get

$$p(0, t) = p_n \exp \{q[V_1 + V_2 \exp (j\omega t)]/kT\}$$
$$= p_n \exp (qV_1/kT) \exp \{qV_2 [\exp (j\omega t)]/kT\}. \qquad (5.26)$$

Now making the small-signal approximation that $\exp [qV_2 (\exp j\omega t)/kT]$ can be represented by the first two terms of its series expansion

$$[1 + qV_2 (\exp j\omega t)/kT],$$

we may write:

$$p(0, t) = p_n e^{qV_1/kT} + p_n(e^{qV_1/kT})(qV_2/kT)e^{j\omega t}. \qquad (5.27)$$

Now equating corresponding terms in (5.22) and (5.27) we have

for holes:

$$P_1 = p_n(e^{qV_1/kT} - 1); \qquad (5.28)$$

$$P_2 = p_n \frac{qV_2}{kT} e^{qV_1/kT}, \qquad (5.29)$$

for electrons:

$$N_1 = n_p(e^{qV_1/kT} - 1); \qquad (5.30)$$

$$N_2 = n_p \frac{qV_2}{kT} e^{qV_1/kT}. \qquad (5.31)$$

The small-signal approximation above requires that $qV_2 \ll kT$, since the third term of the expansion must be negligible. At room temperature this means that $V_2 \ll 25$ mv. The necessity of introducing such an approximation arises because of the exponential relation between bias voltage and excess minority-carrier density. In view of this, it is usually advisable to work out results using the current–minority-carrier density relations (5.20), reserving the transformation of excess minority-carrier density to voltage for the last step.

Admittance of the diode. Defining i in a form similar to the definition of v, we may write

$$i = I_1 + I_2 e^{j\omega t}. \qquad (5.32)$$

Now substituting (5.32) and (5.42) in Eq. (5.20), we may write the diode admittance as

$$Y = \frac{I_2}{V_2} = \frac{(I_{n0}/n_p)N_2(1 + j\omega\tau_n)^{1/2} + (I_{p0}/p_n)P_2(1 + j\omega\tau_p)^{1/2}}{V_2}$$

$$= I_{n0}(1 + j\omega\tau_n)^{1/2} + I_{p0}(1 + j\omega\tau_p)^{1/2}(q/kT)e^{qV_1/kT}, \qquad (5.33)$$

where we have also substituted the definition of N_2 and P_2 from (5.31) and (5.29). This expression can be simplified under a low-frequency assumption that $\omega\tau \ll 1$ so that $(1 + j\omega\tau)^{1/2}$ can be approximated by $(1 + j\omega\tau/2)$. Now the admittance becomes:

$$Y = [(q/kT)e^{qV_1/kT}][I_{n0} + I_{p0} + (j\omega/2)(I_{n0}\tau_n + I_{p0}\tau_p)], \qquad (5.34)$$

giving a conductance of

$$G = (qI_0/kT)e^{qV_1/kT} \qquad (5.35)$$

in parallel with an effective capacitance

$$C = [I_{n0}\tau_n + I_{p0}\tau_p](q/2kT)e^{qV_1/kT}, \qquad (5.36)$$

where $I_0 = I_{n0} + I_{p0}$, the total reverse diffusion leakage-current of the diode.

The capacitance of Eq. (5.36) is often called the *diffusion capacitance* to distinguish it from the *depletion capacitance* (Eq. 4.22), which is also in parallel with the conductance of the junction. Figure 5.2 shows the $p(x, t)$-curve of a diode in which $N_1 \ll P_1$ and $N_2 \ll P_2$. This corresponds to heavy doping of the P-region compared to the N-region $(N_A \gg N_D)$. It should be noted that the use of Eqs. (5.31) and (5.29) for N_2 and P_2 places this admittance equation under the small-signal restriction.

By reference to Fig. 5.2, we may discover the physical interpretation of Eq. (5.20) in which the terms in N_1 and N_2 are neglected and $(1 + j\omega\tau_p)^{1/2}$ is represented by $1 + j\omega\tau_p/2$. Since $\omega \ll \tau_p$, the injected hole density $p(x, t)$ will always be in quasi-equilibrium as P_1 is harmonically modulated with the amplitude P_2. The displacement current which flows in such a case will determine the imaginary part of the *current-density immittance* (I_2/P_2) and will be determined by the charge stored when P_1 changes. This charge will effectively not be the total ΔQ for a given ΔP_1, since part of the total ΔQ will represent injected carriers which recombine, as well as stored carriers. If there were no recombination, the instantaneous $p(x)$ would be given by the straight lines to the point $x = L_p$ in the figure,

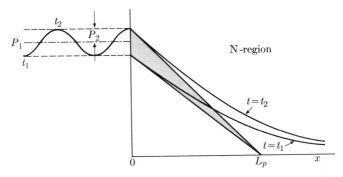

FIG. 5.2. Variation of stored charge with a change in P_1.

and the ohmic contact to the N-region would have to be at this point to yield the correct terminal densities and density gradients at the junction. In this latter case the effective stored charge is

$$\Delta Q = qA\, \Delta P_1 L_p/2, \tag{5.37}$$

which is just one-half of the total ΔQ represented by the difference between the two expontential curves at $t = t_1$ and $t = t_2$. Now the current-density analog of the capacitance is given by

$$X_{IP} = \frac{\Delta Q}{\Delta P_1} = \frac{qAL_p}{2} = \frac{I_{p0}}{p_n}\frac{\tau_p}{2}. \tag{5.38}$$

The current-density analog of the conductance is given by

$$G_{IP} = \frac{\Delta I}{\Delta P_1} = \frac{qAD_p}{L_p} = \frac{I_{p0}}{p_n}, \tag{5.39}$$

since $(dp/dx) = (\Delta P_1/L_p)$ along the straight lines of Fig. 5.2. The total *current-density immittance* is then

$$\frac{I_2}{P_2} = G_{IP} + j\omega X_{IP} = \frac{I_{p0}}{p_n}\left(1 + \frac{j\omega\tau_p}{2}\right). \tag{5.40}$$

This can be seen to be identical to the last term of (5.20) when set equal to the last term of (5.32) under the low-frequency assumption ($\omega \ll \tau_p$).

Large-signal graphical analysis. We will consider the storage time, or turn-off delay time, of a diode. Let us assume that we have a forward-biased junction diode operating at a constant current determined by the voltage supply and the series resistance of the circuit. At $t = 0$ let the polarity of the supply voltage be reversed. The behavior of the diode under these conditions is illustrated in Fig. 5.3. The time Δt is called the recovery

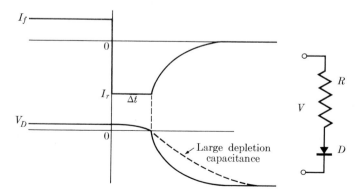

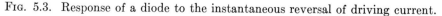

FIG. 5.3. Response of a diode to the instantaneous reversal of driving current.

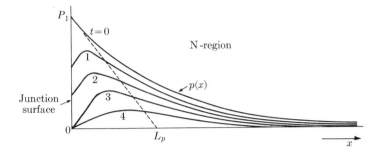

FIG. 5.4. The depletion of the stored charge in a diode when driven by a reverse current.

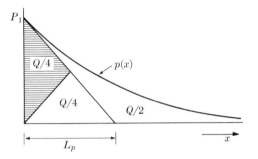

FIG. 5.5. Charge removed during diode recovery.

time of the diode. Physically it is the time required for the excess injected current carriers to be removed from the neighborhood of the junction. Figure 5.4 shows the distribution of stored carriers, and the sequence of their removal from a diode with a P-region which is heavily doped compared to the N-region.

The steady-state forward-bias current I_f is given by

$$I_f = qAD_p(P_1/L_p). \tag{5.41}$$

The initial slope of the hole distribution is given by $-P_1/L_p$. If the series resistance of the circuit limits the reverse current I_r to the same numerical value but the opposite polarity, it follows that immediately after the supply voltage reversal, the slope of the hole distribution at the junction will be P_1/L_p, as shown in the curve for $t = 1$. As time goes on, this slope will be maintained (curves 1, 2, and 3) until the excess concentration of holes at the junction is zero (curve 3). After that, the excess hole distribution will rapidly flatten out, and the current I_r will drop as the dp/dx at the junction drops. The time for the hole distribution to reach the condition of curve 3 will be Δt, the storage or recovery time of the diode.

Figure 5.5 illustrates a simple method of calculating this recovery time Δt to a reasonable approximation. If the total charge under the excess carrier-distribution curve $p(x)$ is Q, then $Q/2$ lies below the line to $x = L_p$. By taking the reciprocal of the initial slope through the origin, we divide this charge into two equal parts of $Q/4$ each. Now, it is clear that if we neglect recombination and assume that the $Q/4$ of the shaded region is removed by I_r, we can calculate Δt. In this case, the continuity equation takes the simple form (assuming that depletion capacitance is negligible, compared with diffusion capacitance)

$$\frac{\Delta Q}{\Delta t} = I_r, \tag{5.42}$$

where $\Delta Q = Q/4$, and we may write $|I_r| = |I_f| = Q/\tau_p$, since all diffusion current in the initial steady state turns to conduction current by recombination. Now Δt becomes

$$\Delta t = \frac{\Delta Q}{I_r} = \frac{Q/4}{Q/\tau_p} = \frac{\tau_p}{4}. \tag{5.43}$$

Equation (5.43) represents a sort of zero-order result, since we have neglected recombination. If we now consider recombination, as well as I_r effective in removing the shaded region of $Q/4$, we write the continuity equation as

$$\frac{\Delta Q}{\Delta t} = I_r + \frac{\Delta Q}{\tau_p}, \tag{5.44}$$

where again $\Delta Q = Q/4$ and $I_r = Q/\tau_p$. From this we get

$$\Delta t = \frac{Q/4}{Q/\tau_p + Q/4\tau_p} = \frac{\tau_p}{5}. \tag{5.45}$$

In actual fact the exact analysis of the above problem is quite complex [2] but yields a value of $\Delta t = 0.22\tau_p$, which is seen to be bracketed by the above results.

This calculation is essentially the discharging time of the diffusion capacitance. If there is appreciable junction depletion capacitance, the voltage across the junction will change more slowly, and part of the current I_r will be used to charge the depletion capacitance. However, the voltage across the diode, V_D, does not change much until state 3 shown in Fig. 5.4 is reached, and therefore the charging of the depletion capacitance merely stretches out the exponential recovery curve after the time Δt and does not affect Δt itself. This is illustrated in the dashed voltage curve of Fig. 5.3.

It is hoped that this example will serve to illustrate the direct graphical approach to large signal problems. The subject will be discussed in more detail in Chapter 6.

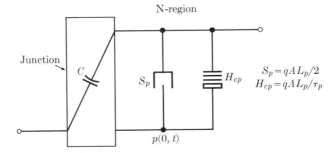

FIG. 5.6.   One-lump, two-element representation of a diode with a heavy P-doping.

5.2   Lumped-Model Diode Analysis [3]

In Chapter 4 a combinance and a storance were defined by lumping the material and geometrical parameters involved in the recombination current and the storage current in a PN-junction. Since these currents flow in parallel in a junction diode, we may use a lumped model to analyze the behavior of the diode. A lumped representation of a diode is shown in Fig. 5.6. This represents a diode with a heavily doped P-region so that all of the action takes place in the N-region. The depletion capacitance C is considered to be negligible compared with the diffusion capacitance when the diode is forward-biased. In this rough one-lump, two-element approximation, the terminal diffusion current is represented by the recombination current through H_{cp}, since all diffusion current eventually reverts to majority-carrier conduction current by means of the recombination process. The stored excess injected carriers are represented by the storance S_p. We may now write the diode current as

$$i_p = p(H_{cp} + j\omega S_p) \tag{5.46}$$

in an analogy to a circuit equation, where the excess minority-carrier density represents voltage, and H_{cp} and S_p are the conductive and reactive circuit elements. By substitution it is easy to verify Eq. (5.46) as the last term of Eq. (5.20), where $p = P_2 e^{j\omega t}$ and $(1 + j\omega\tau_p)^{1/2}$ is approximated by $1 + j\omega\tau_p/2$.

It should be noted that even though this one-lump approximation gives the correct low-frequency behavior of the diode, it gives only one-half of the actual stored charge, since the storance when multiplied by its terminal charge density P_2 gives only one-half of the charge under the curve $qP_2 A e^{-x/L_p}$ (see Fig. 5.5). To obtain a good agreement with both stored charge and low-frequency response, we should take a high-order approximation using two lumps with a total of five elements. This two-lump approximation is shown in Fig. 5.7.

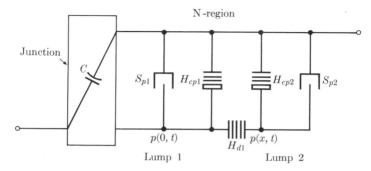

Fig. 5.7.   Two-lump, five-element representation of a diode with a heavy P-doping.

In the one-lump representation, the lower side of S_p and H_{cp} are to be considered "charged" to a density $p(0, t)$, which is the excess hole density at the surface of the junction. The terminal side of the elements is "grounded" with respect to any excess carrier density, and current in the terminal connection represents majority-carrier flow only.   In the two-lump representation the elements of the first lump (nearest the junction) are considered to be "charged" to the $p(0, t)$ excess density, while the elements of the second lump are "charged" to an excess density $p(x, t)$, representative of the point x at some distance from the junction.

If the diode consists of relatively equally doped N- and P-regions, the one-lump representation requires two sides, as shown in Fig. 5.8.   The operation of this representation is explained as follows. Starting with the terminal on the P-region side, we see that there is a majority hole current in the terminal lead, a portion of which is converted, at the junction, to an excess minority-carrier current in the N-region.   The hole density $p(0, t)$ at the junction surface supports this current.   This excess density charges S_p and recombines through H_{cp} to give a portion of the majority

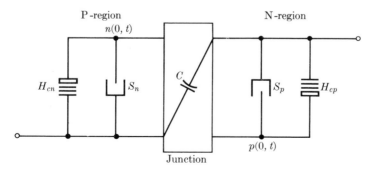

Fig. 5.8.   One-lump representation of diode with relatively equal doping.

electron current in the N-type side terminal. The remainder of the majority electron-terminal current flows along the right-hand terminal lead and is converted at the junction into an excess minority electron current in the P-region supported by the density $n(0, t)$, shown at the top of the P-region. This excess density charges S_n and recombines through H_{cn} to give the remainder of the majority hole current in the P-region terminal lead. It should be pointed out that the doping levels involved determine the $n(0, t)$- and $p(0, t)$-levels, and that the lifetimes on the two sides determine both the storances and combinances.

Evaluation of lumped elements. The evaluation of the elements of the lumped model from physical or electrical measurements is relatively straightforward. We will first consider the one-lump approximation. From the equations given in Fig. 5.6,

$$S_p/H_{cp} = \tau_p/2. \tag{5.47}$$

From Eq. (5.46) we see that we may write H_{cp} in terms of the dc reverse-bias leakage current $I_0 = I_{p0}$, since p_n is the excess density for reverse bias:

$$H_{cp} = I_{p0}/P_n. \tag{5.48}$$

Here $p_n n_n = n_i^2$ and $n_n = 1/q\mu_n\rho_n$. If the physical properties of the N-region are known, we have τ_p and ρ_n, the lifetime and resistivity of the material from which the N-region was made. We can measure I_0, and at the temperature of measurement n_i^2 and μ_n can be looked up for the material of the diode. Finally we have

$$H_{cp} = I_0/q\mu_n n_i^2\rho_n, \tag{5.49}$$

and

$$S_p = I_0\tau_p/2q\mu_n n_i^2\rho_n. \tag{5.50}$$

We are now able to calculate these lumped elements from the parameters of the diode material and a measurement of its dc reverse leakage current. The measurement of I_0 essentially serves to determine the effective area of the diode. If the diode material parameters are unknown, the lumped elements can be measured only within the common multiplier p_n.

For the two-lump model illustrated in Fig. 5.7, one may take the exact current-hole density function of the last term of Eq. (5.20), which is

$$i_p = \frac{I_{p0}}{p_n} P_2(1 + j\omega\tau_p)^{1/2}, \tag{5.51}$$

divide by P_2 to get a current-hole density immittance, and use the five available parameters of the two-lump model to fit the curve as closely as possible over the low-frequency range. When this is done one obtains:

$$S_{p1} = 0.243qAL_p, \qquad H_{cp1} = 0.243qAL_p/\tau_p,$$
$$H_{d1} = 1.285qAL_p/\tau_p, \qquad H_{cp2} = 1.84qAL_p/\tau_p, \qquad S_{p2} = 1.84qAL_p.$$
$$(5.52)$$

From this result, where the elements more distant from the junction seem to carry more weight, it is seen that there is little direct correlation with physical intuition, where it would be assumed that the elements in the region of high minority-carrier density should carry most weight. Nevertheless, the electrical behavior can be represented quite accurately by such a five-parameter model.

5.3 Numerical Example

Given a silicon abrupt PN-junction diode made from 1.0 ohm-cm P-type and 0.2 ohm-cm N-type material. Let $\tau_n = 10^{-6}$ sec and $\tau_p = 10^{-8}$ sec. Sketch the majority- and minority-carrier currents as functions of distance from the junction (on both sides of the junction) and calculate the position of the point or points where they are equal for a forward bias of 0.3 v.

Since the N-region is most heavily doped, most of the minority-carrier injection will be found in the P-region. Also, since $\tau_n \gg \tau_p$, the extent of the injection will be much greater in the P-region. With these guides in mind, we sketch the currents as shown in Fig. 5.9. Since the minority current is larger than the majority current only in the lightly doped P-region, it can be seen that there is only one point of equality between minority- and majority-carrier currents and that it is in the P-region at position x_1. The curves of Fig. 5.9 should not be mistaken for curves of

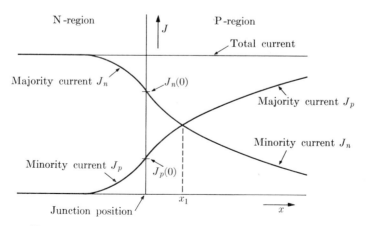

FIG. 5.9. Current components in a PN-junction diode.

carrier density, even though they look the same. Each of the minority-current components drops off exponentially as we move away from the junction because these currents are diffusion currents proportional to the gradient of $p(x)$ and $n(x)$, which are exponential functions with exponential gradients.

From the symmetry of Fig. 5.9 it is clear that x_1 occurs where the minority-carrier injection current J_n is equal to half the total diode current. (We are ignoring the very small minority-carrier drift currents in the two regions.) Our first task is to calculate the total diode current at a forward bias of 0.3 v. From Eq. (4.10), for dc-operation, we find that

$$J = q\left[\frac{D_n n_p}{L_n} + \frac{D_p p_n}{L_p}\right][e^{40 \times 0.3} - 1] = 2.7 \times 10^{-14}\left[\frac{D_n n_p}{L_n} + \frac{D_p p_n}{L_p}\right]\frac{amp}{cm^2},$$

$$(5.53)$$

where we must evaluate the constants in the bracket from the given material parameters and the curves of D_n and D_p given in Section 6.7, Fig. 6.16(b).

Calculating n_p for the P-region, we first estimate N_A for this region, using Eq. (2.21) and μ_p for a pure material given in the Appendix. From this we get $N_A = 1/\rho_p q \mu_p = 1.3 \times 10^{16}/cm^3$. With this value of N_A, we find $D_p = 10 \; cm^2/sec$ from Fig. 6.16(b). Using the Einstein relation $\mu_p = qD_p/kT$ and the value of q/kT for 300°K given in the Appendix, we find a corrected μ_p valid for 1.0-ohm-cm material as $\mu_p = 40 \times 10 = 400 \; cm/sec$ per unit field. The corresponding corrected value of N_A is $1.55 \times 10^{16}/cm^3$. From the Appendix, n_i^2 for silicon at 300°K is 2.5×10^{20}. Now $n_p = n_i^2/N_A = 1.6 \times 10^4/cm^3$. By the same procedure we find p_n in the N-region to be $0.5 \times 10^4/cm^3$.

From Fig. 6.16(b) we find D_n in the P-region to be about 12 cm/sec per unit field and D_p in the N-region to be about 8 cm/sec per unit field. Since the lifetimes are given, we get $L_n = (D_n \tau_n)^{1/2} = 3.5 \times 10^{-3} \; cm$ and $L_p = 2.8 \times 10^{-4} \; cm$. Substituting these values in Eq. (5.53) gives the total diode current density as $J = 2.7 \times 10^{-14}(5.5 + 14)10^7 = 5.3 \; \mu a/cm^2$.

We must finally calculate the position x_1 in the P-region where $J_n = 5.3/2 = 2.65 \; \mu a/cm^2$. Here J_n is given by the dc-term of Eq. (5.17) evaluated by using (5.16). We must be careful of our signs and reverse the signs of Eq. (5.17) for our example because we are considering the P-region to be in the positive x-direction, as shown in Fig. 5.9, rather than in the negative x-direction as shown in Fig. 5.1, which was used to set up Eq. (5.17). The minority electron current now can be written as

$$J_n = -(qD_n N_1/L_n)e^{-x/L_n}, \qquad (5.54)$$

where $N_1 = n_p(e^{40 \times 0.3} - 1)$. Solving Eq. (5.54) for x, we find x_1 to be

$$x_1 = L_n \ln (J_n L_n / q D_n N_1), \tag{5.55}$$

where J_n is $2.65\,\mu a$. Evaluating, we find $x_1 = 3.5 \times 10^{-3} \ln (1.78) = 2 \times 10^{-3}$ cm.

Problems

5.1 Given a silicon PN-junction diode made of 0.1-ohm-cm P-type and 1-ohm-cm N-type material, let $\tau_n = 10^{-7}$ sec and $\tau_p = 10^{-6}$ sec. Calculate the density of minority carriers as a function of distance from the junction for a 0.2-v forward bias. [Assume $T = 300°K$. Other properties of silicon are given in the Appendix and Fig. 6.16(b).]

5.2 Calculate the reverse-bias saturation current density of the diode of Problem 5.1.

5.3 Many diodes are fabricated using a thin epitaxially grown layer of material of relatively high resistivity as one of the regions of the device. Assume that the total thickness (between the surface of the junction and the surface of the ohmic contact) of the N-region of the diode of Problem 5.1 is only 10^{-3} cm. Calculate the reverse-bias saturation current density and compare it with the result of Problem 5.2.

5.4 In the diode of Problem 5.1 calculate the diffusion capacity and the depletion capacity and compare them at a forward bias of 0.2 v.

5.5 Given that the diode of Problem 5.1 has been operated at 5 amp/cm² forward current density and this is suddenly switched to a reverse current density of 2 amp/cm², calculate the recovery time of the diode.

5.6 Given a germanium diode with the following specifications: area, $A = 0.002$ cm²; P-region, $\rho_p = 1$ ohm-cm, $\tau_n = 10^{-5}$ sec; N-region, $\rho_n = 0.01$ ohm-cm, $\tau_p = 10^{-6}$ sec. (Assume that $T = 300°K$. See the Appendix for other properties of germanium.) Calculate the elements of a one-lump approximation to this diode. Using these lumps, calculate the reverse leakage current of the diode.

5.7 A small current given by $i = 10^{-8} \cos 10^5 t$ drives the diode of Problem 5.6. Calculate the voltage developed across the terminals.

Bibliography

1. D. LeCroissette, *Transistors*, Prentice-Hall, Englewood Cliffs, New Jersey, 1963, Chapter 4.
2. B. Lax and S. F. Neustradter, "Transient Response of a PN Junction," *J. Appl. Phys.* **25**, 1148–1154 (1954).
3. J. G. Linvill and J. F. Gibbons, *Transistors and Active Circuits*, McGraw-Hill, New York, 1961.
4. W. Shockley, *Electrons and Holes in Semiconductors*, D. Van Nostrand, Princeton, New Jersey, 1950, pp. 309–317.

CHAPTER 6

TRANSISTORS

A transistor consists of one rectifying junction separated from a second rectifying junction by a web of semiconductor material which is thin compared with the minority-carrier diffusion length in that material (see Fig. 6.1). One junction (the collector junction) is reverse-biased, and the other junction (the emitter junction) is forward-biased. Because the web of material (the base region) separating the emitter and collector junctions is thin compared with a diffusion length, the minority carriers injected into the base region by the forward-biased emitter junction find their way almost without loss to the reverse-biased collector junction and determine its current. In modern transistors the transport of minority carriers across the base region involves a combination of the processes of diffusion and drift in an electric field. To understand the transport mechanism, it is preferable to consider the two processes separately. The alloy-junction transistor is a device in which minority-carrier transport proceeds exclusively by diffusion. Although other fabrication processes have largely replaced the alloy process, the alloy-junction structure has been the workhorse transistor of the past decade. We shall introduce our subject with a discussion of such a transistor.

6.1 The Diffusion Analysis of the Transistor

Figure 6.1(a) shows an idealized cross section of a PNP alloy-junction transistor. Typically these devices are made from wafers of N-type semiconductor material upon which two dots of alloy material containing P-

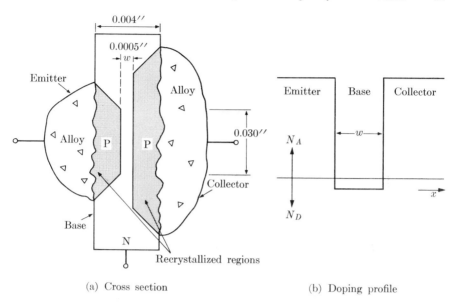

(a) Cross section   (b) Doping profile

Fig. 6.1. Alloy-junction transistor.

type impurity are positioned and then cycled to a high temperature and back. The P-type emitter and collector regions are formed by a recrystallization of the semiconductor material upon cooling from the high-temperature cycle. We shall make our example more specific by considering a germanium device. The recrystallization process is necessary in order for the emitter and collector regions to acquire sufficient P-type impurity to convert the germanium from its original N-type conductivity. The alloy material must contain both P-type impurities (elements from column III of the periodic table) and material which, when molten, will dissolve a significant amount of germanium. In the molten state, at the peak of the temperature cycle, the alloy is permeated by the P-type impurity so that on recrystallization the germanium will contain this impurity almost to the limit of its solid solubility. This recrystallized material builds on the undisturbed web of N-type single-crystal germanium which forms the base region of the device.

In the case of germanium it turns out that indium alone is a reasonably good P-type alloy material. If very heavy doping of the alloy regions is required, gallium is added, since it has a higher solid solubility in germanium than does pure indium. The doping profile is shown in Fig. 6.1(b) in expanded scale. It is seen that the junctions are very abrupt, since they mark the limits of solution of the germanium by the indium during the heating cycle. There is very little smearing out of this boundary by solid-state diffusion because the temperature cycle is usually fast enough to allow no time for impurity diffusion. The impurity density in the emitter and collector regions is about equal and very much greater than the impurity density in the base region.

If the proper crystallographic orientation of the original germanium is used, the limits of the solution of the alloy will be planes parallel to each other and to the original surfaces of the crystal wafer. This preferential solution of the germanium along (111) crystal planes allows very accurate control of the base width by controlling the total amount of dissolving alloy, its area of contact, and its maximum temperature (and therefore its maximum solubility).

Simple dc case. As mentioned above, the emitter injects minority carriers into the base where they find their way by diffusion to the collector. We will first consider this current transfer ratio α_{FB} defined as $\partial I_C / \partial I_E$ at a constant collector voltage V_C, where I_C is a collector current, I_E is emitter current, and the subscript FB refers to "Forward Base" meaning that the current transfer ratio is from emitter to collector with the base common.

We can write α_{FB} as the product of four factors, $\alpha^* \beta \gamma M$, where α^* is called the collector efficiency, β the base-region transport efficiency, γ the emitter injection efficiency, and M is a multiplication factor which represents the multiplication of current carriers by collision in the high-field region of the reverse-biased collector junction. These factors are defined by the following equations:

$$\alpha^* = \frac{\partial(I_C/M)}{\partial I_{pC}}, \quad \beta = \frac{\partial I_{pC}}{\partial I_{pE}}, \quad \gamma = \frac{\partial I_{pE}}{\partial I_E}, \quad M = \left[1 - \left(\frac{V_C}{BV_C}\right)^m\right]^{-1},$$

$$(6.1)$$

where

$\quad I_C =$ total collector-junction current,
$\quad I_{pC} =$ hole current through collector junction,
$\quad I_{pE} =$ hole current through emitter junction,
$\quad I_E =$ total emitter-junction current,
$BV_C =$ avalanche breakdown voltage of the collection junction.

(The equation for M is an empirical approximation.) The factor α^* is seen to be the incremental collector current represented as a fraction of the hole collector current exclusive of those holes created by avalanche multiplication; β is the incremental collector hole current represented as a fraction of the emitter hole current; and γ is the incremental emitter hole current represented as a fraction of the emitter current.

Figure 6.2 shows the energy-band diagram of an alloy-junction transistor with forward bias applied to the emitter junction and reverse bias applied

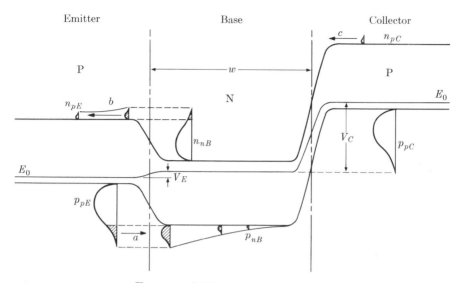

FIG. 6.2. PNP-transistor with bias.

to the collector junction. Holes in this situation will move from left to right across the base region and "fall" up into the collector region. Injected holes are represented by the small shaded distributions at the bottom of the figure. The diminishing size of the hole distribution as it moves to the right represents the concentration gradient of the diffusing holes. In the following analysis it is assumed that the injected density of excess minority carriers in a given region is always small compared with the equilibrium value of the majority-carrier density in that region. This is called the assumption of low-level injection.

First, we shall calculate the emitter efficiency for the dc case. From the definition of Eq. (6.1) we may write

$$\gamma = \frac{\partial I_{pE}}{\partial I_E} = \frac{\partial I_{pE}/\partial V_E}{\partial I_E/\partial V_E}.$$ (6.2)

To compute I_E and its partial derivative, we must evaluate both the hole and electron components of I_E. From Eqs. (4.8) and (4.9) we may write

$$I_{pE} = (qAD_p p_{nB}/w)e^{qV_E/kT},$$
$$I_{nE} = (qAD_n n_{pE}/L_{nE})(e^{qV_E/kT} - 1),$$ (6.3)

where the (-1) term is omitted from the I_{pE}-expression because, at the collector junction, the hole distribution actually approaches zero rather than p_{nB}. Leaving the (-1) term in the I_{nE}-expression implies that the thickness of the emitter is large compared to L_{nE}.

Differentiating (6.3) and substituting in (6.2) gives

$$\gamma = \frac{D_p p_{nB}/w}{(D_p p_{nB}/w) + (D_n n_{pE}/L_{nE})}. \tag{6.4a}$$

We may express γ in terms of measured resistivities since

$$(n_{pE}/p_{nB}) = (n_{nB}/p_{pE}) \quad \text{and} \quad (\rho_E/\rho_B) = (n_{nB}q\mu_n/p_{pE}q\mu_p).$$

Using the Einstein relation $D = \mu kT/q$, we may write

$$\gamma = [1 + (\rho_E w/\rho_B L_{nE})]^{-1}. \tag{6.4b}$$

From Eq. (6.4b) it can be seen that in order to get a high injection efficiency, it is necessary to dope the emitter quite heavily compared to the base. For an alloy-junction transistor this doping is automatic, since the recrystallized semiconductor contains the P-type dope nearly to the limit of solid solubility. A very narrow base width will also help.

The transport efficiency β can be approximated quite simply for the dc-case when $L_{pB} \gg w$. In this case the hole-concentration gradient (dp/dx) in the base region is essentially a constant, and p decreases almost linearly from its injection density $p(0)$ on the emitter side of the base to zero on the reverse-biased collector side. Using a linear approximation, we calculate the charge stored in the base region to be $A_E q w p(0)/2$, and using this value, the recombination current can be written as

$$A_E q w p(0)/2\tau_p. \tag{6.5}$$

The total hole current is equal to the input diffusion current which is

$$A_E q D_p p(0)/w. \tag{6.6}$$

The output hole current is diminished by the recombination hole current, and β can be expressed by the ratio of the incremental output and input hole currents giving

$$\beta = \frac{A_E q D_p \Delta p(0)/w - A_E q w \Delta p(0)/2\tau_p}{A_E q D_p \Delta p(0)/w} = 1 - \frac{w^2}{2L_{pB}^2}. \tag{6.7}$$

This evaluation of β involves only the bulk recombination losses in the base region. It takes no account of surface recombination losses at the periphery of the emitter which may be significant in many transistor geometries at high current levels.

To evaluate α^* we must consider space-charge neutrality in the region of the collector near the collector junction and take into account the field currents in this region. As the holes from the emitter diffuse across the base and fall into the collector, they tend to increase the majority hole density near the collector junction. Such an increase is impossible because the minority electrons are being depleted as they fall into the base and space-charge neutrality must be preserved. The only alternative is for the excess holes to be swept into the collector by an electric field (very slight unbalance of space charge). This field is of the right sign to accelerate the minority electrons toward the base, thus giving us a positive feedback action and an α^* somewhat greater than unity. To evaluate this effect we write for the collector region,

$$I_{nC} = -Aq(n_C \mu_n \operatorname{grad} V + D_n \operatorname{grad} n_C),$$
$$I_{pC} = -Aq(p_C \mu_p \operatorname{grad} V - D_p \operatorname{grad} p_C). \qquad (6.8)$$

Setting grad n_C = grad $p_C = n_{pC}/L_{nC}$ from the space-charge neutrality condition, and eliminating grad V, we get

$$I_{nC} = I_{pC} \frac{n_C \mu_n}{p_C \mu_p} - Aq \frac{D_n n_{pC}}{L_{nC}} \left(\frac{n_C}{p_C} + 1 \right), \qquad (6.9)$$

giving a total collector current of

$$I_C = I_{nC} + I_{pC}$$
$$= I_{pC} \left(1 + \frac{n_C \mu_n}{p_C \mu_p} \right) - Aq \frac{D_n n_{pC}}{L_{nC}} \left(\frac{n_C}{p_C} + 1 \right). \qquad (6.10)$$

Taking $\partial I_C / \partial I_{pC}$ for a PNP-transistor, we get

$$\alpha^* = 1 + \frac{n_C \mu_n}{p_C \mu_p}. \qquad (6.11)$$

Equation (6.11) shows that unless there is an appreciable minority-carrier density n_C in the P-type collector region, α^* is essentially unity. Here n_C represents the average electron density in the region of grad V, and is directly proportional to n_{pC} but somewhat smaller. For an alloy transistor, where the collector region is very heavily doped, n_C is utterly negligible and α^* is indeed unity. Other types of transistors can, however, show α^*-values measurably greater than unity.

Finally, we will evaluate the collector saturation current to complete the dc analysis. The electron current through the collector junction for large reverse bias is $I_{nC} = A_C q D_n n_{pC} / L_{nC}$ when no emitter current is flowing. The hole current through the collector junction is

$$I_{pC} = (A_E q D_p p_{nB}/w) e^{q V_E / kT}. \qquad (6.12)$$

Since we are requiring zero net current through the emitter junction, the emitter voltage must adjust itself to equalize the flow of electrons and

holes across the junction. Solving for $e^{qV_E/kT}$ under the condition that
$I_E = I_{nE} + I_{pE} = 0$ we find that

$$I_E = 0 = A_Eq\left(\frac{D_pp_{nB}}{w} + \frac{D_nn_{pE}}{L_{nE}}\right)e^{qV_E/kT} - \frac{A_EqD_nn_{pE}}{L_{nE}}, \quad (6.13)$$

giving

$$e^{qV_E/kT} = \left(\frac{D_pp_{nB}L_{nE}}{D_nn_{pE}w} + 1\right)^{-1}.$$

The diffusion components of I_{C0} can now be written as:

$$I_{C0} = -(I_{nC} + I_{pC}) = -q\left[\frac{A_CD_nn_{pC}}{L_{nC}} + \frac{A_ED_pp_{nB}}{w}(1 - \gamma)\right], \quad (6.14)$$

where γ is given by Eq. (6.4a). In addition to this diffusion current, there
is a regeneration current which consists of carriers generated in the collector-junction depletion region. This regeneration current will be considered later and is given by Eq. (6.103).

In the above discussion only the bulk recombination is considered.
Actually much of the transport loss in the base is due to surface recombination on the surface of the base region near the edges of the emitter region.
This adds a term to $1/\beta$ and will be left to a future discussion of the
current dependence of α_{FB}.

Transport-mechanism analysis.   In this section we again consider
the transport of injected holes across the base region of a PNP-transistor.
We include the effects of surface recombination and of driving frequency.
We first set up the continuity equation including these factors and then
solve it under the boundary condition that $p(x) = 0$ at $x = w$, the edge
of the base region nearest the back-biased collector.

To consider a situation as near to reality as possible, we shall attempt to
take geometry into account while retaining the simplicity of a one-
dimensional analysis. Figure 6.3 shows a schematic section of a typical
planar PNP-transistor.   Here, although the vertical scale of section
$A A$ is exaggerated, it is clear that the base width w is very small compared with the diameter of the emitter region. We shall assume that
holes injected into the base from the emitter region are lost by surface
recombination only in an annular ring of width w surrounding the emitter.
In general, then, the active surface of the base region directly affecting
the base transport losses is the perimeter of the emitter region multiplied
by w.

If we define the current density flowing into this active surface as
$J_s = spq$, where s is a constant of proportionality, it is seen that s has the
dimensions of velocity. The quantity s is called the surface recombination

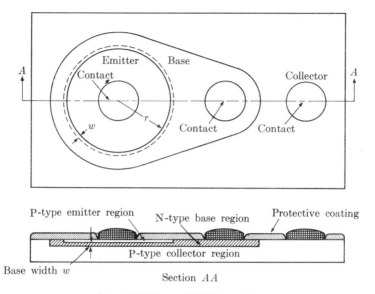

P-type emitter region   N-type base region   Protective coating

P-type collector region

Base width w

Section AA

Fig. 6.3 Planar PNP-transistor.

velocity and is controlled by the physical and chemical treatment of the active surface. Here p is the density of excess holes just beneath the surface.

We are now in a position to write the continuity equation for current crossing the base region under the above geometrical assumptions and conditions. Assuming cylindrical symmetry, we let the total holes in the volume element $\pi r^2 \, \partial x$ be $\mathcal{P}$. Then we may write

$$\frac{\partial \mathcal{P}}{\partial t} = -(p - p_n)\left(\frac{\pi r^2 \, \partial x}{\tau_B} + s_B 2\pi r \, \partial x\right) + D_p \frac{\partial p}{\partial x}\, \pi r^2. \qquad (6.15)$$

Dividing by the volume element, we have

$$\frac{\partial p}{\partial t} = -(p - p_n)\left(\frac{1}{\tau_B} + \frac{2s_B}{r_E}\right) + D_p \frac{\partial^2 p}{\partial x^2}, \qquad (6.16)$$

where r_E is the radius of the emitter region. Here we have considered the annular area around the emitter as though it were the lateral area of a cylinder surrounding the active base region. The continuity equation (6.16) is seen to be the same as Eq. (5.8) in form. From this point on, we will use a single subscript E, B, or C to identify emitter, base, or collector material properties. Thus L_{nE}, L_{pB}, etc. become simply L_E, L_B, etc. The double subscript is retained in connection with current carrier density to indicate the thermodynamic equilibrium density. We will now solve (6.16) under the boundary condition that $p = 0$ at $x = w$ for a reverse-biased collector junction. Again using (5.9) as the general solution we get the time-independent (dc) equation

$$0 = -p_1 \left(\frac{1}{\tau_B} + \frac{2s_B}{r_E} \right) + D_p \frac{d^2 p_1}{dx^2}, \qquad (6.17)$$

and the time-dependent (ac) equation

$$j\omega p_2 = -p_2 \left(\frac{1}{\tau_B} + \frac{2s_B}{r_E} \right) + D_p \frac{d^2 p_2}{dx^2}. \qquad (6.18)$$

Now at the emitter side of the base, $x = 0$ and the minority hole density is $p_1(0) = P_1$. At the collector side of the base, $x = w$ and the minority hole density is zero so that $p_1(w) = -p_{nB}$. We may now write the solution to (6.17) as

$$p_1(x) = A_1 \exp \left[(1 + 2s_B \tau_B / r_E)^{1/2} x / L_B \right]$$
$$+ B_1 \exp \left[-(1 + 2s_B \tau_B / r_E)^{1/2} x / L_B \right]. \qquad (6.19)$$

We find from the boundary conditions that

$$-p_{nB} = A_1 \exp \left[(1 + 2s_B \tau_B / r_E)^{1/2} w / L_B \right]$$
$$+ B_1 \exp \left[-(1 + 2s_B \tau_B / r_E)^{1/2} w / L_B \right], \qquad (6.20)$$

$$P_1 = A_1 + B_1,$$

yielding

$$A_1 = \frac{P_1 \exp \left[-(1 + 2s_B \tau_B / r_E)^{1/2} w / L_B \right] + p_{nB}}{\exp \left[-(1 + 2s_B \tau_B / r_E)^{1/2} w / L_B \right] - \exp \left[(1 + 2s_B \tau_B / r_E)^{1/2} w / L_B \right]},$$

$$\qquad (6.21)$$

$$B_1 = \frac{P_1 \exp \left[(1 + 2s_B \tau_B / r_E)^{1/2} w / L_B \right] + p_{nB}}{\exp \left[(1 + 2s_B \tau_B / r_E)^{1/2} w / L_B \right] - \exp \left[-(1 + 2s_B \tau_B / r_E)^{1/2} w / L_B \right]}.$$

The solution may be given in terms of hyperbolic functions:

$$p_1(x) =$$
$$\frac{P_1 \sinh \left[\left(1 + \frac{2s_B \tau_B}{r_E} \right)^{1/2} \frac{w - x}{L_B} \right] - p_{nB} \sinh \left[\left(1 + \frac{2s_B \tau_B}{r_E} \right)^{1/2} \frac{x}{L_B} \right]}{\sinh \left[\left(1 + \frac{2s_B \tau_B}{r_E} \right)^{1/2} \frac{x}{L_B} \right]}.$$
$$\qquad (6.22)$$

The solution of Eq. (6.18) can be written in a similar manner as

$$p_2(x) = \frac{P_2 \sinh \left[(1 + 2s_B \tau_B / r_E + j\omega \tau_B)^{1/2} (w - x) / L_B \right]}{\sinh \left[(1 + 2s_B \tau_B / r_E + j\omega \tau_B)^{1/2} w / L_B \right]}, \qquad (6.23)$$

where the boundary conditions are

$$p_2(w) = 0 \quad \text{and} \quad p_2(0) = P_2.$$

We have now obtained the dc and ac solutions for the minority hole density in the base region. From these solutions we may calculate the various currents in this region. By evaluating the currents at both sides of the base region, we can find the transport efficiency of the base. We now proceed to calculate the currents.

The minority hole current entering the emitter side of the base can be written

$$J_p = -q D_p \frac{dp}{dx} (0). \qquad (6.24)$$

From Eqs. (5.9), (6.22), and (6.23) we can evaluate (dp/dx) at $x = 0$, giving

$$\frac{dp}{dx} (0) =$$

$$-\frac{(1 + 2 s_B \tau_B / r_E)^{1/2}}{L_B} \left\{ P_1 \coth\left[\left(1 + \frac{2 s_B \tau_B}{r_E}\right)^{1/2} \frac{w}{L_B}\right]\right.$$

$$+ p_{nB} \operatorname{csch}\left[\left(1 + \frac{2 s_B \tau_B}{r_E}\right)^{1/2} \frac{w}{L_B}\right]\right\} - \frac{(1 + 2 s_B \tau_B / r_E + j\omega\tau_p)^{1/2}}{L_B}$$

$$\times \left\{ P_2 \coth\left[\left(1 + \frac{2 s_B \tau_B}{r_E} + j\omega\tau_B\right)^{1/2} \frac{w}{L_B}\right]\right\}. \qquad (6.25)$$

The dc current at the emitter side of the base region is determined from the first two terms of Eq. (6.25),

$$J_{pE} = \frac{q D_p}{L_B}\left(1 + \frac{2 s_B \tau_B}{r_E}\right)^{1/2} \left\{ P_1 \coth\left[\left(1 + \frac{2 s_B \tau_B}{r_E}\right)^{1/2} \frac{w}{L_B}\right]\right.$$

$$+ p_{nB} \operatorname{csch}\left[\left(1 + \frac{2 s_B \tau_B}{r_E}\right)^{1/2} \frac{w}{L_B}\right]\right\}. \qquad (6.26)$$

The ac current at the emitter side of the base region is determined from the last term of Eq. (6.25):

$$J_{pE} = \frac{q D_p}{L_B}\left(1 + \frac{2 s_B \tau_B}{r_E} + j\omega\tau_B\right)^{1/2}$$

$$\times P_2 e^{j\omega t} \coth\left[\left(1 + \frac{2 s_B \tau_B}{r_E} + j\omega\tau_B\right)^{1/2} \frac{w}{L_B}\right]. \qquad (6.27)$$

At the collector side of the base we must evaluate the (dp/dx) at $x = w$ to calculate the corresponding currents:

$$\frac{dp}{dx}(w) =$$

$$- \frac{(1 + 2s_B \tau_B / r_E)^{1/2}}{L_B} \left\{ P_1 \operatorname{csch}\left[\left(1 + \frac{2s_B \tau_B}{r_E}\right)^{1/2} \frac{w}{L_B}\right]\right.$$

$$\left. + p_{nB} \coth\left[\left(1 + \frac{2s_B \tau_B}{r_E}\right)^{1/2} \frac{w}{L_B}\right]\right\} - \frac{(1 + 2s_B \tau_B / r_E + j\omega\tau_B)^{1/2}}{L_B}$$

$$\times P_2 \operatorname{csch}\left[\left(1 + \frac{2s_B \tau_B}{r_E} + j\omega\tau_B\right)^{1/2} \frac{w}{L_B}\right]. \tag{6.28}$$

The currents at the collector side of the base are

$$J_{pC} = \frac{qD_p}{L_B}\left(1 + \frac{2s_B \tau_B}{r_E}\right)^{1/2}\left\{P_1 \operatorname{csch}\left[\left(1 + \frac{2s_B \tau_B}{r_E}\right)^{1/2} \frac{w}{L_B}\right]\right.$$

$$\left. + p_{nB} \coth\left[\left(1 + \frac{2s_B \tau_B}{r_E}\right)^{1/2} \frac{w}{L_B}\right]\right\}, \tag{6.29}$$

$$j_{pC} = \frac{qD_p}{L_B}\left(1 + \frac{2s_B \tau_B}{r_E} + j\omega\tau_B\right)^{1/2}$$

$$\times P_2 e^{j\omega t} \operatorname{csch}\left[\left(1 + \frac{2s_B \tau_B}{r_E} + j\omega\tau_B\right)^{1/2} \frac{w}{L_B}\right]. \tag{6.30}$$

We are now in a position to calculate the transport efficiency β as defined in Eq. (6.1). Since the ac currents can be considered differential currents, we may write

$$\beta = \frac{\partial I_{pC}}{\partial I_{pE}} = \frac{j_{pC}}{j_{pE}} = \operatorname{sech}\left[\left(1 + \frac{2s_B \tau_B}{r_E} + j\omega\tau_B\right)^{1/2} \frac{w}{L_B}\right]. \tag{6.31}$$

For the low-frequency case $\omega \to 0$, and we have

$$\beta = \operatorname{sech}\left[\left(1 + \frac{2s_B \tau_B}{r_E}\right)^{1/2} \frac{w}{L_B}\right]. \tag{6.32}$$

If, in addition, $(2s_B \tau_B / r_E) \ll 1$, we have negligible surface recombination and

$$\beta = \operatorname{sech}(w/L_B). \tag{6.33}$$

Also, if $w \ll L_B$, we may write

$$\beta = \frac{1}{1 + w^2/2L_B^2} \simeq 1 - \frac{w^2}{2L_B^2}, \tag{6.34}$$

which is identical to Eq. (6.7) obtained above. We are now better able to appreciate the approximations involved in the simple relation (6.7).

The low-frequency approximation means that $\omega \tau_B \ll 1$. If $\tau_B \sim 10^{-6}$ sec, then any frequency below 5 kc is considered low. The negligible surface-recombination approximation indicates that $2s_B\tau_B \ll r_E$. Again letting $\tau_B \sim 10^{-6}$ sec and $r_E \sim 10^{-2}$ cm, we see that any surface recombination velocity less than 200 cm/sec can be considered negligible. Such a value is within the reach of modern technology, but is not too easy to maintain over the useful life of a device. A gradual rise in s will cause a decrease in α_{FB} and therefore in α_{FE}.

Since β is very nearly unity for good transistors, we will discuss the above results in terms of the function $|1 - \beta|$. If we assume that the argument of the sech in (6.31) is nearly zero, we may expand the sech as

$$\text{sech}\left[\left(1 + \frac{2s_B\tau_B}{r_E} + j\omega\tau_B\right)^{1/2} \frac{w}{L_B}\right] \simeq 1 - \frac{w^2}{2L_B^2}\left(1 + \frac{2s_B\tau_B}{r_E} + j\omega\tau_B\right),$$

giving

$$(1 - \beta) = \frac{w^2}{2D_p}\left(\frac{1}{\tau_B} + \frac{2s_B}{r_E} + j\omega\right); \tag{6.35}$$

and the absolute value of $(1 - \beta)$ is

$$|1 - \beta| = \frac{w^2}{2D_p}\left[\left(\frac{1}{\tau_B} + \frac{2s_B}{r_E}\right)^2 + \omega^2\right]^{1/2}. \tag{6.36}$$

Plotting $|1 - \beta|$ vs. ω in Fig. 6.4, we see that curves for various values of τ_B and s_B are asymptotic to the curve $(w^2\omega/2D_p)$. Experimentally a plot of base current vs. ω will show this behavior, since $|1 - \beta|$ is in fact the normalized base current of the device if the injection efficiency γ is unity. From the first term of Eq. (6.36) it can be seen that an increase in surface-recombination velocity cannot be distinguished from a decrease in

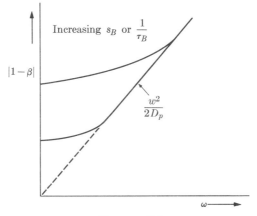

FIGURE 6.4

bulk lifetime. In most devices, however, the normal aging of the α_{FB} of
the device is usually attributed to a changing s_B, since it is hard to imagine
that τ_B is susceptible to anything in the device ambient.

Returning to the expansion of sech, we may write it in the form

$$\beta = \frac{1}{1 + (w^2/2D_p)(1/\tau_B + 2s_B/r_E + j\omega)} . \tag{6.37}$$

From (6.37) it is easy to determine the so-called cutoff frequency of the
transistor. This is defined as the frequency at which β has dropped to
0.707 of its low-frequency value. If we define β_0 as the low-frequency β,
then we can write

$$\beta = \frac{\beta_0}{1 + j\omega\beta_0 w^2/2D_p} . \tag{6.38}$$

The cutoff frequency ω_0 can be calculated by equating the real and
imaginary parts of the denominator of (6.38) giving

$$\omega_0 = 2D_p/\beta_0 w^2 = 2D_p/w^2 \tag{6.39}$$

for $\beta_0 \simeq 1.0$. In many practical cases, this base cutoff frequency may well
be overshadowed by the bypass effects of the emitter- and collector-
junction depletion capacitances, but it does represent a fundamental limit
in the frequency response of a transistor.

The injection efficiency γ also has a small intrinsic frequency dependence
since the injected minority-carrier density in the base region also shows a
frequency dependence, as indicated in Eq. (6.23).

We may calculate the frequency dependence of the injection efficiency
γ as follows:

$$\gamma = \frac{j_{pE}}{j_{pE} + j_{nE}} , \tag{6.40}$$

where j_{pE} is given by Eq. (6.27) and j_{nE} is given by the first term of
Eq. (5.20) as

$$j_{nE} = \frac{qD_n N_2}{L_E} (1 + j\omega\tau_E)^{1/2} e^{j\omega t} . \tag{6.41}$$

Making the approximation that the coth can be represented by the first
two terms of its series expansion, we find that $x \coth x = 1 + x^2/2$ so
that

$$j_{pE} = \frac{qD_p P_2}{w} \left[1 + \left(1 + \frac{2s_B\tau_B}{r_E} + j\omega\tau_B \right) \frac{w^2}{2L_B^2} \right] e^{j\omega t} . \tag{6.42}$$

By substituting in Eq. (6.40) and making the appropriate identifications using the small-signal approximation, we find that γ can be written as

$$\gamma = \left[1 + \frac{\rho_E w}{\rho_B L_E} \frac{(1 + j\omega\tau_E)^{1/2}}{1 + (1 + 2s_B\tau_B/\tau_E + j\omega\tau_B)w^2/2L_B^2} \right]^{-1}. \quad (6.43)$$

Here we have evaluated P_2 and N_2 by defining the excess hole density as $p - p_{nB} = p_{nB}(e^{qv_E/kT} - 1)$, where $v_E = V_E + V_e e^{j\omega t}$. Substituting v_E and making the small-signal approximation, we get an expression for p which can be identified term by term with Eq. (5.9), giving

$$P_2 = p_{nB}(qV_e/kT)e^{qV_E/kT}.$$

By a similar process we find that $N_2 = n_{pE}(qV_e/kT)e^{qV_E/kT}$.

Continuing the usual assumption that

$$(1 + 2s_B\tau_B/\tau_E + j\omega\tau_B)w^2/2L_B^2 \ll 1,$$

we can express Eq. (6.43) in terms of β:

$$\gamma = 1 - \frac{\rho_E w}{\rho_B L_E} (1 + j\omega\tau_E)^{1/2}\beta. \quad (6.44)$$

From this we can express the overall frequency dependence of the current transfer ratio α_{FB} by forming the product $\gamma\beta \simeq \alpha_{FB}$. From this we find that

$$\alpha_{FB} = \beta - \frac{\rho_E w}{\rho_B L_E} (1 + j\omega\tau_E)^{1/2}\beta^2,$$

$$\alpha_{FB} = 1 - \frac{\rho_E w}{\rho_B L_E} (1 + j\omega\tau_E)^{1/2} \quad (6.45)$$

$$+ \frac{w^2}{2L_B^2} \left(1 + \frac{2s_B\tau_B}{\tau_E} + j\omega\tau_B \right) \left[\frac{2\rho_E w}{\rho_B L_E} (1 + j\omega\tau_E)^{1/2} - 1 \right].$$

This expression neglects the product of small terms and is good for most practical devices at low bias levels, since $\alpha^* M$ is usually unity at low bias and reasonable doping levels. From the first form of Eq. (6.45), it can be seen that the primary frequency dependence of α_{FB} is that of its first term β unless τ_E is comparable to τ_B. In most transistors $\tau_E \ll \tau_B$ because of the heavy doping of the emitter.

Diffusion capacitance. As in the case of the diode, the transistor has a so-called diffusion capacitance which is determined by the charge which must be stored in the base in order to provide a diffusion gradient for current flow. If we write the emitter current as

$$I_E = A_E q D_p p_E / w \quad (6.46)$$

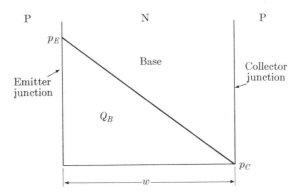

FIG. 6.5. Transistor base-region charge storage.

(see Fig. 6.5), the average hole density in the base region under the emitter is given by $p_E/2$, and the stored charge is

$$Q_B = (qp_E/2)A_E w. \tag{6.47}$$

Here $p_E = p_{nB}e^{qV_E/kT}$, giving

$$Q_B = (A_E qw/2)p_{nB}e^{qV_E/kT}. \tag{6.48}$$

By definition, the diffusion capacitance $C_D = (dQ_B/dV_E)$, yielding

$$C_D = (A_E qw/2)(q/kT)p_{nB}e^{qV_E/kT}, \tag{6.49}$$

and by substituting (6.46) we get

$$C_D = I_E(q/kT)(w^2/2D_p). \tag{6.50}$$

In this calculation it is assumed that current flow from the emitter to the collector only involves a carrier density gradient immediately beneath the area of the emitter. For this reason, only the area A_E appears in the above expression. In actual fact a slightly larger area is probably involved, but the edge corrections are considered negligible, since it is hard to imagine that the base-region charge will expand laterally much more than a distance w beyond the area of the emitter for a transistor not in saturation.

It will be instructive to estimate the magnitude of the diffusion capacitance in a typical switching transistor. For a 100-mc unit, $w \sim 10^{-3}$ cm so that at room temperature and $I_E = 10$ ma, we have

$$C_D = 0.01(39)(10^{-6}/100) = 3.9 \times 10^{-3}\,\mu\text{f}.$$

This represents the largest capacitance involved with the unit, being typically 10 times the emitter depletion-region capacitance and 100 times the collector junction capacitance. Since it depends on w^2, it can be drastically reduced in thin base units, but even in the extreme case of a 1-μ base width, it is still 39 pf.

The admittance of the ports. From Eqs. (6.27), (6.30), and (6.41) we may calculate the transistor admittances under the following definitions:

$$v_E = V_E + V_e e^{j\omega t}, \qquad v_C = V_C + V_c e^{j\omega t},$$

$$i_E = I_E + I_e e^{j\omega t}, \qquad i_C = I_C + I_c e^{j\omega t}, \tag{6.51}$$

and

$$I_e = Y_{ee} V_e + Y_{ec} V_c, \qquad I_c = Y_{ce} V_e + Y_{cc} V_c. \tag{6.52}$$

The total ac emitter current may be written

$$I_e = (j_{pE} + j_{nE}) A_E = q A_E \left\{ \frac{D_p}{L_B} \left(1 + \frac{2 s_B \tau_B}{r_E} + j\omega\tau_B \right)^{1/2} \right.$$

$$\times P_2 \coth \left[\left(1 + \frac{2 s_B \tau_B}{r_E} + j\omega\tau_B \right)^{1/2} \frac{w}{L_B} \right] + \frac{D_n}{L_E} N_2 (1 + j\omega\tau_E)^{1/2} \right\}.$$

$$\tag{6.53}$$

Similarly, the ac collector current amplitude may be written

$$I_c = A_E j_{pC} = q A_E \frac{D_p}{L_B} \left(1 + \frac{2 s_B \tau_B}{r_E} + j\omega\tau_B \right)^{1/2}$$

$$\times P_2 \operatorname{csch} \left[\left(1 + \frac{2 s_B \tau_B}{r_E} + j\omega\tau_B \right)^{1/2} \frac{w}{L_B} \right]. \tag{6.54}$$

Here again we use the emitter area because it is assumed that the collector is active only in an area directly beneath the emitter. We now identify P_2 as the change in the p_E of Fig. 6.5 as V_E changes:

$$P_2 = \Delta p_E = (q/kT) p_{nB} e^{q V_E / kT} \Delta V_E, \tag{6.55}$$

and we see that $\Delta V_E = V_e$. Making a similar identification of N_2, we may write

$$Y_{ee} = \frac{I_e}{V_e}$$

$$= A_E q \left(\frac{q}{kT} e^{q V_E / kT} \right) \left\{ \frac{D_p p_{nB}}{L_B} \left(1 + \frac{2 s_B \tau_B}{r_E} + j\omega\tau_B \right)^{1/2} \right. \tag{6.56}$$

$$\times \coth \left[\left(1 + \frac{2 s_B \tau_B}{r_E} + j\omega\tau_B \right)^{1/2} \frac{w}{L_B} \right] + \frac{D_n n_{pE}}{L_E} (1 + j\omega\tau_E)^{1/2} \right\},$$

and similarly,

$$Y_{ce} = \frac{-I_c}{V_e} = -A_E q \left(\frac{q}{kT} e^{qV_E/kT}\right) \left\{\frac{D_p p_{nB}}{L_B} \left(1 + \frac{2s_B \tau_B}{r_E} + j\omega\tau_B\right)^{1/2}\right.$$
$$\left. \times \operatorname{csch}\left[\left(1 + \frac{2s_B\tau_B}{r_E} + j\omega\tau_B\right)^{1/2} \frac{w}{L_B}\right]\right\}. \qquad (6.57)$$

Here, there is no electronic component of I_c because the leakage over the back-biased collector barrier is essentially a dc current. The remaining two admittances are

$$Y_{ec} = -A_E q \left(\frac{q}{kT} e^{qV_C/kT}\right) \left\{\frac{D_p p_{nB}}{L_B} \left(1 + \frac{2s_B\tau_B}{r_E} + j\omega\tau_B\right)^{1/2}\right.$$
$$\left. \times \operatorname{csch}\left[\left(1 + \frac{2s_B\tau_B}{r_E} + j\omega\tau_B\right)^{1/2} \frac{w}{L_B}\right]\right\}, \qquad (6.58)$$

$$Y_{cc} = A_E q \left(\frac{q}{kT} e^{qV_C/kT}\right) \left\{\frac{D_p p_{nB}}{L_B} \left(1 + \frac{2s_B\tau_B}{r_E} + j\omega\tau_B\right)^{1/2}\right.$$
$$\left. \times \coth\left[\left(1 + \frac{2s_B\tau_B}{r_E} + j\omega\tau_B\right)^{1/2} \frac{w}{L_B}\right]\right\}. \qquad (6.59)$$

Here, $\Delta p_C = (q/kT)p_{nB}e^{qV_C/kT}\,\Delta V_C = P_2$, and in (6.59) the N_2-term of I_e is omitted because the electronic term from the collector (the n_{pC}-distribution) contributes essentially a dc component only.

If one approximates the hyperbolic functions by the first two terms of their series expansions and recognizes that

$$(A_E q D_p p_{nB}/w)e^{qV_E/kT} = I_E,$$

then, excluding the n_{pE}-term, one may write

$$Y_{ee} = \frac{qI_E}{kT}\left[1 + \left(1 + \frac{2s_B\tau_B}{r_E} + j\omega\tau_B\right)\frac{w^2}{2L_B^2}\right], \qquad (6.60)$$

$$Y_{ce} = \frac{-qI_E/kT}{1 + (1 + 2s_B\tau_B/r_E + j\omega\tau_B)w^2/3L_B^2}. \qquad (6.61)$$

Also, since $(A_E q D_p p_{nB}/w)e^{qV_C/kT} = I_{p0}$ (the hole component of I_{C0}), we may write

$$Y_{ec} = \frac{-qI_{p0}/kT}{1 + (1 + 2s_B\tau_B/r_E + j\omega\tau_B)w^2/3L_B^2}, \qquad (6.62)$$

$$Y_{cc} = \frac{qI_{p0}}{kT}\left[1 + \left(1 + \frac{2s_B\tau_B}{r_E} + j\omega\tau_B\right)\frac{w^2}{2L_B^2}\right]. \qquad (6.63)$$

These equations are more tractable than Eqs. (6.56) through (6.59) and are quite good approximations under the condition that

$$(1 + 2s_B\tau_B/r_E + j\omega\tau_B)^{1/2}w/L_B$$

is small compared to unity. It should be noted that the imaginary part of (6.60) gives the expression for diffusion capacitance found in (6.50).

6.2   Lumped-Model Analysis of the Transistor [3]

In terms of the Linvill lumped components described in Chapter 4 and applied to a diode in Chapter 5, we may represent a PNP-transistor to the first order by the circuit of Fig. 6.6. Here, it can be seen that the transistor representation consists of two one-lump diode approximations (representing the collector and emitter diodes) connected by a diffusance. This is a minimum representation. Each diode is represented by only two elements and the diffusion-charge transport of the base region is represented by a single element. Such a model can give the effect of charge build-up in the base region but cannot give the effect of base transit time because there is no transit-time mechanism represented. If more than one lump is used for each diode, the effect of transit-time delay can be approximated by the effective charging of each lump partially in series, beginning at the emitter and progressing toward the collector. To illustrate the lumped approach, we will use the one-lump five-element model of Fig. 6.6.

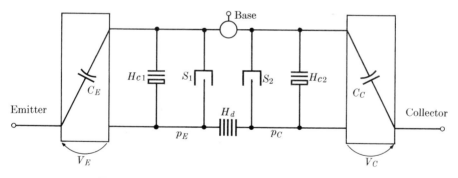

Fig. 6.6. Lumped representation of a transistor.

We will first write the emitter current using the node equations and the definitions of the lumped elements given in Chapter 4:

$$i_E = p_E H_{c1} + (p_E - p_C)H_d + S_1\left(\frac{dp_E}{dt}\right). \tag{6.64}$$

If p_E and p_C are excess minority-carrier densities, we will have $p_C = -p_{nB}$

for a reverse-biased collector junction (total hole density being zero at the collector side of the base). Recalling the definitions of i_E and v_E given in Eq. (6.51), we may write

$$p_E = p_{nB} [\exp (qv_E/kT) - 1]$$
$$= p_{nB} \{[\exp (qV_E/kT)] \exp [(qV_e \exp j\omega t)/kT] - 1\}, \quad (6.65)$$

and under the small-signal approximation, where the second exponential may be replaced by the expansion $[1 + (qV_e/kT)e^{j\omega t}]$, we have

$$dp_E/dt = p_{nB} [\exp (qV_E/kT)](qV_e/kT)j\omega \exp j\omega t. \quad (6.66)$$

Equation (6.64) may now be written

$$i_E = p_{nB}\{[\exp (qV_E/kT)][1 + (qV_e/kT) \exp j\omega t] - 1\}H_{c1}$$
$$+ p_{nB}[\exp (qV_E/kT)][1 + (qV_e/kT) \exp j\omega t]H_d \quad (6.67)$$
$$+ p_{nB}[\exp (qV_E/kT)][(qV_e/kT) \exp j\omega t]j\omega S_1,$$

where we may identify the dc and ac components of the emitter current, respectively, as

$$I_E = p_{nB}\{[\exp (qV_E/kT)](H_{c1} + H_d) - H_{c1}\}, \quad (6.68)$$

$$I_e = p_{nB}\{[\exp (qV_E/kT)](qV_e/kT)(H_{c1} + H_d + j\omega S_1)\}. \quad (6.69)$$

In a similar manner we may calculate i_C as

$$i_C = p_C H_{c2} + (p_C - p_E)H_d + S_2(dp_C/dt). \quad (6.70)$$

Since $p_C = -p_{nB}$, the constant equilibrium density of holes in the base region, $(dp_C/dt) = 0$, and the last term of Eq. (6.70) vanishes. Using the same equation (6.65) for p_E as before, we get

$$i_C = -p_{nB}\{H_{c2} + e^{qV_E/kT}[1 + (qV_e/kT)e^{j\omega t}]H_d\}, \quad (6.71)$$

where we identify I_C and I_c as

$$I_C = -p_{nB}\{H_{c2} + [\exp (qV_E/kT)]H_d\}, \quad (6.72)$$

$$I_c = -p_{nB}[\exp (qV_E/kT)](qV_e/kT)H_d. \quad (6.73)$$

We may now calculate the admittances

$$Y_{ee} = (I_e/V_e) = p_{nB}(q/kT)[\exp (qV_E/kT)](H_{c1} + H_d + j\omega S_1), \quad (6.74)$$

$$Y_{ce} = (I_c/V_e) = -p_{nB}(q/kT)[\exp (qV_E/kT)]H_d. \quad (6.75)$$

By symmetry, the other two admittances are given by

$$Y_{cc} = (I_c/V_c) = p_{nB}(q/kT)[\exp{(qV_C/kT)}](H_{c2} + H_d + j\omega S_2),$$
$$(6.76)$$
$$Y_{ec} = (I_e/V_c) = -p_{nB}(q/kT)[\exp{(qV_C/kT)}]H_d.$$
$$(6.77)$$

In Eq. (6.68) we have the dc emitter current under the assumption that $p_C = -p_{nB}$. If the collector is not reverse-biased, this assumption is not valid and we must have $p_C = p_{nB}(e^{qV_C/kT} - 1)$ in the general case. In any dc case it is recognized that $(dp_C/dt) = (dp_E/dt) = 0$, so that there are no storance terms. The general dc currents I_E and I_C can then be written:

$$I_E = p_{nB}[(e^{qV_E/kT} - 1)(H_{c1} + H_d) - (e^{qV_C/kT} - 1)H_d], \quad (6.78)$$

$$I_C = p_{nB}[(e^{qV_C/kT} - 1)(H_{c2} + H_d) - (e^{qV_E/kT} - 1)H_d]. \quad (6.79)$$

To derive the expressions for the leakage currents I_{C0} and I_{E0}, we recognize that for I_{C0}, V_C is large and negative and $I_E = 0$. Under these conditions we may solve for $(e^{qV_E/kT} - 1)$ from Eq. (6.78), giving

$$(e^{qV_E/kT} - 1) = -H_d/(H_{c1} + H_d), \quad (6.80)$$

which when substituted into Eq. (6.79) gives

$$I_{C0} = -p_{nB}\left[\frac{-H_d^2}{H_{c1} + H_d} + (H_{c2} + H_d)\right] = -p_{nB}\left(H_{c2} + \frac{H_{c1}H_d}{H_{c1} + H_d}\right).$$
$$(6.81)$$

In a similar manner we can find I_{E0}:

$$I_{E0} = p_{nB}\left[\frac{H_d^2}{H_{c2} + H_d} - (H_{c1} + H_d)\right] = -p_{nB}\left(H_{c1} + \frac{H_{c2}H_d}{H_{c2} + H_d}\right).$$
$$(6.82)$$

The constants of the above lumped model of the transistor may be evaluated by suitable terminal measurements. A dc measurement of I_{C0} and I_{E0}, together with the measurement of the above admittances at a single frequency, should suffice to determine the five parameters H_{c1}, S_1, H_d, S_2, and H_{c2} within the common multiplier p_{nB}. If the resistivity of the base material is known, or if the admittances are measured at more than one frequency, all parameters can be determined by curve fitting.

Finally, it should be noted that since the above lumped model concerns the base region only, we may define the base transport efficiency $\beta = I_c/I_e$, which from Eqs. (6.73) and (6.69) yields

$$\beta = \frac{H_d}{H_d + H_{c1} + j\omega S_1}. \quad (6.83)$$

Insofar as γ and $-\alpha^*$ are unity, Eq. (6.83) gives the α_{FB} of the transistor. Also, since $H_d = qAD_p/w$ and $I_E = (qAD_p p_{nB}/w)e^{qV_E/kT}$, we may express the admittances of Eqs. (6.74) and (6.75) in the simple form

$$Y_{ee} = \frac{qI_E}{kT}\frac{1}{\alpha_{FB}}, \qquad Y_{ce} = -\frac{qI_E}{kT}. \tag{6.84}$$

6.3 Large-Signal Analysis

Equations (6.78) and (6.79) show a certain symmetry and are written in a general form. Ebers and Moll [4] have expressed the collector and emitter currents in such a general form as follows:

$$I_E = a_{EE}(e^{qV_E/kT} - 1) + a_{EC}(e^{qV_C/kT} - 1),$$
$$I_C = a_{CE}(e^{qV_E/kT} - 1) + a_{CC}(e^{qV_C/kT} - 1). \tag{6.85}$$

The constants of these phenomenological equations can be evaluated in terms of the terminal parameters I_{C0}, I_{E0}, α_{FB}, and α_{RB}. We now proceed with this evaluation.

For a reverse-biased collector, V_C is large and negative, causing the $e^{qV_C/kT}$-terms to vanish in equations (6.85), giving

$$I_E = a_{EE}(e^{qV_E/kT} - 1) - a_{EC}, \qquad I_C = a_{CE}(e^{qV_E/kT} - 1) - a_{CC}. \tag{6.86}$$

Eliminating $(e^{qV_E/kT} - 1)$, we get

$$I_C = a_{CE}(I_E + a_{EC})/a_{EE} - a_{CC}. \tag{6.87}$$

Under the conditions of a reversed-biased emitter, $e^{qV_E/kT} \to 0$, and by eliminating $(e^{qV_C/kT} - 1)$ we obtain

$$I_E = a_{EC}(I_C + a_{CE})/a_{CC} - a_{EE}. \tag{6.88}$$

Since we define α_{FB} as $-(\partial I_C/\partial I_E)$ and I_{C0} as I_C for $I_E = 0$, we may write Eq. (6.87) as

$$I_C = -\alpha_{FB}I_E + I_{C0}. \tag{6.89}$$

Also, we may define a reverse current transfer ratio $\alpha_{RB} = -(\partial I_E/\partial I_C)$ and I_{E0} as I_E for $I_C = 0$, when the emitter is reverse-biased. Equation (6.88) now becomes

$$I_E = -\alpha_{RB}I_C + I_{E0}. \tag{6.90}$$

We may evaluate the a's in terms of the parameters α_{FB}, α_{RB}, I_{C0}, and I_{E0}, using the equations obtained by equating the coefficients in Eqs.

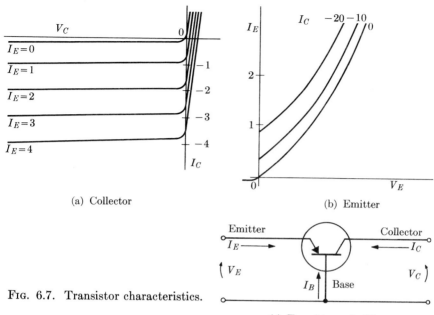

(a) Collector

(b) Emitter

FIG. 6.7. Transistor characteristics.

(c) Transistor polarities

(6.87) and (6.89) and in Eqs. (6.88) and (6.90). This gives

$$-\alpha_{FB} = a_{CE}/a_{EE}, \qquad -\alpha_{RB} = a_{EC}/a_{CC},$$

$$(6.91)$$

$$I_{C0} = (a_{EC}a_{CE}/a_{EE}) - a_{CC}, \qquad I_{E0} = (a_{EC}a_{CE}/a_{CC}) - a_{EE},$$

which yield

$$a_{EE} = -I_{E0}/(1 - \alpha_{FB}\alpha_{RB}), \qquad a_{EC} = \alpha_{RB}I_{C0}/(1 - \alpha_{FB}\alpha_{RB}),$$

$$(6.92)$$

$$a_{CE} = \alpha_{FB}I_{E0}/(1 - \alpha_{FB}\alpha_{RB}), \qquad a_{CC} = -I_{C0}/(1 - \alpha_{FB}\alpha_{RB}),$$

and equations (6.85) become

$$I_E = \frac{-I_{E0}}{1 - \alpha_{FB}\alpha_{RB}} (e^{qV_E/kT} - 1) + \frac{\alpha_{RB}I_{C0}}{1 - \alpha_{FB}\alpha_{RB}} (e^{qV_C/kT} - 1),$$

$$(6.93)$$

$$I_C = \frac{\alpha_{FB}I_{E0}}{1 - \alpha_{FB}\alpha_{RB}} (e^{qV_E/kT} - 1) - \frac{I_{C0}}{1 - \alpha_{FB}\alpha_{RB}} (e^{qV_C/kT} - 1).$$

These equations can be used to plot the dc characteristics of a transistor. If we again eliminate $(e^{qV_E/kT} - 1)$ from equations (6.93), we get

$$I_C = -\alpha_{FB}I_E - I_{C0}(e^{qV_C/kT} - 1). \qquad (6.94)$$

This equation gives the familiar collector family of characteristics shown in Fig. 6.7(a). In a similar manner the emitter family shown in Fig. 6.7(b) is given by

$$I_E = -\alpha_{RB}I_C - I_{E0}(e^{qV_E/kT} - 1). \qquad (6.95)$$

The bias polarity for these characteristic curves and for Eqs. (6.85) through (6.95) is shown in Fig. 6.7(c).

6.4 Transistor Switching

The above large-signal analysis lends itself readily to switching analysis. As an example, we will calculate the dc voltage drop and ac impedance of a "closed" transistor switch. By "closed" we mean a transistor held in saturation by high emitter current. The circuit is shown in Fig. 6.8(a), and the "open" and "closed" conditions are illustrated in Fig. 6.8(b). Here the switch is controlled by the base current of the transistor, and the control terminal is slightly negative when the switch is closed and is open or at ground when the switch is open. By Kirchhoff's law, the sum of the base and collector currents must equal the emitter current. When the transistor is not biased to the closed saturation condition, we know from (6.94) that $I_C = -\alpha_{FB}I_E + I_{C0}$, and since $I_B + I_C + I_E = 0$, we obtain

$$I_B = I_C(1 - \alpha_{FB})/\alpha_{FB} - I_{C0}/\alpha_{FB}. \qquad (6.96)$$

Now if we define the open condition of the switch to be found with $I_B = 0$, we see that the dc leakage current is given by

$$I_C = I_{C0}/(1 - \alpha_{FB}). \qquad (6.97)$$

If we define the open condition to be found for $V_B = 0$, we may calculate the dc leakage current from equations (6.93) by letting $V_E = 0$. This

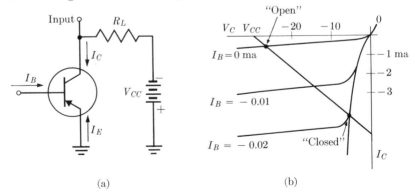

(a)   (b)

Fig. 6.8. Transistor switch configuration.

eliminates the first terms in both equations, giving from the second equation,

$$I_C = I_{C0}/(1 - \alpha_{FB}\alpha_{RB}) \tag{6.98}$$

(when V_C is still large and negative), and since α_{FB} is nearly unity, we find that $I_C \simeq I_{C0}/(1 - \alpha_{RB})$ under this condition. From this we see that there may be an order-of-magnitude difference in the open-switch leakage current between the $I_B = 0$ and the $V_B = 0$ criteria.

Turning our attention to the closed condition of the switch, we may calculate the voltage drop across the switch by solving Eqs. (6.94) and (6.95) for the voltage V_C and V_E, respectively, giving

$$V_C = \frac{kT}{q} \ln\left(-\frac{I_C + \alpha_{FB}I_E}{I_{C0}} + 1\right), \tag{6.99}$$

$$V_E = \frac{kT}{q} \ln\left(-\frac{I_E + \alpha_{RB}I_C}{I_{E0}} + 1\right). \tag{6.100}$$

Recognizing that both I_{C0} and I_{E0} are small compared to I_C and I_E, we see that we may neglect the unit terms in Eq. (6.100). Using the relation $I_B + I_C + I_E = 0$ to eliminate I_E and adding V_C and V_E algebraically, we find that

$$V_{CE} = V_C - V_E = \frac{kT}{q} \ln \frac{\alpha_{RB}[1 - (I_C/I_B\alpha_{FB})(1 - \alpha_{FB})]}{[1 + (I_C/I_B)(1 - \alpha_{RB})]}. \tag{6.101}$$

Here V_C and V_E are subtracted because both junctions are forward-biased with respect to the base when the switch is in the closed condition.

Having found V_{CE}, we may calculate the ac impedance of the closed switch by evaluating the derivative (dV_{CE}/dI_C). Differentiating Eq. (6.101) gives

$$z_{CE} = \frac{kT}{q}\left[\frac{1}{\alpha_{FB}I_B/(1 - \alpha_{FB}) - I_C} + \frac{1}{I_B/(1 - \alpha_{RB}) + I_C}\right]. \tag{6.102}$$

There are a number of processes which significantly modify the above results. First, only the "intrinsic" transistor has been considered. In any real transistor there is usually appreciable series resistance in the bulk material of the base and collector regions to significantly increase the V_{CE}-drop. Also the presence of the collector and emitter depletion capacitances will be quite significant at high frequencies.

From Fig. 6.3 it is clear that the base current must flow radially out of the thin base region between the emitter and collector in order to reach the thicker, relatively low-resistance, portion of the base region surrounding the emitter. This radial flow will create a voltage drop which will tend to bias the center of the emitter region off and concentrate the emitter-current injection around the rim of the emitter. Since the major loss involved in α_{FB} is due to the surface recombination near the rim of the emitter, it is clear that as base current is increased, α_{FB} will fall off. Estimates of this effect can be made for specific geometries, and it is usually found to be significant when the transistor is driven into saturation.

The ac impedance of the open switch is just the slope of the I_{C0}-line of the dc characteristic in parallel with the collector depletion capacitance. The slope of the I_{C0}-characteristic is determined by thermal generation in the collector depletion region and by avalanche multiplication in this region. The thermal-generation current is voltage dependent simply because the thickness of the depletion region is voltage dependent. The voltage dependence of the avalanche process is given in equations (6.1). The depletion capacitance is also voltage dependent, as shown in Eq. (4.22). At low frequencies and relatively low voltages only the slope of the dc I_{C0}-curve is significant.

As an example we will calculate the open impedance using only the effect of the thermal-generation current in the collector-junction depletion region. If we assume a heavily doped collector region, we will find the entire depletion region in the base material and that its depth will be given by Eq. (4.21),

$$x_{\mathrm{N}} = \left[\frac{2\epsilon(\phi - V)}{qN_D} \right]^{1/2},$$ (4.21)

where $N_A \gg N_D$. The current produced by thermal generation in this region is given by

$$I = -qAx_{\mathrm{N}}n_i/\tau,$$ (6.103)

which may be compared with Eq. (5.22). Here τ is the effective lifetime of both carriers in the depletion region, and n_i represents the deficiency of carriers of each type in this region.

Substituting (4.21) in (6.103) and differentiating, we find that

$$\frac{dV}{dI} = z_{CE} = \frac{2\tau}{An_i} \left[\frac{N_D (\phi - V)}{2q\epsilon} \right]^{1/2}.$$ (6.104)

This will give about 100 megohms for a silicon transistor with an effective $\tau = 10^{-7}$ sec, and at relatively low collector bias voltage. At collector voltages greater than about one-half the breakdown voltage of the junction, the avalanche multiplication effect will control this impedance, and at frequencies above 10 kc, the collector depletion capacitance will be significant.

Transient behavior and charge control. In Section 5.1 we considered the problem of diode recovery time from the point of view of a direct evaluation of the continuity equation by various approximations. Involved

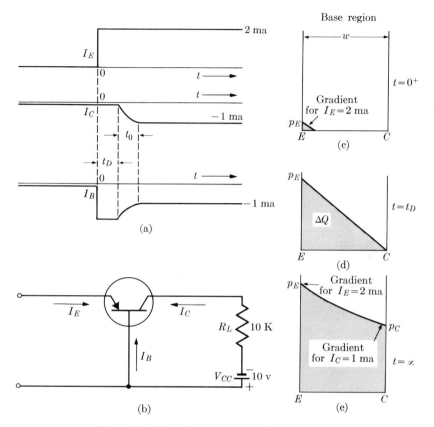

Fig. 6.9. Transistor common-base turn-on.

in this was the concept that the stored excess minority current carriers controlled the impedance of the junction. In a transistor the density of stored minority carriers in the base region also controls the emitter and collector currents and the device impedance. Analyzing the device behavior from the point of view of these stored carriers (or charge) is called the charge-control method. We will proceed to analyze the transient behavior of a transistor from this point of view.

Figure 6.9 shows a series of steps involved in turning on a PNP-diffusion transistor and driving it into saturation. All currents are considered positive when directed into a terminal of the device. Figure 6.9(a) illustrates the behavior of the terminal currents and Fig. 6.9(b) shows the circuit. Figures 6.9(c), (d), and (e) show the excess minority-carrier densities in the base region for three different times, $t = 0^+$, just after the emitter is switched on, $t = t_D$, just as the first injected carriers reach the collector, and $t = \infty$, after all the base has been charged sufficiently to allow base recombination current to equal the difference between the emitter and collector currents.

Figure 6.9(c) shows the condition of the device an instant after the constant emitter current drive is applied. At this point there is a charge gradient in the base sufficient to carry the full emitter current but only an infinitesimal amount of stored charge. This requires that the small amount of charge injected must be confined to the emitter side of the base region to provide the required diffusion gradient, as shown. As time goes on, the stored charge will increase by moving the hypotenuse of the triangle shown in the figure upward and outward so that the required constant diffusion gradient is maintained. At time t_D the triangle will have expanded until it reaches the collector side of the base. Up until this time there has been no effect on the collector due to the emitter current. After time t_D, the injected carriers begin to charge up the collector junction, and the current in the load begins to rise. The charging time of the collector depletion capacitance is denoted by t_0 in the figure. All during the capacitance-charging time t_0, the total stored charge in the base region remains constant because the collector is using the entire emitter current by dividing it between the load and the charging of the depletion capacitance.

The common base turn-on time consists of the delay time t_D, which is the time required for the collector current to start to rise after the emitter current has started, plus the collector rise time t_0. The base current rises as soon as the emitter is turned on because the injection current through the emitter-base junction must be balanced by a majority-carrier current from the base lead to maintain space-charge neutrality in the base region. Here we are neglecting the charging of the emitter-base depletion region because it varies only slightly in voltage when the emitter is forward-biased. The collector-base depletion region, however, must be discharged from the full value of V_{CC} when the transistor saturates at $t = t_D + t_0$.

At the end of t_0, all terminal currents have reached their final values, but the minority-carrier density in the base is still that shown for $t = t_D$. More time must elapse before the base region receives its full charge, shown for $t = \infty$. The final equilibrium charge density is determined by the total recombination in the base region so that to a first approximation, $I_B = P/\tau_B$, where P is the total excess hole storage in the base and τ_B is the effective base-region lifetime. The emitter current is now divided between the load and base-region recombination current, and both the emitter and collector junctions are forward-biased.

The delay time t_D may be calculated by determining the charge ΔQ injected into the base region during t_D and equating it to $I_E t_D$. The injected charge is given by

$$\Delta Q = \tfrac{1}{2}qA p_E w = I_E w^2/2D_p, \tag{6.105}$$

where $p_E = I_E w/qA D_p$, and we see that the factor $w^2/2D_p = 1/\omega_0$, the cutoff frequency of the device. Since $\Delta Q = I_E t_D$, we find that the delay time is

$$t_D = w^2/2D_p = 1/\omega_0. \tag{6.106}$$

For very high-speed transistors the charging of the emitter depletion capacitance to give sufficient forward bias to supply the emitter current drive will be comparable to, or larger than the t_D calculated above. This emitter-barrier charging time is typically of the order of a few nanoseconds for a 2-ma emitter current. It is clear, therefore, that a transistor with a cutoff frequency above 100 mc will have a significant switching turn-on delay due to the emitter-capacitance charging time as well as the t_D calculated above.

The collector rise time t_0 is determined by the current $[I_E - I_C(t)]$ charging the collector-barrier depletion-region capacitance from a value of $(V_{CC} - I_{C0}R_L)$ to nearly zero. From Eq. (4.22) we find the collector-barrier capacitance to be

$$C_C = A_C \left[\frac{qN_A N_D \epsilon}{2(N_A + N_D)(\phi - V_C)} \right]^{1/2}, \tag{6.107}$$

where V_C is the voltage across the collector barrier, ϕ is the barrier height, N_D is the doping of the base of the PNP-transistor, and N_A is the doping of the collector region. Here, A_C is the area of the collector junction. An increment of charge dQ is removed from the collector barrier by the current $I_E + I_C(V)$ in the time

$$dt = \frac{dQ(V)}{I_E + I_C(V)}. \tag{6.108}$$

Here $dQ(V) = A_C C(V)\, dV$ and $I_C(V)$ is given by $(V_{CC} - V_C)/R_L$, and we assume that $\alpha_{FB} \simeq 1$. Integrating we find that

$$t_0 = \int_{V_{CC}}^0 \frac{A_C C(V_C)\, dV}{I_E + (V_{CC} - V_C)/R_L}. \tag{6.109}$$

Here, the upper limit of zero is really an approximation, since as the collector junction enters saturation, it will be forward-biased by a voltage up to one-half of the voltage corresponding to the energy gap of the semiconductor involved. This will be negligible in determining t_0 if the supply voltage V_{CC} is of several volts magnitude. Also, we have considered $I_{C0}R_L$ negligible by omitting it from the lower limit. Of course, if the initial condition is determined by a finite I_E, there will be a comparable I_C which cannot be neglected. Substituting (6.107) in (6.109), we have

$$t_0 = A_C R_L \left[\frac{qN_A N_D \epsilon}{2(N_A + N_D)} \right]^{1/2} \int_{V_{CC}}^0 \frac{dV_C}{(I_E R_L + V_{CC} - V_C)(\phi - V_C)^{1/2}}, \tag{6.110}$$

and integrating, we have

$$t_0 = A_C R_L \left[\frac{2\epsilon q N_A N_D}{(N_A + N_D)(I_E R_L + V_{CC} - \phi)} \right]^{1/2}$$

$$\times \left[\tan^{-1} \left(\frac{\phi - V_{CC}}{I_E R_L + V_{CC} - \phi} \right)^{1/2} - \tan^{-1} \left(\frac{\phi}{I_E R_L + V_{CC} - \phi} \right)^{1/2} \right].$$

$$(6.111)$$

Finally, in terms of the parametric voltage $V_s = (I_E R_L + V_{CC} - \phi)$ we may write

$$t_0 = 2 R_L C_C(V_s) \left[\tan^{-1} \left(\frac{\phi - V_{CC}}{V_s} \right)^{1/2} - \tan^{-1} \left(\frac{\phi}{V_s} \right)^{1/2} \right], \qquad (6.112)$$

where $C_C(V_s)$ refers to the collector capacitance evaluated at V_s. This relation (6.112) is valid only in saturation where the voltage drop $I_E R_L$ exceeds $|V_{CC}|$ by more than ϕ. At lower values of I_E we must integrate (6.110) to 90% of the final equilibrium value of collector voltage, since an exponential relation requires an infinite time to reach equilibrium.

It should be noted that at the threshold of saturation, $V_s \sim \phi$ and deep in saturation, $|V_s| \gg |V_{CC}|$. If switching is just into saturation, Eq. (6.112) reduces to $t_0 = (\pi/2) R_L C_C(\phi)$, which is a maximum value. With an overdrive into deep saturation, t_0 is a minimum given by

$$t_0 = 2 R_L C_C(V_s)[-V_{CC}/V_s]^{1/2}.$$

Our next task is to calculate the storage time of the transistor. The storage time is defined as the time required to remove the excess density (p_C) of minority carriers at the collector junction once the input is either turned off or driven off. It is necessary first to calculate the final values of p_E and p_C to which the base-region excess current carrier density will rise in order to have the proper initial conditions for a calculation of storage time. In this way we will find the storage time as a function of both turn-on and turn-off drives.

In saturation both the emitter and collector are forward-biased so that we may let the base-region stored charge be represented by the superposition of the charge distributions of two opposed diffusion currents, as illustrated in Fig. 6.10. To calculate the final values of p_E and p_C, we will define the diffusion currents $I_{EF} = qAD_p p_E/w$ and $I_{CR} = qAD_p p_C/w$. The forward emitter current I_{EF} represents the current of holes diffusing to the right in Fig. 6.10, associated with the gradient indicated by the diagonal drawn from p_E to C. The reverse collector current I_{CR} represents the current of holes diffusing to the left, associated with the gradient indicated by the diagonal drawn from p_C to E. The linear superposition

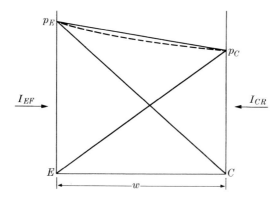

Fig. 6.10. Superimposed diffusion currents in a saturated transistor.

of these currents gives the net current of holes flowing into the emitter and out of the collector, which is I_C. Therefore $-\alpha_{FB}I_{EF} + I_{CR} = I_C$. The portion of I_{EF} which contributes to recombination current is $(1 - \alpha_{FB})I_{EF}$, where α_{FB} is the forward-current transfer ratio measured by using the emitter as input and the collector as output with a common base. The portion of I_{CR} which contributes to recombination current is $(1 - \alpha_{RB})I_{CR}$, where α_{RB} is the reverse-current transfer ratio measured by using the collector as input and the emitter as output. Here A represents the effective area of the active base region.

We can now write a continuity equation for charge conservation as follows:

$$\Delta Q = (I_E + I_C)\,\Delta t - [(1 - \alpha_{RB})I_{CR} + (1 - \alpha_{FB})I_{EF}]\,\Delta t, \tag{6.113}$$

where $I_E + I_C$ is the excess current available for charging up the base, and the term in brackets represents the rate at which base-region charge is lost by recombination. The steady state of all currents is reached when $\Delta Q/\Delta t = 0$, giving two simultaneous equations determining I_{CR} and I_{EF}:

$$I_E + I_C = (1 - \alpha_{RB})I_{CR} + (1 - \alpha_{FB})I_{EF},$$
$$-I_C = \alpha_{FB}I_{EF} - I_{CR}. \tag{6.114}$$

The solution of equations (6.114) gives for final equilibrium $(t = \infty)$:

$$I_{EF}(\infty) = \frac{I_E + \alpha_{RB}I_C}{1 - \alpha_{FB}\alpha_{RB}} = \frac{qAD_p}{w}\,p_E(\infty), \tag{6.115}$$

$$I_{CR}(\infty) = \frac{\alpha_{FB}I_E + I_C}{1 - \alpha_{FB}\alpha_{RB}} = \frac{qAD_p}{w}\,p_C(\infty). \tag{6.116}$$

At zero time we know that $I_E(0) = (qAD_p/w)p_E(0)$, giving

$$p_E(\infty) = p_E(0) \frac{I_E(\infty) + \alpha_{RB}I_C(\infty)}{(1 - \alpha_{FB}\alpha_{RB})I_E(0)},$$ (6.117)

$$p_C(\infty) = p_E(0) \frac{\alpha_{FB}I_E(\infty) + I_C(\infty)}{(1 - \alpha_{FB}\alpha_{RB})I_E(0)},$$ (6.118)

where the parenthetical (∞) and (0) denote final and initial equilibrium values of the variables. We may now use these values of $p_E(\infty)$ and $p_C(\infty)$ to calculate the storage time of the device. Of course, the device

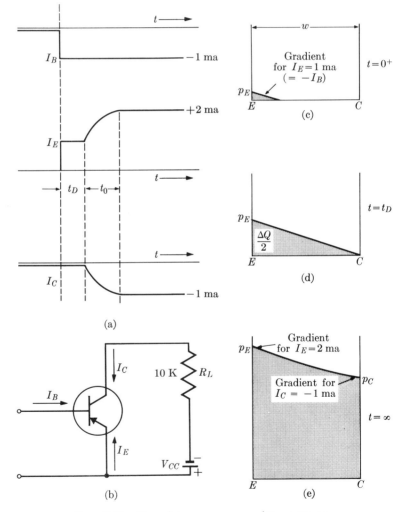

FIG. 6.11. Transistor common-emitter turn-on.

must be left on long enough to let p_E and p_C approach their equilibrium values, or the storage time will not be very reproducible.

If the transistor is turned on by using the base as input in a common emitter connection, the initial base-charging current will be $I_E = -I_B$. The delay time $t_D = 1/\omega_0$ is the same as before, since it is independent of current. Using the examples of Fig. 6.11, we see that a step of -1 ma in the base current would in time create the same $p_E(\infty)$ and $p_C(\infty)$ hole densities as are shown in Fig. 6.9, but in the meantime there would be only one-half the stored charge in the base at time $t = t_D$, since the charging current is only half as large as in the common-base example.

Next, we will calculate the time required for the establishment of $p_E(\infty)$ and $p_C(\infty)$ to within 0.9 of their equilibrium values. Referring to the continuity equation (6.113) for the common-base configuration, we will adapt it for easy use by defining an average $\bar{\alpha} = (\alpha_{FB} + \alpha_{RB})/2$ so that we may write

$$\Delta Q = (I_E + I_C)\,\Delta t - (1 - \bar{\alpha})(I_{CR} + I_{EF})\,\Delta t. \qquad (6.119)$$

We shall now evaluate the initial and final stored charges. From Fig. 6.9 we see that at the end of time $t_D + t_0$, we still have the charge involved in maintaining I_E across the base. This can be written

$$Q(0) = qAw\frac{p_E}{2} = \frac{w^2}{2D_p}I_E = \frac{I_E}{\omega_0}. \qquad (6.120)$$

This is the initial stored charge for our problem. For this initial condition we are assuming negligible base-region recombination so that there is a uniform charge-density gradient from the emitter to the collector.

When base charging is complete we have twice as much emitter current as collector current so that the density gradient at the emitter is twice that at the collector (see Fig. 6.11). This means that we no longer have a straight line between p_E and p_C, and the recombination current of the entire stored-charge distribution is just sufficient to equal the difference between the emitter and collector currents. Nevertheless, as can be seen from the figure, the average of p_E and p_C, multiplied by the area and thickness of the base region will give a good approximation to the total stored charge. From Eqs. (6.117) and (6.118) we may write

$$Q(\infty) = qAw\left(\frac{p_E(\infty) + p_C(\infty)}{2}\right) = \frac{I_E + I_C}{\omega_0(1 - \bar{\alpha})}, \qquad (6.121)$$

where we have used the average $\bar{\alpha}$ and recognized that

$$I_E(\infty) = I_E \qquad \text{and} \qquad I_C(\infty) = I_C$$

throughout the base-charging time.

We may write (6.119) as a differential equation

$$\frac{dQ}{dt} = I_E + I_C - (1 - \bar{\alpha})\omega_0 Q, \tag{6.122}$$

where $(I_{CR} + I_{EF}) = \omega_0 Q$ [see Eq. (6.127)]. Separating variables and integrating gives

$$t_C = \int_{Q(0)}^{0.9Q(\infty)} \left[\frac{dQ}{I_E + I_C - (1 - \bar{\alpha})\omega_0 Q} \right]$$

$$= \frac{-1}{\omega_0(1 - \bar{\alpha})} \left[\ln \{ I_E + I_C - (1 - \bar{\alpha})\omega_0 Q \} \right]_{Q(0)}^{0.9Q(\infty)}. \tag{6.123}$$

Remembering that $t_D = 1/\omega_0$, we get

$$t_C = \frac{t_D}{1 - \bar{\alpha}} \ln \left[\frac{\bar{\alpha} I_E + I_C}{0.1(I_E + I_C)} \right], \tag{6.124}$$

where we integrated to 90% of the final value of charge in order to get an arbitrary finite charging time [$Q(\infty)$ is by definition reached only in infinite time]. Here, t_C is measured from the end of t_0 which was arbitrarily used as a new zero time in defining $Q(0)$. From this equation it is clear that t_C must be considerably greater than t_D, since $(1 - \bar{\alpha})$ is much less than one and if $\bar{\alpha}$ is nearly one, the argument of the logarithm is nearly ten. Computing t_C for the numerical values of Fig. 6.9 and assigning $\bar{\alpha} = 0.9$, we find that $-t_C = 10t_D \ln 8 = 21t_D$. This gives an idea of the length of time required for p_E and p_C to come to equilibrium in the base region.

In the case of the common-emitter situation shown in Fig. 6.11, we would get the same time for t_C, since the same terminal currents are operating. Expressing Eq. (6.124) in terms of base drive gives

$$t_C = \frac{t_D}{1 - \bar{\alpha}} \ln \left[\frac{\bar{\alpha} I_B - (1 - \bar{\alpha}) I_C}{0.1 I_B} \right] \tag{6.125}$$

(since $I_E + I_C = -I_B$).

Although the area of the base region does not enter explicitly into the results above since it is contained in the substitution of currents for charge densities, there is the implicit assumption that the effective area is the same area that is involved in current flow. Furthermore, we have used the same area for I_{CR} and I_{EF}, implying that the emitter and collector are the same size. In actual fact, the area involved may well exceed that of either the emitter or collector, and a transistor in deep saturation may store some charge in parts of the base relatively remote from the active base region for Class A operation. For this reason, t_C may be longer because transit time would be required to diffuse charge to these remote regions, and yet if the minority-carrier lifetime is low in such regions, they may shorten t_C by requiring the accumulation of much less total stored charge. In summary, it is probably true that an average base lifetime $\bar{\tau}_B$, evaluated on the above area assumptions and a measurement of observed storage time, will allow a reasonably good phenomenological theory. Accordingly, we will now calculate the turn-off time of the transistor switch, using such an average base lifetime or, what is the same thing, an average $\bar{\alpha}$-parameter.

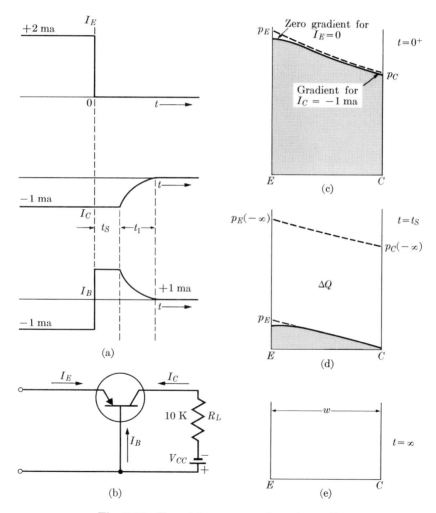

Fig. 6.12. Transistor common-base turn-off.

The storage time t_S, defined as the time required to reduce p_C from $p_C(\infty)$ to zero, will be calculated first. In Fig. 6.12 is shown the relation between the various currents and the stored charge during turn-off. Here, it is assumed that the emitter circuit is opened at $t = 0$. Immediately, the hole gradient at the emitter side of the base goes to zero, as shown for the time $t = 0^+$ in Fig. 6.12(c). When the time t_S is reached, the hole density on the collector side of the base goes to zero, as shown in Fig. 6.12(d). During this time, t_S, the quantity of charge ΔQ, has been removed by a combination of collector current and recombination current. The simple continuity equation expressing the detailed balance during this time is

$$\frac{dQ}{dt} = I_C - Q/\bar{\tau}_B, \tag{6.126}$$

where $\bar{\tau}_B$ is the average lifetime of excess holes in the base region (including both surface and bulk recombination).

We may express $\bar{\tau}_B$ in terms of the terminal quantity $\bar{\alpha}$ as follows. According to Eq. (6.119), the recombination current can be written as $(1 - \bar{\alpha})(I_{CR} + I_{EF})$. From the definitions of I_{CR} and I_{EF} we may write

$$(I_{CR} + I_{EF}) = \frac{2qAD_p}{w} \frac{(p_E + p_C)}{2} = \frac{2D_p}{w^2} Q = \omega_0 Q. \tag{6.127}$$

Equating the two expressions for recombination current, we find that

$$Q/\bar{\tau}_B = (1 - \bar{\alpha})\omega_0 Q \quad \text{or} \quad (1 - \bar{\alpha})\omega_0 = 1/\bar{\tau}_B. \tag{6.128}$$

Returning to the calculation of storage time, we substitute in the continuity equation (6.126) and remembering that I_C is constant during t_S, we write the differential equation

$$\frac{dQ}{dt} = I_C - (1 - \bar{\alpha})\omega_0 Q, \tag{6.129}$$

which is identical in form to (6.122) and is solved in the same way to give

$$t_S = \frac{-t_D}{1 - \bar{\alpha}} [\ln \{I_C - (1 - \bar{\alpha})\omega_0 Q\}]_{Q(\infty)}^{Q(t_S)}, \tag{6.130}$$

where the initial stored charge density is $Q(\infty)$, as given before in Eq. (6.121), and the final charge density $Q(t_S)$ can be found by calculating the base charge necessary to maintain I_C (see Fig. 6.12d):

$$Q(t_S) = qAwp_E(t_S)/2 = -I_C/\omega_0. \tag{6.131}$$

By substituting limits in Eq. (6.130) we find that

$$t_S = \frac{t_D}{1 - \bar{\alpha}} \ln\left[\frac{I_E}{I_C(\bar{\alpha} - 2)}\right], \tag{6.132}$$

where it is understood that I_E is the emitter current for $t = 0^-$. Again assigning $\bar{\alpha} = 0.9$, we find for the currents given in Fig. 6.12 that $t_S = 10t_D \ln (1.82) = 6t_D$. This is for an open emitter. If the emitter is driven to some negative current value, the t_S will be much shorter. As an example let the emitter current be -2 ma while I_C is still -1 ma. Now, roughly two-thirds of the stored charge will be removed by the collector, as shown in Fig. 6.13.

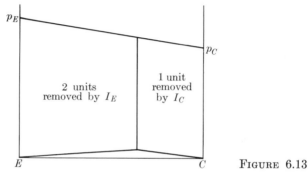

$$p_E$$

$$p_C$$

2 units
removed by I_E

1 unit
removed
by I_C

E C FIGURE 6.13

The storage time can then be calculated from (6.130) by using limits of $Q(t_S)/3$ and $Q(\infty)/3$ for the integral involving collector current only. In general, we may calculate these limits from the ratio of the collector current to the total current draining the base region during t_S. If I_E^- represents the negative emitter current used to turn off the transistor, we will use limits of $Q(t_S)[I_C/(I_C + I_E^-)]$ and $Q(\infty)[I_C/(I_C + I_E^-)]$ in (6.130), obtaining

$$t_S = \frac{t_D}{1 - \bar{\alpha}} \ln\left[\frac{I_E^- - I_E}{I_C(2 - \bar{\alpha}) + I_E^-}\right]. \tag{6.133}$$

The remaining part of the turn-off time is the time indicated as t_1 in Fig. 6.12. This is the time required to charge the collector barrier from zero to $-V_{CC}$ and may be calculated in a manner similar to the calculation of t_0 above [of the order of $R_L C_C(\phi)$ for most conditions].

In a common-emitter configuration we may compute the storage time directly by transformation of Eq. (6.133) using Kirchhoff's law. We define the base current during saturation as $I_B = -(I_E + I_C)$ and the base current after time zero when turn-off is initiated by $I_B^- = (I_E^- + I_C)$. During the storage time interval all these currents are constant so that we may substitute in Eq. (6.133), obtaining

$$t_S = \frac{t_D}{1 - \bar{\alpha}} \ln\left[\frac{I_B - I_{\bar{B}}}{I_C(1 - \bar{\alpha}) - I_{\bar{B}}}\right] \tag{6.134}$$

for t_S in terms of base current drive.

In the above discussion we have implied that the charge density at the collector side of the base would be drawn down by the collector current at a certain rate and just as the density reached zero, the same collector current would start charging the collector depletion capacitance. Figure 6.12 indicates this by showing a sharp breakaway of I_C at the end of t_S. Actually, in many transistor geometries this breakaway is far from sharp. Rounding of this corner results from the spreading out of the stored charge into the relatively remote parts of the base region so that the charge density at different parts of the collector junction may reach zero at different times. In this case, there will be a rounded characteristic if the lateral resistivity of the device is large enough to support appreciable lateral voltage drops.

The same type of effect can be seen in the delay time during turn-on. Here, in certain geometries the spreading of the base-region charge may be such that only at the center of the emitter will the injected charge density reach the collector at the time t_D calculated above. The remaining collector areas may be brought into action at successively later times, giving a rounded characteristic for turn-on delay time as well. Because of these effects, it is hard to compare measured and calculated t_D and t_S times to better than a factor of two or so.

6.5   Effects of Temperature

The factors involved in the thermal runaway of a transistor are I_{C0}, α_{FE}, r_B, and r_E. Only I_{C0} and α_{FE} are of primary importance as we will show by consideration of a common-emitter connection under the conditions of either constant base current or constant base voltage drive.

If power is dissipated in the collector junction faster than it can be removed by thermal conduction, the transistor will burn up. The thermal conductivity of the transistor structure can be expressed in watts/°C. This is just the reciprocal of the K-factor used in the literature, which is expressed in degrees of temperature rise of the collector junction per watt of dissipated power. If the dissipated power is represented by the expression $I_C(V_{CC} - I_C R_L)$, we may differentiate it with respect to temperature and express the condition for thermal stability as

$$K\frac{\partial I_C}{\partial T}(V_{CC} - 2I_C R_L) < 1. \tag{6.135}$$

In a common-emitter connection we may express I_C as

$$I_C = \alpha_{FE}(I_{C0} + I_B). \tag{6.136}$$

For constant current drive we then have

$$\frac{\partial I_C}{\partial T} = \frac{\partial(\alpha_{FE}I_{C0})}{\partial T} + I_B\frac{\partial\alpha_{FE}}{\partial T}. \tag{6.137}$$

If we have a constant voltage drive, then

$$I_B = V_B/r_{BB} = V_B/(r_B + \alpha_{FE}r_E), \tag{6.138}$$

giving

$$I_C = \alpha_{FE}I_{C0} + \frac{\alpha_{FE}V_B}{r_B + \alpha_{FE}r_E}, \tag{6.139}$$

where $r_E = kT/qI_E$. We may assume that $r_B \ll \alpha_{FE}r_E$ if we have a reasonable α_{FE} of the order of 100, giving

$$\frac{\partial I_C}{\partial T} = \frac{\partial(\partial_{FE}I_{C0})}{\partial T} + \frac{qV_B}{k}\frac{\partial(I_E/T)}{\partial T}. \tag{6.140}$$

Evaluating the second term first, we assume that $\gamma = 1$ and let $I_E = I_0e^{qV_E/kT}$, where $I_0 = qAD_pp_{nB}/w$ and $V_E = -V_B$. Since $p_{nB} = n_i^2/N_D = (N_cN_v/N_D)e^{-\Delta E/kT}$, we find that

$$\frac{qV_B}{k}\frac{\partial(I_E/T)}{\partial T} = \frac{qA}{w}\left[e^{(qV_B-\Delta E)/kT}\frac{\partial(D_p/T)}{\partial T} + \frac{D_p}{T}\frac{\partial}{\partial T}e^{(qV_B-\Delta E)/kT}\right]. \tag{6.141}$$

Assuming that $D_p \sim 1/T^{1/2}$, we may evaluate (6.141) as

$$\frac{qV_B}{k}\frac{\partial(I_E/T)}{\partial T} = f(V_B, T^{-7/2})e^{(qV_B-\Delta E)/kT}, \tag{6.142}$$

where $f(V_B, T^{-7/2})$ is a function whose maximum dependence on T is the $-\frac{7}{2}$ power, as indicated. In the first term of Eq. (6.140) we are concerned with the temperature dependence of α_{FE} and I_{C0} as for the case of constant I_B-drive. In the case of α_{FE} we find from Eqs. (6.91), (6.34), and (6.106) the relation

$$\alpha_{FE} \simeq 1/(1 - \alpha_{FB}) \simeq 1/(1 - \beta) = \tau_B/t_D, \tag{6.143}$$

where it can be seen that the temperature dependence of α_{FE} is, to the first order, the temperature dependence of the effective base-region lifetime.

In Chapter 3 we outlined the Shockley-Read [6] theory of minority-carrier lifetime. In Eq. (3.12) we found for N-type material that

$$\tau_B = \tau_p(1 + e^{(E_T-E_0)/kT}), \tag{6.144}$$

where τ_p is the limiting hole lifetime found when the Fermi level coincides with the bottom of the conduction band, and E_T is the energy of the recombination trapping centers. Inspection of Fig. 3.1 shows that the lifetime τ_B increases rapidly with temperature because E_0 moves toward the center of the energy gap with rising temperature. When the Fermi level coincides with the trap energy E_T, then τ_B is already double the limiting τ_p-value. We are now in a position to evaluate the temperature dependence of α_{FE} as

$$\frac{\partial \alpha_{FE}}{\partial T} = -\frac{\tau_p}{t_D} \frac{(E_T - E_0)}{kT^2} e^{(E_T-E_0)/kT}. \tag{6.145}$$

Inspection of Eq. (6.145) shows that if $(E_T - E_0)$ is negative and several times kT, the α_{FE} will increase quite rapidly with increasing T.

For the case of I_{C0} we have from Eq. (6.14) the diffusion contribution to I_{C0}:

$$I_d = -qA\left[\frac{D_n n_{pC}}{L_{nC}} + \gamma \frac{D_n n_{pE}}{L_{nE}}\right]. \tag{6.146}$$

From Eq. (5.22) we find the regeneration contribution to I_{C0} to be

$$I_r = -\frac{qAn_i}{\tau_B}\left[\frac{2\epsilon(\phi - V_C)}{qN_D}\right]^{1/2}, \tag{6.147}$$

where we assume that the collector doping level is large compared to the base doping level ($N_A \gg N_D$) and therefore that the collector depletion region is entirely in the base region. For a large-gap semiconductor such as silicon, the regeneration current dominates, but at elevated temperatures the diffusion leakage takes over. Equation (5.23) may be used to estimate the relative size of I_d and I_r under a given set of conditions. Here we will proceed with $I_{C0} = I_r$ only. Using Eq. (6.147) we may write the product $\alpha_{FE} I_{C0}$ as

$$\alpha_{FE} I_{C0} = -\frac{qAn_i}{t_D}\left[\frac{2\epsilon(\phi - V_C)}{qN_D}\right]^{1/2}. \tag{6.148}$$

Since $n_i^2 = N_c N_v e^{-\Delta E/kT}$, we may evaluate the temperature dependence of the $\alpha_{FE} I_{C0}$ product as

$$\frac{\partial(\alpha_{FE} I_{C0})}{\partial T} = \frac{qA \, \Delta E}{kT^2 t_D}\left[\frac{\epsilon N_c N_v(\phi - V_C)}{2qN_D}\right]^{1/2} e^{-\Delta E/2kT}. \tag{6.149}$$

Over a significant range of temperature the product ($\alpha_{FE} I_{C0}$) will have an activation energy of $\Delta E/2$ for large-gap semiconductors.

For a small-gap semiconductor such as germanium, the diffusion process will dominate I_{C0}. Since $n_{pC} = n_i^2/N_{AC}$ and $n_{pE} = n_i^2/N_{AE}$ in Eq. (6.146), we see that I_{C0} will have the full temperature dependence of n_i^2, which is an activation energy of ΔE. There will be no lifetime term since

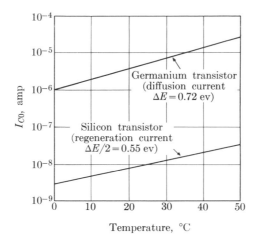

FIG. 6.14. I_{C0} vs. temperature.

we assume that both the emitter and collector are doped heavily enough that the lifetime τ_n is a constant near its limiting value.

Putting these results together, we find for a constant I_B-drive that $\partial I_C/\partial T$ is proportional to $e^{-\Delta E/2kT}$ or to $e^{(E_T-E_0)/kT}$, depending on whether the first or second term of Eq. (6.137) is larger. Since I_B is usually much larger than I_{C0}, the temperature dependence of I_C should be proportional to $e^{(E_T-E_0)/kT}$.

For a constant V_B-drive we must evaluate the relative sizes of the terms in Eq. (6.140). Again, since I_E is usually orders of magnitude larger than I_{C0}, we expect the second term to dominate, giving a temperature dependence of $e^{(qV_B-\Delta E)/kT}$. This is much larger than the temperature dependence for the constant I_B-drive, since $(qV_B - \Delta E)$ is of the order of ΔE, whereas $(E_T - E_0)$ is probably much less than $\Delta E/2$ in the constant I_B-case.

In Fig. 6.14 is shown the experimental variation of I_{C0} with temperature for germanium and silicon transistors. We have seen that I_r dominates I_d for silicon so that I_{C0} should be proportional to $e^{-\Delta E/2kT}$ in this case. In germanium at room temperature the reverse is true so that I_{C0} is proportional to $e^{-\Delta E/kT}$, as is shown experimentally.

6.6 High-Level Injection [7]

Up to this point we have assumed low-level injection. This requires the density of injected minority carriers to be small, compared with the density of majority carriers present. We will now consider some of the effects to be expected if the density of injected carriers becomes comparable to the equilibrium density of majority carriers normally present in the region.

Focusing our attention on the base region of the transistor, we will first consider the effect of high-level injection on the diffusion transport of holes across the base region. Writing the hole and electron currents in the base region, we have

$$I_{nB} = -qA_E[n_B\mu_n \text{ grad } (V) - D_n \text{ grad } (n_B)], \qquad (6.150)$$

$$I_{pB} = -qA_E[p_B\mu_p \text{ grad } (V) + D_p \text{ grad } (p_B)], \qquad (6.151)$$

where n_B and p_B are the majority- and minority-carrier densities in the base region and are functions of x as we move from $x = 0$ at the emitter junction to $x = w$ at the collector junction. From detailed balance and space-charge neutrality we know that at any point x, $n_B = N_D + (p_B - p_{nB})$. Since N_D and p_{nB} are constants, it is clear that grad $(n_B) =$ grad $(p_B) \simeq p_E/w$ throughout the base. This assumes very small recombination loss in the base region as usual. Since the electron current across the base region is limited to the leakage over the collector barrier, we may assume $I_{nB} \simeq 0$. Setting Eq. (6.150) equal to zero and solving for grad (V) we find that

$$\text{grad } (V) = D_n p_E/w n_B \mu_n. \qquad (6.152)$$

Substituting in Eq. (6.151) gives

$$I_{pB} = -qA_E\left[\frac{p_B}{n_B}\left(\frac{\mu_p}{\mu_n} D_n\right)\frac{p_E}{w} + D_p \frac{p_E}{w}\right]. \qquad (6.153)$$

Since $(\mu_p/\mu_n)D_n = D_p$, we may write Eq. (6.153) in the form

$$I_{pB} = -qA_E\left[\left(1 + \frac{p_B}{n_B}\right) D_p\right]\frac{p_E}{w}. \qquad (6.154)$$

Here, we can see that Eq. (6.154) is identical to Eq. (6.46) used in all the previous diffusion analysis, except that it contains an effective diffusion constant

$$D_p^* = \left[1 + \frac{p_B}{n_B}\right] D_p. \qquad (6.155)$$

So long as we have low-level injection, $p_B \ll n_B$, and the effective diffusion constant is just D_p. When p_B is comparable to n_B, we may use the effective diffusion constant (6.155) in our previous results. In this connection, however, it must be pointed out that since $p_B(0) = p_E$ and $p_B(w) = 0$, the effective diffusion constant is a function of x so that we cannot directly substitute. Moreover, this effective D_p^* only obtains when there is negligible electron diffusion current in the same region. This was a condition in the above derivation and is actually the physical cause of the increased effective D_p^* because the blocking of the electronic diffusion current by the establishment of the effective field, $-\text{grad}\ (V)$, is the cause of speeding up the holes. For very high injection levels, $p_B \to n_B$ and $D_p^* \to 2D_p$ as a limit.

Turning to another effect of high-level injection, we will consider the factors of α_{FB}. The first factor of interest is the transport efficiency β. From Eq. (6.36) it is clear that as D_p increases $|1 - \beta|$ decreases. This is true even though D_p may be affected only at the emitter side of the base. Any speeding of the holes on their way will allow a larger percentage to arrive at the collector without recombining. Since $p_B(0) = p_E$ and p_E is proportional to the emitter current I_E, we would expect α_{FE} to increase with emitter current. In some transistors this is true initially, but soon α_{FE} begins to fall as I_E continues to increase (see Fig. 6.15). This is due to two factors, a drop in the emitter injection efficiency γ and the crowding of base current toward the perimeter of the emitter, thus increasing the surface recombination term in β.

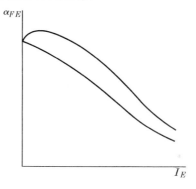

Fig. 6.15. Typical curves of α_{FE} vs. I_E for germanium transistors.

To see these effects more clearly we write $1/\alpha_{FE}$ as

$$(1/\alpha_{FE}) = (1 - \alpha_{FB})/(\alpha_{FB}) \simeq (1 - \alpha_{FB}) = 1 - \gamma\beta$$
$$\simeq (1 - \gamma) + (1 - \beta), \qquad (6.156)$$

where we are assuming that α_{FB}, γ, and β are nearly unity and that α^* is unity. From Eq. (6.4a) we find the dc-injection efficiency loss to be $(1 - \gamma) \simeq D_n n_E w/D_p p_B L_{nE}$. From Eq. (6.36) we find the corresponding transport efficiency loss to be

$$(1 - \beta) \simeq (w^2/2D_p)(1/\tau_B + 2s_B/r_E).$$

Equation (6.156) is now evaluated:

$$\frac{1}{\alpha_{FE}} = \frac{D_n n_E w}{D_p p_B L_{nE}} + \frac{w^2}{2D_p}\left[\frac{1}{\tau_B} + \frac{2s_B}{r_E}\right]. \qquad (6.157)$$

Considering first the effect of a high injection level on the first term, we note that it contains D_p in the denominator and n_E in the numerator. The n_E-factor entered through Eq. (6.3), where the electrons diffusing from the base to the emitter were given by $n_E(e^{qV_E/kT} - 1)$. From Eq. (4.3) we can write an effective n_E^* as

$$n_E^* = n_B(0)e^{-q\phi/kT}, \tag{6.158}$$

where $n_B(0) = N_D + p_E$ and the equilibrium $n_{pE} = N_D e^{-q\phi/kT}$. Substituting in Eq. (6.158), we find

$$n_E^* = n_{pE} + p_E e^{-q\phi/kT} = n_{pE}(1 + p_E/N_D). \tag{6.159}$$

This effective n_E^* should be used in (6.157) to give the high-injection level effect. Using the same quantities, we can evaluate (6.155) at $x = 0$ to be

$$D_p^* = D_p\left(1 + \frac{p_E}{N_D + p_E}\right). \tag{6.160}$$

Combining these two factors we find that the first term of (6.157) should carry the overall factor

$$\left[1 + \frac{p_E^2}{N_D(N_D + 2p_E)}\right]. \tag{6.161}$$

Here we have taken the worst case for D_p^* since the emitter current of holes will certainly not be increased as much as using p_E in the D_p^* would indicate. In most cases the factor of Eq. (6.159) is better. In any event we see from these considerations that the first term of Eq. (6.157) monotonically increases as p_E becomes comparable with N_D, even when we have used D_p^* at full value; that is, as though it were equally effective throughout the base region.

The second term contains D_p^* in the denominator so that it may initially decrease. However, the relative sizes of the two terms at low injection levels will determine the initial behavior of α_{FE}. If the injection efficiency term (the first term) dominates, α_{FE} will monotonically decrease with I_E. If the transport efficiency term dominates at low injection levels, α_{FE} may increase initially with I_E and then fall off.

Even in this latter case, increasing I_E may cause sufficient crowding of the base current toward the edge of the emitter that increasing surface recombination may offset the D_p^*-effect. This current crowding is directly due to the radial $I_B R_B$-drop in the base region. This voltage drop tends to bias the center of the emitter off, thus causing most of the injection to occur around the perimeter of the emitter. Typical curves of α_{FE} are shown in Fig. 6.15.

6.7 Doping-Level Effects

In most of the foregoing discussion the only effects of doping level considered were those associated directly with charge density. In the case of depletion-layer capacitance, the doping level was found to determine the dipole-layer charge density. In the case of injection efficiency the doping level determined the ratio of electron and hole densities at the forward-biased emitter junction. Here we will consider more indirect effects of doping level.

Diffusion constant. As the doping level increases, the density of ionized donors and acceptors increases. At some point in each type of semiconductor material, these, rather than the normal semiconductor lattice atoms, become the dominant scattering centers for current carriers. Above this doping level the mobility drops off monotonically. Since the diffusion constant is directly proportional to the mobility, it will show the same behavior. Figure 6.16 shows the relation between the diffusion constants for electrons and holes in silicon and germanium.

If we now consider injection efficiency we see that Eq. (6.4) partially accounts for the doping variation of D_p and D_n by expressing the result in terms of the resistivities. However, L_{nE} still depends on D_{nE} and is therefore doping dependent. In Chapter 3 we found that τ_n depended on the Fermi level and therefore on the doping level. In the case of the emitter region of a transistor, however, we may assume that the doping is so heavy that τ_n is essentially at its saturation value, leaving D_{nE} as the remaining doping-dependent factor in the injection efficiency loss.

Charge transport across the base region is dependent primarily on the diffusion constant through the diffusion transit time, $w^2/2D_p$. This

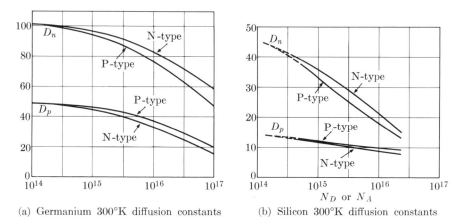

(a) Germanium 300°K diffusion constants   (b) Silicon 300°K diffusion constants

FIG. 6.16. Graph taken from mobility measurements of Prince [8], [9].

quantity enters as the reciprocal of the α_{FB} cutoff frequency, as the turn-on delay time (t_D), and as a factor in the transport efficiency loss term $(1 - \beta)$ [see Eq. (6.36)]. Consideration of these factors shows that a high base-region doping level will decrease the cutoff frequency, increase the turn-on delay, and decrease the transport efficiency.

Resistivity effects. There are resistivity effects beyond those considered in connection with the injection efficiency. The terminal currents must flow through the resistances of the emitter, base, and collector regions. The depletion-region capacitances and the diffusion capacitance must be charged through these resistances. In modern transistors the effective base-region resistance is usually the largest and most restrictive of these transistor-body resistances. We can calculate such a base resistance for the circular emitter geometry shown in Fig. 6.3. Under the assumption of low-level injection we will be able to eliminate current crowding. We will also assume that the base-region material is thick enough and of low enough resistivity outside of the emitter area that it does not contribute to R_B. Considering an annular ring of radius r, thickness dr, and height w, we may write

$$dV_{rB} = J_r \pi r^2 \left[\frac{\rho_B \, dr}{2\pi r w} \right], \tag{6.162}$$

where J_r is the majority-carrier current density in the base region. The factor in brackets is the resistance of the annular ring, and $J_r \pi r^2$ is the current flowing through the ring from the inside out. Integrating Eq. (6.162) gives

$$V_{rB} = J_r A_E \left[\frac{\rho_B}{4\pi w} \right] = I_r R_B, \tag{6.163}$$

where $R_B = \rho_B/4\pi w$. Evaluating R_B for $\rho_B = 0.1$ ohm-cm and $w = 1 \mu$ gives 80 ohms. This base doping level markedly degrades D_p in silicon so that it is clear that an engineering compromise is called for. Also, in practice, the speed of response of a transistor may be limited by $R_B C_C$. Here, both factors depend upon the base doping level, but R_B dominates so that heavy doping monotonically decreases the time constant. Such an advantage must be balanced against a decreasing β-factor.

The voltage V_{rB} is measured between the center and the perimeter of the emitter and represents the differential bias on the emitter junction tending to create current crowding. For an α_{FB} of 0.99 and an emitter current of 1 ma, we see that V_{rB} is only 0.8 mv, which is quite negligible compared to an emitter bias of a few tenths of a volt. A significant change in emitter bias requires about (kT/q) volts. At room temperature this is 25 mv, which can be seen to be large compared to V_{rB}.

6.8   Numerical Example

Given a PNP abrupt junction germanium transistor connected in a common emitter configuration, find expressions which are valid for the diffusion capacitance in both the active and saturation regions of the transistor's operating range.   Plot the diffusion capacitance against I_B from $I_B = 0$ to $I_B = -100\,\mu a$ for a transistor with $\alpha_{FB} = 0.99$, $\alpha_{RB} = 0.70$, $w = 10^{-3}$ cm, collector supply voltage $V_{CC} = -10$ v, and a 5000-ohm load resistor.

We first calculate the base-region charge (Q_B) as a function of base-emitter voltage (V_B) and then the diffusion capacitance will be given by $C_D = dQ_B/dV_B$. Base current is always recombination current, so for the active region of the device characteristic, we may write

$$I_B = -(1 - \alpha_{FB})I_E = -(1 - \alpha_{FB})qAD_p p_E/w. \qquad (6.164)$$

In this case the base-region charge is just

$$Q_B = qAwp_E/2, \qquad (6.165)$$

and by the law of the junction, Eq. (4.6),

$$p_E = p_{nB}[e^{-qV_B/kT} - 1]. \qquad (6.166)$$

(Here it is understood that all currents are considered positive when they are directed into the device, and for a PNP-transistor, hole injection by the emitter corresponds to a positive I_E and a negative I_B.)   Substituting Eq. (6.166) into Eq. (6.165), we find

$$Q_B = (qAw/2)p_{nB}(e^{-qV_B/kT} - 1). \qquad (6.167)$$

Differentiating and substituting Eq. (6.164) gives

$$C_D = \frac{w^2}{2D_p} \frac{q}{kT} \frac{-I_B}{(1 - \alpha_{FB})}. \qquad (6.168)$$

Equation (6.168) is valid only in the active region of the device characteristic, where the base-region charge is given by Eq. (6.165). In the saturation region of the device characteristic, the base-region charge is well approximated by

$$Q_B = qAw(p_E + p_C)/2 \qquad (6.169)$$

(refer to Fig. 6.10). In this example we find that the device enters saturation at $I_B = -20.2\,\mu a$, since at this current, $I_C = \alpha_{FB}I_B/(1 - \alpha_{FB}) = V_{CC}/R_L$. At the limit of our specified range of $I_B(-100\,\mu a)$, the emitter current will exceed the collector current by about $80\,\mu a$, and the base-region charge must be increased by an amount sufficient to give an extra 80 μa of recombination current.

Evaluating Eq. (6.169), we use the definitions of I_{EF} and I_{CR} given in Eqs. (6.115) and (6.116). We now write

$$I_C = I_{CR} - \alpha_{FB}I_{EF} = qAD_p(p_C - \alpha_{FB}p_E)/w. \qquad (6.170)$$

Solving for p_C we find that $p_C = \alpha_{FB}p_E + I_Cw/qAD_p$, and substituting in Eq. (6.169) gives

$$Q_B = (qAw/2)(p_E + \alpha_{FB}p_E + I_Cw/qAD_p). \qquad (6.171)$$

Substituting Eq. (6.166) and differentiating, we find

$$C_D = \left(\frac{q}{kT}\right)\left(\frac{qAw}{2}\right)p_E(1 + \alpha_{FB}). \qquad (6.172)$$

From the definition of I_{EF} we have $I_{EF} = qAD_pp_E/w$, which may be substituted in Eq. (6.172), giving

$$C_D = \frac{w^2}{2D_p}(1 + \alpha_{FB})\frac{qI_{EF}}{kT}. \qquad (6.173)$$

This equation can be compared with Eq. (6.50). It is seen that we have replaced I_E in Eq. (6.50) with $(1 + \alpha_{FB})I_{EF}$ in Eq. (6.173). This is reasonable if one considers that both p_C and p_E are increased when the emitter-base voltage is increased for a saturated transistor.

Using the definition of I_{EF} given in Eq. (6.115) with the substitution of $I_E = -(I_B + I_C)$, we may rewrite Eq. (6.173) as

$$C_D = \frac{w^2}{2D_p}\frac{q}{kT}\frac{-[I_B + I_C(1 - \alpha_{RB})](1 + \alpha_{FB})}{(1 - \alpha_{RB}\alpha_{FB})}. \qquad (6.174)$$

Here $I_C = V_{CC}/R_L$ and I_B is given. We are now ready to calculate the diffusion capacitance in the saturation region from Eq. (6.174) and in the active region from Eq. (6.168). Evaluating these equations, we find the common factor $(w^2q/2D_pkT) = 0.4\ \mu$f/amp. In our example

$$(1 + \alpha_{FB}) = 1.99, \qquad (1 - \alpha_{RB}\alpha_{FB}) = 0.297,$$

$$(1 - \alpha_{RB}) = 0.300, \qquad \text{and} \qquad (1 - \alpha_{FB}) = 0.01.$$

Substituting these numbers and using Eq. (6.168) up to $I_B = -20.2\ \mu$a and Eq. (6.174) for $I_B = -20.3\ \mu$a and up, we find the curve of C_D, shown in Fig. 6.17.

In the idealized model we have used, it is seen that there is a discontinuity of a factor of two in the diffusion capacitance at the threshold of saturation of the device. This discontinuity can be understood by comparing Fig. 6.5 with Fig. 6.10. If in Fig. 6.5 we raise p_E by an increment Δp_E, we see that we add a triangular increment to Q_B. This is for the active region of the device characteristic. In the other case we see from Fig. 6.10 that an increment of Δp_E will add a parallel-sided increment to Q_B in the saturation region of the device characteristic, since no more current can flow in the collector, and p_C must rise with p_E until ΔQ_B is sufficient to give a recombination current equal to the added emitter current. The discontinuity is then a result of suddenly doubling the ΔQ_B required for a given Δp_E.

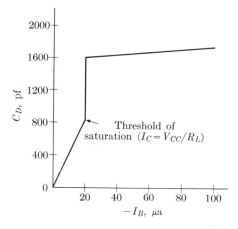

FIG. 6.17. Diffusion capacitance of a PNP-transistor.

This result is also dependent on the assumption of constant α_{FB} and α_{RB} throughout the range of base currents considered. In a real transistor these effective current transfer ratios may change rapidly at the onset of saturation as excess current carriers spread out beyond the active region of the base. This effect usually masks the rapid change of C_D shown at the onset of saturation in this example.

The relatively constant C_D found in the saturation region is due to the fact that C_D is really proportional to I_{EF} as given in Eq. (6.173), while we are plotting against I_B. In the active region,

$$I_{EF} = I_E = -I_B/(1 - \alpha_{FB})$$

so that C_D must grow with I_B multiplied by a large factor. In the saturation region I_{EF} grows only as $-I_B/(1 - \alpha_{RB}\alpha_{FB})$, which is a much smaller factor of proportionality. If we plotted C_D vs. I_E, we would not find the flattening out of the C_D-dependence after the onset of saturation as we did in the example just discussed.

Problems

6.1 Given a PNP germanium transistor with the properties listed in the table below.

Emitter	Base, w	Collector
$A_E = 1 \times 10^{-3}$ cm $\rho_p = 0.01$ ohm-cm $\tau_n = 10^{-8}$ sec	$w = 5 \times 10^{-4}$ cm $\rho_n = 1$ ohm-cm $\tau_p = 10^{-6}$ cm	$A_C = 2 \times 10^{-3}$ cm $\rho_p = 0.1$ ohm-cm $\tau_n = 10^{-7}$ sec

Also given are:

$$n_i = 2.5 \times 10^{13} \text{ carriers/cm},$$
$$\epsilon = 16\epsilon_0 = 1.41 \text{ pf/cm},$$
$$\mu_n = 3600 \text{ cm/sec/v/cm for the base region},$$
$$\mu_p = 300 \text{ cm/sec/v/cm for the emitter region}.$$

Calculate (a) the injected efficiency γ as a function of collector voltage and evaluate it at $V_C = -2, -5,$ and -10 v; (b) the I_{C0} at the same voltages; (c) the voltage at which the collector-barrier depletion region contacts the emitter (punch-through voltage).

6.2 Compare the injection efficiency of the emitter junction of Problem 6.1 with the injection efficiency of the same junction if fabricated between two thick semiconductor regions.

6.3 Derive an expression for the injection efficiency of a PNP-transistor including the effect of the emitter depletion capacitance C_E.

6.4 Given a transistor with $\alpha_{FB} = 0.98$, $\alpha_{RB} = 0.80$, $I_{C0} = 10^{-8}$ amp, and $I_{E0} = 0.82 \times 10^{-8}$ amp. Calculate and compare the open-circuit leakage current and the closed-circuit voltage drop for this transistor used in a common-emitter and in a common-collector connection. (The base is used as the control electrode in both cases.) For the closed condition let the switch current be four times the control current.

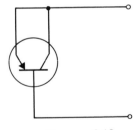

6.5 Given a transistor connected as shown in Fig. 6.18. Derive an expression for the impedance of the circuit, using the five-element one-lump model shown in Fig. 6.6 (neglect the transition capacitances).

FIGURE 6.18

6.6 Given a PNP-transistor with the following characteristics: $\alpha_{FB} = 0.98$, $\alpha_{RB} = 0.70$, collector barrier height $\phi = 0.3$ v, collector capacitance at zero bias $C_C(\phi) = 10$ pf, cutoff frequency $\omega_0 = 10^8$ cycles/sec, which is connected in the circuit shown in Fig. 6.19(b) and operated according to the time chart (Fig. 6.19a). Calculate the storage time measured from the closing of switch position 2. [*Hint:* Note that full base charging is not achieved before the switch is thrown. Assume that the impedance of the load is negligible compared to 5 K.]

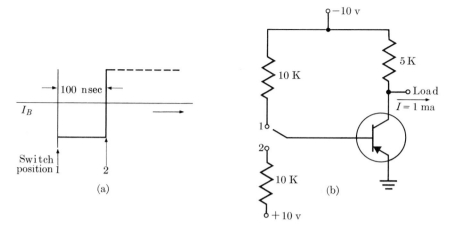

FIGURE 6.19

6.7 Given a PNP-transistor with base width w. Calculate the turn-on delay time if a step voltage pulse is applied across the emitter junction at $t = 0$ biasing the emitter in the forward direction. (Assume the series resistance and the charging time of the emitter depletion capacitance to be negligible.)

6.8 Using the data for the transistor of Problem 6.1, calculate the upper limit of the surface recombination velocity s_B so that surface recombination will not reduce the α_{FE} more than 2%. (Assume low frequency and $V_C = -10$ v.)

Bibliography

1. W. SHOCKLEY, "The Theory of PN Junctions in Semiconductors and PN Junction Transistors," *Bell System Tech. J.* **28**, 435–489 (1949).
2. R. D. MIDDLEBROOK, *An Introduction to Junction Transistor Theory*, John Wiley and Sons, New York, 1957.
3. J. G. LINVILL and J. F. GIBBONS, *Transistors and Active Circuits*, McGraw-Hill, New York, 1961.
4. J. J. EBERS and J. L. MOLL, "Large Signal Behavior of Junction Transistors," *Proc. IRE* **42**, 1761–1772 (1954).
5. R. BEAUFOY and J. J. SPARKES, "The Junction Transistor as a Charge Controlled Device," *ATE Journal* **13**, 310–327 (1957).
6. W. SHOCKLEY and W. T. READ, JR., "Statistics of the Recombination of Holes and Electrons," *Phys. Rev.* **87**, 835–842 (1952).
7. W. M. WEBSTER, "On the Variation of Junction Transistor Amplification Factor with Emitter Current," *Proc. IRE* **42**, 914–920 (1954).
8. M. B. PRINCE, "Drift Mobility in Semiconductors, I Germanium," *Phys. Rev.* **92**, 681 (1953).
9. M. B. PRINCE, "Drift Mobility in Semiconductors, II Silicon," *Phys. Rev.* **93**, 1204 (1954).

CHAPTER 7

TRANSISTOR STRUCTURES

In this chapter we will consider the major aspects of the operation of several multiple-junction structures. Some of these structures are operated as two-terminal devices but can be understood in terms of transistor mechanisms and are therefore considered together with the transistors.

7.1 The Drift Transistor[1]

The drift transistor differs from the diffusion transistor considered in Chapter 6 in that the current carriers injected at the emitter side of the base region are transported across the base region by drift in a built-in electric field rather than by diffusion. Most modern transistors fabricated by a solid-state diffusion process are drift transistors, although they usually go by the names "graded-base" or "diffused-base," which refer to the method of fabrication rather than the mechanism of charge transport. Figure 7.1 shows the physical origin of such a built-in electric field. The donor levels are crowded together at the left (emitter) side of the base region, indicating a heavy doping. At the collector side, the doping is light. If there is no bias applied to either junction, the current-carrier distribution in the base is as illustrated in the figure. At every point of the base, $p_{nB}n_{nB} = n_i^2$, and the Fermi level must be close to the conduction band near the emitter to yield such a large n_{nB} when multiplied by the density of conduction band states. Conversely, it must be much farther from the conduction band at the collector side of the base to yield the small n_{nB}

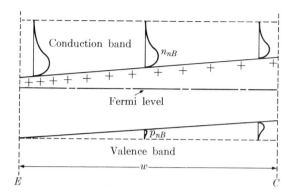

Fig. 7.1. Drift-transistor base region showing the effect of a doping gradient.

when multiplied by the same conduction-band density of states function. Since the Fermi level is always at a constant energy in the absence of bias, the band edges must be tilted as shown to accommodate the doping gradient which determines n_{nB} at each point.

If the collector is reverse-biased to create a sink for holes at the collector side of the base, the density p_{nB} will go to zero at the collector. Any hole injected at the emitter will then gain energy moving along the upward sloping valence-band edge as it traverses the base region to the collector. This effect can be considered as motion in a built-in electric field represented by the sloping band edge. (See Fig. 1.5 and accompanying discussion.)

We will now determine the doping gradient necessary to achieve a uniform slope or electric field. If we consider two points a and b in the base region, we know from Eq. (4.6) that

$$n_a = n_b e^{qV_{ab}/kT}, \tag{7.1}$$

where V_{ab} is the voltage difference between points a and b. Since $n_a = N_D(a)$ and $n_b = N_D(b)$, we may write

$$V_{ab} = V(a) - V(b) = \frac{kT}{q} \ln \frac{N_D(a)}{N_D(b)}, \tag{7.2}$$

or as a difference equation,

$$\Delta V = \frac{kT}{q} \Delta \ln N_D. \tag{7.3}$$

Dividing by Δx and passing to the limit, we find an electric field

$$\varepsilon = -\frac{dV}{dx} = -\frac{kT}{q} \frac{d \ln N_D}{dx}. \tag{7.4}$$

We know that if we define $N_D(x) = N_D(0)e^{-Bx}$, Eq. (7.4) becomes

$$\mathcal{E} = -\frac{kT}{q}\frac{d}{dx}[\ln N_D(0) - Bx] = B\left(\frac{kT}{q}\right), \qquad (7.5)$$

showing that an exponential doping gradient will give a constant built-in field with the value of the field equal to (kT/q) times the constant in the exponent of the doping function.

Transport across the base region in the absence of recombination can be described for a PNP-transistor by the relation

$$I_p = qA\left[\mu_p\mathcal{E}p(x) - D_p\frac{dp}{dx}\right]. \qquad (7.6)$$

Here, the constant built-in field $\mathcal{E}$ is positive since according to Fig. 7.1 we will be accelerating holes in the positive x-direction. The diffusion gradient of holes will also drop away to the right from emitter to collector, giving a diffusion current which enhances the drift current. The first-order linear differential equation (7.6) has the solution

$$p(x) = \left[\exp\left(\frac{\mu_p\mathcal{E}x}{D_p}\right)\right]\left[\frac{I_p}{qA\mu_p\mathcal{E}}\exp\left(-\frac{\mu_p\mathcal{E}x}{D_p}\right) + C\right]. \qquad (7.7)$$

Here we consider the zero of x at the emitter-junction surface so that the collector junction is at $x = w$. Assuming that the collector is reverse-biased, we let $p(w) = 0$, giving

$$C = -\frac{I_p}{qA\mu_p\mathcal{E}}\exp\left(-\frac{\mu_p\mathcal{E}w}{D_p}\right), \qquad (7.8)$$

and the final solution

$$p(x) = -\frac{I_p}{qA\mu_p\mathcal{E}}\left\{\exp\left[-\frac{(w-x)\mu_p\mathcal{E}}{D_p}\right] - 1\right\}. \qquad (7.9)$$

In order to interpret the constants of Eq. (7.9), we note that $\mu_p\mathcal{E}t_w = w$, where t_w is the time required for a hole to drift the distance w. From our switching analysis of the diffusion transistor we found that the delay time $t_D = w^2/2D_p$ is really the time required for a hole to diffuse a distance w. From these two relations we find that

$$\mu_p\mathcal{E}w/D_p = 2t_D/t_w. \qquad (7.10)$$

The function $(w - x)(\mu_p\mathcal{E}/D_p)$ is then twice the ratio of the diffusion to drift transit time for the distance $(w - x)$.

At the emitter side of the base we find the excess hole density to be

$$p_E(\mathcal{E}) = -\frac{I_p}{qA\mu_p\mathcal{E}}\left[\exp\left(-\frac{\mu_p\mathcal{E}w}{D_p}\right) - 1\right]. \qquad (7.11)$$

Here $p_E(\mathcal{E})$ designates the hole density at the emitter side of the base for the case of pure drift transport of holes across the base region. If we define a similar $p_E(D)$ as the hole density at the emitter side of the base required to carry the same current by pure diffusion transport, we see that $p_E(D) = I_p w/qAD_p$, and substituting in (7.11), we find that

$$p_E(\mathcal{E}) = -p_E(D)(t_w/2t_D)(e^{-2t_D/t_w} - 1). \qquad (7.12)$$

Figure 7.2 shows the hole density distribution in the base region of a drift transistor as given by Eq. (7.9). Differentiating Eq. (7.9) with respect to x and evaluating dp/dx at $x = w$, we find that

$$\frac{dp}{dx}(w) = -\frac{I_p}{qA\mu_p\mathcal{E}}\left[\exp\left(\frac{\mu_p\mathcal{E}w}{D_p}\right)\exp\left(-\frac{\mu_p\mathcal{E}w}{D_p}\right)\right]\frac{\mu_p\mathcal{E}}{D_p} = -\frac{p_E(D)}{w}.$$
$$(7.13)$$

In other words, the hole gradient at the collector is the same in a drift transistor as it is in a diffusion transistor, and when this slope is extrapolated back to the emitter (as in Fig. 7.2), we find a direct comparison between the stored carriers in the two cases. From this comparison it is clear that for a given base width there is much less stored charge in a drift transistor and therefore a better transport efficiency and a lower "diffusion" capacitance. Here, we will retain the name "diffusion capacitance" (even though the main charge transport process is now drift) to mean the capacitance involved in changing the level of the stored charge in order to cause a change in emitter current.

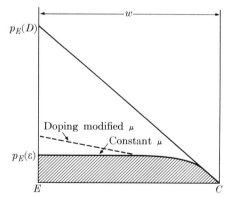

FIG. 7.2. Hole density in the base region of a drift transistor.

Figure 7.2 suggests that the drift mechanism transports the charge on the emitter side of the base, since there is only a very small concentration gradient, and that the diffusion mechanism transports the charge near the collector, since here the gradient can support nearly the entire current.

We will now calculate the base transport efficiency to a first-order approximation. Since the current at the emitter side of the base is nearly pure drift current, we may write the input hole current assuming constant μ_p and $\mathcal{E}$:

$$I_p = qA\mu_p\mathcal{E}p_E(\mathcal{E}). \qquad (7.14)$$

Since $(2t_D/t_w)$ is usually of the order of 10 to 100, $p_E(\mathcal{E})$ is very much less than $p_E(D)$ so that we may approximate the stored charge as $qAwp_E(\mathcal{E})$, and the recombination current due to a base region lifetime of τ_B is

$$I_r = qAwp_E(\mathcal{E})/\tau_B. \qquad (7.15)$$

The base transport efficiency is now

$$\beta = (I_p - I_r)/I_p = 1 - I_r/I_p = 1 - w/\mu_p\mathcal{E}\tau_B. \qquad (7.16)$$

This may be compared with Eq. (6.7) for the diffusion transistor. If we make the substitution $\tau_B D_p = L^2{}_B$, we find that

$$\beta = 1 - (t_w/t_D)(w^2/2L^2{}_B) = 1 - t_w/\tau_B. \qquad (7.17)$$

From a comparison of (7.17) and (6.7) we see that $(1 - \beta)$ is decreased by the factor (t_w/t_D) when we compare drift and diffusion transistors of identical base width and base-region lifetime. It should be noted that the transit time ratio (t_w/t_D) is independent of variations of mobility with doping density since it depends on the ratio (μ/D) which is a constant at a given temperature, as shown by the Einstein relation $\mu = qD/kT$.

Next, considering injection efficiency in the same elementary manner we find that

$$\gamma = \frac{\Delta I_{pE}}{\Delta(I_{pE} + I_{nE})} = \frac{\partial I_{pE}/\partial V_E}{\partial I_E/\partial V_E}, \qquad (7.18)$$

where $I_{pE} = qA\mu_p\mathcal{E}(p_E + p_{nB})$ and $I_{nE} = qAD_n n_E/L_E$ and the excess carrier densities on the base and emitter sides of the emitter-junction depletion region are given by $p_B = p_{nB}(e^{qV_E/kT} - 1)$ and $n_E = n_{pE}(e^{qV_E/kT} - 1)$. Substituting these relations into (7.18) gives

$$\gamma \simeq 1 - \frac{D_n n_{pE}}{L_E\mu_p\mathcal{E}p_{nB}} = 1 - \frac{t_{LE}}{2t_{DE}}\frac{\rho_E}{\rho_B}, \qquad (7.19)$$

where $(t_{LE}/2t_{DE}) = (D_n/\mu_n\mathcal{E}L_E)$ and $(\mu_n n_{pE}/\mu_p p_{nB}) = (\rho_E/\rho_B)$; t_{LE} is the electronic drift transit time for the distance L_E, and t_{DE} is the electronic diffusion transit time for the same distance. The drift field involved is, of course, the built-in base-region field. It must be understood that there is no drift field in the emitter region where the charge transport is solely by diffusion. The use of the fictitious time t_{LE} is simply for convenience.

From (7.19) we see that there is a limit to the ρ_B at the emitter side of the base if we wish to maintain a reasonable injection efficiency. If we assume $(t_{LE}/2t_{DE})$ to be of the order of 0.1 and if we let ρ_E represent essentially degenerate doping, then ρ_B cannot represent more than 0.1 degenerate doping ($\rho_B \simeq 10\rho_E$) if we wish to maintain a γ of 0.99.

On the collector side of the base, the highest resistivity possible may be obtained by doping the material so that it is just short of intrinsic at the lowest operating temperature of the device. Such doping would give a voltage drop across the base region of roughly $\Delta E/2$, less a voltage equal to $(kT/q) \ln 10$, since $N_{AE} > 10N_{DB}$ to maintain γ. For germanium this gives a limiting voltage of $(0.72/2 - 0.059) = 0.301$ v. For silicon it is $(1.12/2 - 0.059) = 0.501$ v. For a nominal base width of 5×10^{-4} cm, these give maximum built-in fields of 600 v/cm and 1000 v/cm, respectively.

Proceeding to calculate the collector leakage current I_{C0}, we find the hole current through the collector junction to be

$$I_{pC} = qA_E\mathcal{E}\mu_p p_{nB}e^{qV_E/kT}. \tag{7.20}$$

The electron current is

$$I_{nC} = qA_C D_n n_{pC}/L_C. \tag{7.21}$$

By definition, $I_{C0} = I_{pC} + I_{nC}$, but we wish to eliminate $e^{qV_E/kT}$ by fixing the condition that $I_E = 0$. The emitter current is

$$I_E = qA_E[\mathcal{E}\mu_p p_{nB}e^{qV_E/kT} + (D_n n_{pE}/L_E)(e^{qV_E/kT} - 1)] = 0. \tag{7.22}$$

Solving for $e^{qV_E/kT}$ gives

$$e^{qV_E/kT} = \left[1 + \frac{2t_{DE}}{t_{LE}}\frac{\rho_B}{\rho_E}\right]^{-1} \simeq (1 - \gamma), \tag{7.23}$$

yielding for I_{C0}:

$$I_{C0} = q[A_E\mathcal{E}_p p_{nB}(1 - \gamma) + A_C D_n n_{pC}/L_C]. \tag{7.24}$$

This may be compared with Eq. (6.14). It must be remembered that all of the base-region minority-carrier densities (p_{nB}) used so far have been the minority-carrier density at the emitter side of the base. In both Eq. (6.14) and Eq. (7.24) there is another contributing factor which has been neglected. This is the regeneration current in the collector depletion region. In many cases this current is negligible, but in some silicon transistors it must be considered. The regeneration current is given by Eq. (6.101), where x_N is now replaced by $(x_N + x_P)$ for the collector-base junction. Since this is usually a graded junction rather than an abrupt junction, (Eq. 6.100) no longer gives the depletion-region width.

It should be pointed out here that the remaining factors in α_{FB}, α^*, and M are determined by the collector region or the collector-barrier depletion region and are, therefore, unaffected by the doping gradient in the base. Hence these factors remain the same as before.

It is also worthy of note that the factor $(\mu_p \mathcal{E} w / D_p)$ which we have interpreted as $(2t_D/t_w)$ also has an interpretation in terms of the base doping gradient. The voltage drop across the base region is $w = V(w) - V(0)$. The Einstein relation gives

$$D_p = \mu_p(kT/q). \tag{7.25}$$

Using these expressions and (7.2), we may write

$$\frac{\mu_p \mathcal{E} w}{D_p} = \ln\left(\frac{N_D(0)}{N_D(w)}\right). \tag{7.26}$$

In order to give an alternative interpretation of this factor we may substitute (7.10) into (7.26). In this case we see how the doping ratio determines the transit time ratio:

$$\frac{t_D}{t_w} = \ln\left(\frac{N_D(0)}{N_D(w)}\right)^{1/2}. \tag{7.27}$$

We will next calculate the so-called diffusion capacitance. This is defined as before as $C_D = dQ_B/dV_E$, where Q_B is the charge stored in the base by the current I_E produced by voltage V_E. From Eq. (7.14) we have for a high field $\mathcal{E}$:

$$I_E = qA_E\mu_p p(\mathcal{E}) = qA_E\mu_p p_{nB}e^{qV_E/kT}. \tag{7.28}$$

The stored charge in the shaded area of Fig. 7.2 is approximated by

$$Q_B = qA_E w p_E(\mathcal{E}) = qA_E w p_{nB}e^{qV_E/kT}, \tag{7.29}$$

giving

$$C_D = \frac{dQ_B}{dV_E} = \frac{qI_E}{kT}\frac{w}{\mu_p\mathcal{E}} = \frac{qI_E}{kT}t_w. \tag{7.30}$$

This result compares directly with Eq. (6.50), where for a diffusion transistor $C_D = (qI_E/kT)t_D$.

It is quite possible to set up the full-scale continuity equation for the drift transistor and solve it as was done in Chapter 6 for the diffusion transistor. The algebra is considerably more formidable but there is no more difficulty in principle. Instead of proceeding in that manner, we will use previous results to deduce the first approximations.

Considering the frequency-dependent transport efficiency β, we note by comparing Eqs. (6.37) and (6.7) that t_D merely multiplies the term $(1/\tau_B + 2s_B/r_E + j\omega)$. By analogy we may extrapolate Eq. (7.17) for the drift transistor to yield

$$\beta = 1 - t_w(1/\tau_B + 2s_B/r_E + j\omega). \tag{7.31}$$

It can be seen that a similar transformation will give the admittances of the drift transistor from Eqs. (6.60) through (6.63) as

$$Y_{ee} = \frac{qI_E}{kT}\left[1 + t_w\left(\frac{1}{\tau_B} + \frac{2s_B}{r_E} + j\omega\right)\right],$$

$$Y_{ce} = \frac{-qI_E}{kT}\left[1 + \frac{t_w}{3}\left(\frac{1}{\tau_B} + \frac{2s_B}{r_E} + j\omega\right)\right]^{-1},$$

$$\tag{7.32}$$

$$Y_{ec} = \frac{-qI_{p0}}{kT}\left[1 + \frac{t_w}{3}\left(\frac{1}{\tau_B} + \frac{2s_B}{r_E} + j\omega\right)\right]^{-1},$$

$$Y_{cc} = \frac{qI_{p0}}{kT}\left[1 + t_w\left(\frac{1}{\tau_B} + \frac{2s_B}{r_E} + j\omega\right)\right].$$

From Eq. (7.31) we find the β cutoff frequency for a drift transistor to be $\omega_{\mathcal{E}} = 1/t_w$ so that the ratio of $\omega_0/\omega_{\mathcal{E}}$ is t_w/t_D. This result depends on the assumption that the excess stored charge is simply $qAwp_E(\mathcal{E})$. This assumption is good to about 15% if $(t_D/t_w) = \ln[N_D(0)/N(w)]^{1/2} > 5$ and if $N(w) > 10n_i$. Figure 7.3 shows a plot of the actual stored charge calculated for the several cases indicated. The assumption of a uniform $p_E(\mathcal{E})$ excess carrier density in the base is equivalent to the assumption of a pure drift process. Actually drift and diffusion mechanisms are working in parallel so a resultant transit time would be closer to $(1/t) = (1/t_D) + (1/t_w)$ or $t = t_Dt_w/(t_D + t_w)$, giving $\omega_{\mathcal{E}} = (1/t)$. This resultant t would replace t_w in the above equations to give a somewhat better result.

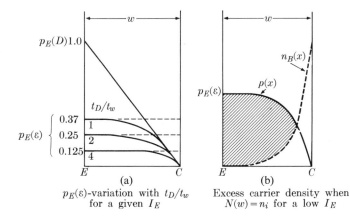

(a)
$p_E(\mathcal{E})$-variation with t_D/t_w for a given I_E

(b)
Excess carrier density when $N(w) = n_i$ for a low I_E

Fig. 7.3. Drift transistor base-region charge.

In Fig. 7.3(a) we see that stored charge under the curves does not approach the constant density approximation (the horizontal dashed lines) until t_D/t_w exceeds 4, as shown in the lowest curve. Figure 7.3(b) shows the excess carrier density (shaded area) for low current levels. Here, the thermal equilibrium carrier density is the exponentially rising dashed line. From this it can be seen that the actual stored charge decreases with current faster than one would expect just from the lowering of the $p_E(\mathcal{E})$-level.

By way of direct comparison, the result of the exact solution of the continuity equation

$$\frac{\partial p}{\partial t} = -\frac{p}{\tau_B} = \mu_p \mathcal{E} \frac{\partial p}{\partial x} + D_p \frac{\partial^2 p}{\partial x^2} \tag{7.33}$$

yields a transport efficiency of [2]

$$\beta = 2[(t_D/t_w)^2 + 2j\omega t_D]^{1/2} e^{t_D/t_w} \{(2t_D/t_w) \sinh [(t_D/t_w)^2 + 2j\omega t_D]^{1/2} \\ + 2[(t_D/t_w)^2 + 2j\omega t_D]^{1/2} \cosh [(t_D/t_w)^2 + 2j\omega t_D]^{1/2}\}^{-1}, \tag{7.34}$$

which for a doping ratio of 100 gives a ratio $\omega/\omega_0 = 4.7$, whereas t_D/t_w gives 2.3 and t_D/t would give 3.3.

For large-signal analysis the generalized transistor equations (6.91) apply equally well to a drift transistor, since they are characterized by measured terminal quantities. For turn-on and turn-off transient analysis we may proceed in the same manner as before, using the basic charge control concept.

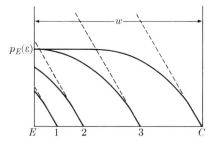

Fig. 7.4. Advancing charge distribution in a drift-transistor base region.

Before starting the transient analysis it will be profitable to contrast the ways in which charge permeates the base region of drift and diffusion transistors under a stepped emitter current drive. Figure 7.4 illustrates the form of the advancing charge distribution in the base region of a transistor. The dashed lines represent the diffusion transistor behavior, and the solid lines represent the drift transistor behavior. At the outset both transistors receive their initial charge by diffusion as shown at position 1 in the figure. As time goes on and p_E rises, the distribution in the drift transistor bends over toward the emitter, since the drift field is sufficient to supply the entire emitter current when a hole density of $p_E(\mathcal{E})$ is reached. In the diffusion transistor, however, the hole density at the emitter must keep increasing in order to maintain a constant (dp/dx) throughout the width of the base region penetrated by the charge. It is clear from the figure that there must be considerably more charge injected into the base region at each step of the process for a diffusion transistor. This means that the delay time for a diffusion transistor will be much greater than that for a drift transistor under constant current drive. It also means that the time required to reach positions 2 and 3 in Fig. 7.4 will be much longer for the diffusion transistor.

We will now calculate the turn-on delay time of a drift transistor. To the zero-order approximation this is just t_w, the drift transit time of the base region plus the charging time of the emitter depletion capacitance. A better approximation for the transit time is found by dividing the base width into a drift distance and a diffusion distance. Referring to Fig. 7.4, we see that the minority hole distribution reaches position 2 essentially by diffusion transport. This distance, x_2, can then be used for the diffusion distance and $(w - x_2)$ will be the drift distance. Now, to calculate the delay time we must first find x_2 and determine its diffusion transit time. This time, added to the drift transit time of $(w - x_2)$, will give us the required total transit time, $t_D(\mathcal{E})$. We find from geometrical considerations that $x_2 = [p_E(\mathcal{E})/p_E(D)]w$, and from Eq. (7.12) for reasonably large doping gradients (neglecting the exponential term), $p_E(\mathcal{E})/p_E(D) = t_w/2t_D$, which gives

$$x_2 = w(t_w/2t_D). \tag{7.35}$$

The total transit time can now be written

$$t_D(\mathcal{E}) = \frac{w - x_2}{\mu_p \mathcal{E}} + \frac{x_2^2}{2D_p} = t_w\left(1 - \frac{t_w}{4t_D}\right). \tag{7.36}$$

For a 100-to-1 doping ratio this gives $t_D(\mathcal{E}) = t_w(1 - 1/9.2) = 0.89t_w = 0.39t_D$. In other words, we have about an 11% correction on the zero-order approximation.

The charging times of the emitter and collector barriers would be the same for a diffusion transistor if the capacities were the same. Actually, the doping ratio of the base region will affect the voltage dependence of the capacities and hence the times. However, $t_0(\mathcal{E})$ will still be of the order of $R_L C_C(\phi)$. The total delay time will be dominated by the emitter-junction charging time for very fast devices, and only in wide-base transistors will the transit time dominate.

There will be a marked difference in the base-region charging time, $t_C(\mathcal{E})$, due to the radically different charge distribution found in the base region of a drift transistor in saturation. If we forward-bias the collector junction of a drift transistor and reverse-bias the emitter, we find $p(x)$ from Eq. (7.7) by letting $p(0) = 0$ to determine $C = -I_p/qA\mu_p\mathcal{E}$, and then, remembering that $I_p = I_C$ for holes into the collector, we may write the $p(x)$ for such a transistor run backward as

$$p(x) = \frac{I_p}{qA\mu_p\mathcal{E}}\left[\exp\left(\frac{\mu_p\mathcal{E}x}{D_p}\right) - 1\right], \tag{7.37}$$

where we have reversed the sign of the equation to take care of the reverse operation and give the proper limit. Here, we have left the sense of x (from emitter to collector) and the field positive. We see that $p(0) = 0$ and $p(w) = p_C(\mathcal{E})$, since $I_p = I_C$, and we may write

$$p_C(\mathcal{E}) = p_C(D)(t_w/2t_D)[e^{2t_D/t_w} - 1]. \tag{7.38}$$

Figure 7.5 shows the superposition of the two $p(x)$-distributions for a drift transistor in saturation. In terms of the two superposed currents I_{EF} and I_{CR} we may write the total excess hole-density distribution as the sum of Eqs. (7.37) and (7.9), obtaining

$$p(x) = \frac{I_{EF}}{qA\mu_p\mathcal{E}}\left\{1 - \exp\left[-\frac{\mu_p\mathcal{E}(w - x)}{D_p}\right]\right\} + \frac{I_{CR}}{qA\mu_p\mathcal{E}}\left[\exp\left(\frac{\mu_p\mathcal{E}x}{D_p}\right) - 1\right]. \tag{7.39}$$

We can now calculate the total stored charge by integrating $p(x)$ over the width of the base region:

$$\begin{aligned}
Q &= qA \int_0^w p(x)\, dx \\
&= \frac{w}{\mu_p\mathcal{E}}(I_{EF} - I_{CR}) - \frac{D_p I_{EF}}{\mu_p^2\mathcal{E}^2}\exp\left(-\frac{\mu_p\mathcal{E}w}{D_p}\right)\left[\exp\left(\frac{\mu_p\mathcal{E}w}{D_p}\right) - 1\right] \\
&\quad + \frac{D_p I_{CR}}{\mu_p^2\mathcal{E}^2}\left[\exp\left(\frac{\mu_p\mathcal{E}w}{D_p}\right) - 1\right] \\
&= \frac{w}{\mu_p\mathcal{E}}\left[(I_{EF} - I_{CR}) + \frac{D_p I_{CR}}{\mu_p\mathcal{E}w}\exp\left(\frac{\mu_p\mathcal{E}w}{D_p}\right)\right], \tag{7.40}
\end{aligned}$$

where we have neglected the term containing $\exp\left(-\mu_p\mathcal{E}w/D_p\right)$ as a factor and have also neglected unity compared to $\exp\left(\mu_p\mathcal{E}w/D_p\right)$ in the last term. Recognizing that $w/\mu_p\mathcal{E} = t_w$, we may express Eq. (7.40) in the form

$$Q = t_w\{I_{EF} + I_{CR}[-1 + (t_w/2t_D)e^{2t_D/t_w}]\}. \tag{7.41}$$

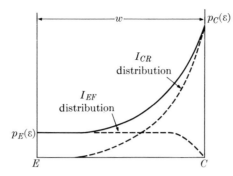

FIG. 7.5. Base-region charge of a drift transistor in saturation.

In order to write Q in terms of the terminal currents, we may write, as before in Eq. (6.112),

$$I_E = I_{EF} - \alpha_{RB}I_{CR},$$
$$I_C = I_{CR} - \alpha_{FB}I_{EF}, \qquad (7.42)$$
$$-I_B = (1 - \alpha_{FB})I_{EF} + (1 - \alpha_{RB})I_{CR},$$

from which we obtain

$$I_{EF} = \frac{I_E + \alpha_{RB}I_C}{1 - \alpha_{FB}\alpha_{RB}} = qA\mu_p\mathcal{E}p_E(\mathcal{E}). \qquad (7.43)$$

From Eq. (7.37) evaluated at $x = w$ and substituting $(\mu_p\mathcal{E}w/D_p) = (2t_D/t_w)$, we find

$$I_{CR} = \frac{\alpha_{FB}I_E + I_C}{1 - \alpha_{FB}\alpha_{RB}} = qA\mu_p\mathcal{E}p_C(\mathcal{E})(e^{-2t_D/t_w}). \qquad (7.44)$$

Now substituting Eqs. (7.43) and (7.44) for I_{EF} and I_{CR} into Eq. (7.41), we find the total stored charge to be

$$Q = \frac{t_w}{1 - \alpha_{FB}\alpha_{RB}}\left[I_E + \alpha_{RB}I_C + (\alpha_{FB}I_E + I_C)\left(1 + \frac{t_w}{2t_D}e^{2t_D/t_w}\right)\right].$$
$$(7.45)$$

This is the charge which must be built up during the base-region charging time and removed during the turn-off storage time of the transistor.

We will complete the discussion of the drift transistor by calculating the turn-off storage time of the device. We assume that the emitter circuit is opened at $t = 0$, giving the sequence of currents and density distributions shown in Fig. 7.6. Here, it is noted that immediately after the emitter circuit is opened, the slope of the hole density distribution at the collector

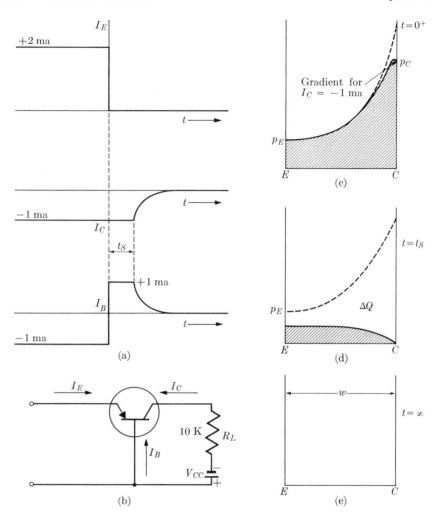

FIG. 7.6. Drift transistor common-base turn-off.

assumes the slope necessary to give the collector current determined by the load resistance and the power supply. The charge ΔQ shown in Fig. 7.6(d) must be removed by I_C and recombined in the time $t_S(\mathcal{E})$.

If we use the average $\bar{\alpha} = (\alpha_{FB} + \alpha_{RB})/2$ as before, we may use Eq. (6.128) for $t_S(\mathcal{E})$ if we replace t_D by t_w. This yields

$$t_S(\mathcal{E}) = \frac{-t_w}{1 - \bar{\alpha}}\left[\ln\left\{I_C - \frac{(1 - \bar{\alpha})Q}{t_w}\right\}\right]_{Q(\infty)}^{Q(t_S)}, \qquad (7.46)$$

where $Q(t_S) \simeq qAwp_E(\mathcal{E})$ and $Q(\infty)$ is given by Eq. (7.45). Evaluating

$p_E(\mathcal{E})$ in terms of I_C, we have

$$p_E(\mathcal{E}) = I_E/qA\mu_p\mathcal{E} = -I_C/\alpha_{FB}qA\mu_p\mathcal{E}. \qquad (7.47)$$

Then we obtain

$$Q(t_S) = -I_C t_w/\alpha_{FB} \qquad (7.48)$$

(remembering that $t_w = w/\mu_p\mathcal{E}$). We may now evaluate $t_S(\mathcal{E})$ as

$$t_S(\mathcal{E}) = \frac{t_w}{(1-\bar{\alpha})}$$

$$\times \ln\left[\frac{I_C - \left(\dfrac{1-\bar{\alpha}}{1-\bar{\alpha}^2}\right)\left[I_E + \alpha_{RB}I_C + (\alpha_{FB}I_E + I_C)\left(1 + \dfrac{t_w}{2t_D}e^{2t_D/t_w}\right)\right]}{I_C + \dfrac{(1-\bar{\alpha})I_C}{\alpha_{FB}}}\right].$$

$$(7.49)$$

Approximating α_{FB} by unity and α_{RB} by $\bar{\alpha}$, we reduce Eq. (7.49) to

$$t_S(\mathcal{E}) = \frac{t_w}{(1-\bar{\alpha})}\ln\left[\frac{(\bar{\alpha}+1)(I_E/I_C) + (1 + I_E/I_C)(t_w/2t_D)e^{2t_D/t_w}}{(\bar{\alpha}+1)(\bar{\alpha}-2)}\right].$$

$$(7.50)$$

Comparing this result numerically with the same case for a diffusion transistor, we use the numerical values of the currents shown in Figs. 7.6 and 6.12 and $\bar{\alpha} = 0.9$, as before. We will adopt a doping ratio of 100, giving $t_w = t_D/2.3$. From this we find $t_S(\mathcal{E}) = (10t_D/2.3)\ln(12.1) = 10.8t_D$, as compared with $6t_D$ for the equivalent diffusion transistor with the same base width.

In Section 6.7 we discussed the variation of the diffusion constant with doping level. Here, in order to get a reasonable field in the base region, the emitter side of the base is heavily doped. This means that the mobility on the emitter side may be significantly degraded, and the mobility and diffusion constants will be a monotonically increasing function of x (measured from the emitter to the collector). The base-region charge distribution will then deviate from the ideal case shown in Fig. 7.2 even when the drift field dominates and is constant. The lowered mobility at the emitter side requires more charge at that side to carry a given current so that the charge distribution would be represented by the dashed line of Fig. 7.2. Such a charge distribution requires more time for establishment and thus slightly slows down the transistor response.

Another deviation from the ideal behavior occurs because of the difficulty of fabricating a truly exponential doping gradient in the base region. Any variation of field in the base will be reflected in an inverse variation of charge density. This usually takes the form of a low field immediately adjacent to the emitter junction, which causes a sharp rise of base charge density next to the emitter [2].

7.2   Unipolar or Field-Effect Transistor [3]

This transistor operates without injection in the ordinary sense and depends upon majority carriers for its current transport. The name "unipolar" is meant to convey the fact that only one type of current carrier is involved. The alternative name "field effect" is often used to convey the fact that the control of the majority-carrier flow is achieved through an electrostatic field permeating the semiconductor material. There are two general types of unipolar transistors, the *depletion* type and the *enhancement* type. In the depletion type the presence of the control field reduces the flow of majority carriers, and in the enhancement type the presence of the control field induces the existence of majority carriers in the working region of the device.

Depletion type. Figure 7.7 shows the structure of a depletion-type field-effect transistor using a cylindrical geometry. The purpose of such a geometry is to give a low resistance for an open channel. The *channel* is the thin disk of N-type material sandwiched between the heavily doped P-regions shown as the shaded sections in the figure. The P-type regions together comprise the control electrode called the *gate*. The current sub-

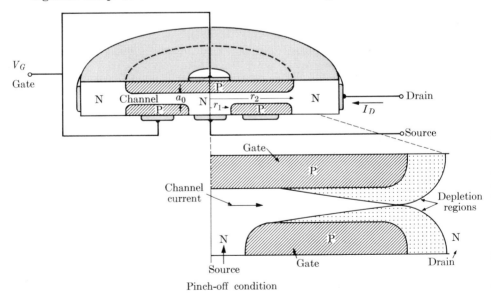

Fig. 7.7.   Cross section of a depletion-mode field transistor.

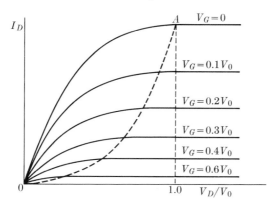

Fig. 7.8. Depletion-mode field-effect transistor characteristics.

ject to control flows by majority-carrier drift from the *source* to the *drain* through the washer-shaped channel. Control is achieved by reverse-biasing the P-regions with respect to the N-type channel, thus decreasing the thickness of the channel by the encroachment of the depletion regions of the junctions. When the depletion regions of the junctions forming the two lateral surfaces of the channel are extended until they contact each other, the channel is said to be *pinched off*. When this occurs, the current through the channel saturates and is essentially independent of drain voltage above the pinch-off voltage. The dynamic range of the device is realized for gate voltages between zero and pinch-off where the working current between source and drain biases the drain end of the channel to pinch-off by its IR-drop in the channel. At the bottom of Fig. 7.7 is shown the form of the depletion regions when the gate and source are tied together and the drain is biased to pinch-off. This arrangement gives the characteristic curve marked $V_G = 0$ in Fig. 7.8, and the point A represents the form of the depletion regions shown in Fig. 7.7. The other curves of Fig. 7.8 are drawn for gate voltages reverse-biased with respect to the source.

This form of the depletion region can be understood as follows. First, we will note that the P-type regions must be heavily doped relative to the N-type channel so that a reverse bias will cause the depletion region to invade primarily the channel material. When the source and gate are grounded and the drain terminal is biased positively, the majority electrons will flow toward the drain through the channel. At the same time the PN-junctions between the gate and drain will be reverse-biased. The magnitude of this reverse bias at each point of the channel will be determined by the IR-drop of the channel current, being zero at the source end (source and gate are common) and a maximum at the drain end of the channel. The depletion-region thickness will then taper along the channel as shown. Pinch-off occurs when the depletion regions from the two sides of the channel just make contact.

We will proceed to calculate the pinch-off voltage and the form of the characteristics of Fig. 7.8. We will assume that the P-regions are very heavily doped relative to the N-region and that the depletion region of the junctions is found essentially in the N-region with a thickness given by Eq. (4.21), where we have assumed $N_A \gg N_D$:

$$x_N = \left[\frac{2\epsilon(\phi - V_G)}{qN_D}\right]^{1/2}. \tag{7.51}$$

If a_0 is the metallurgical thickness of the channel, we may express the channel thickness as a function of gate voltage:

$$a = a_0 - 2\left[\frac{2\epsilon(\phi - V_G)}{qN_D}\right]^{1/2}. \tag{7.52}$$

Pinch-off occurs when $a = 0$, giving the pinch-off voltage $V_G = V_0$ as

$$V_0 = \phi - \frac{qN_D a_0^2}{8\epsilon}. \tag{7.53}$$

We may now write a in terms of the pinch-off voltage:

$$a = a_0\left[1 - \left(\frac{\phi - V_G}{\phi - V_0}\right)\right]^{1/2}. \tag{7.54}$$

We are now ready to calculate the channel current under specific bias conditions. We will first choose the situation where the source and gate are common and the only applied voltage is a positive voltage at the drain terminal. In this situation the source end of the channel will remain at full thickness while the drain end will tend toward pinch-off as the drain voltage is increased. Under this condition we may write the drain current as

$$I_D = \frac{dV}{dR_C} = \frac{dV}{\rho \, dr/2\pi ra}, \tag{7.55}$$

where dR_C is the incremental channel resistance and r is the radial distance to the volume element $(2\pi ra \, dr)$ in the channel (see Fig. 7.7). Integrating

$$I_D \int_{r_1}^{r_2} \frac{dr}{r} = \frac{2\pi a_0}{\rho} \int_0^{V_D}\left[1 - \left(\frac{\phi - V}{\phi - V_0}\right)^{1/2}\right] dV, \tag{7.56}$$

we get

$$I_D = \frac{2\pi a_0 V_D}{\rho \ln (r_2/r_1)}\left[1 - \frac{2}{3}\left(\frac{\phi - V_D}{\phi - V_0}\right)^{1/2}\right]. \tag{7.57}$$

The uppermost curve ($V_G = 0$) of Fig. 7.8 is represented by Eq. (7.57), where ϕ has been neglected compared to V_0. Checking this last assumption numerically, we use the following typical values of the constants of Eq. (7.53):

$$a_0 = 3 \times 10^{-3} \text{ cm}, \qquad N_D = 10^{14} \text{ donors/cm}^3,$$
$$q = 1.6 \times 10^{-19} \text{ coul}, \qquad \epsilon = 1.4 \text{ pf/cm}.$$

From these we find that the last term of Eq. (7.53) is evaluated as -13 v. If $\phi = 0.3$ v, it is seen to be negligible. If a_0 is reduced by a factor of three, ϕ is no longer negligible and must be retained for very thin channels of high-resistivity material.

The maximum saturation current given by Eq. (7.57) for $V_D = V_0$ as found for the same parameters with $V_2 = 0.05$ cm and $r_1 = 0.03$ cm is 10.2 ma for germanium. In Fig. 7.8 the portion of the curve for $V_G = 0$ between the origin and point A is given by Eq. (7.57). If we consider this equation as the product of two factors, a channel conductivity factor (neglecting ϕ)

$$G_C(0) = \frac{2\pi a_0}{\rho \ln (r_2/r_1)} \left[1 - \frac{2}{3} \left(\frac{V_D}{V_0} \right)^{1/2} \right], \tag{7.58}$$

and a driving voltage factor V_D, we see that the conductivity factor will be changed by applying a gate voltage:

$$G_C(V_G) = \frac{2\pi a_0}{\rho \ln (r_2/r_1)} \left[1 - \frac{2}{3} \left(\frac{V_D - V_G}{V_0} \right)^{1/2} \right], \tag{7.59}$$

and the drain current will be obtained, as before, by multiplying by the drain voltage:

$$I_D = G_C V_D = \frac{2\pi a_0}{\rho \ln (r_2/r_1)} \left[1 - \frac{2}{3} \left(\frac{V_D - V_G}{V_0} \right)^{1/2} \right] V_D. \tag{7.60}$$

Equation (7.60) gives the remaining curves of Fig. 7.8 up to the pinch-off point. We are subject to the limits $(V_D - V_G) \leq V_0$ or $V_D \leq (V_0 + V_G)$. In view of these limits it is clear that (7.60) represents the curve of (7.57) from the point A back to a voltage equal to $(V_0 + V_G)$. Therefore the curves of Fig. 7.8 may be generated by displacing the $V_G = 0$ curve parallel to itself in the linear region and passing through the origin. The locus of the pinch-off point A is then the dashed line, which can be seen to be the $V_G = 0$ curve reflected in the midpoint of the line OA.

To the right of the dashed curve (beyond initial pinch-off) it is difficult to simply derive an analytical expression for the current-voltage relation. However, it is clear that the voltage drop in the portion of the channel beyond pinch-off must be sufficient to maintain the current flowing in the

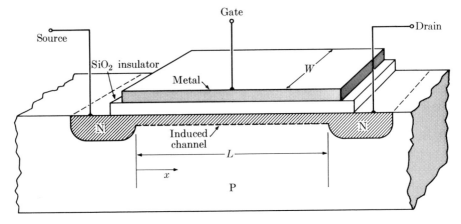

FIG. 7.9. Enhancement field-effect transistor.

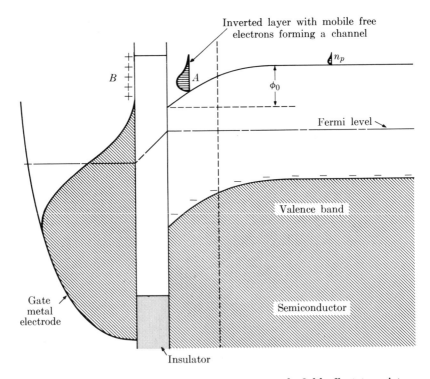

FIG. 7.10. Band scheme of an enhancement-mode field-effect transistor.

channel just before pinch-off, since there is no feedback mechanism present which would lead to a negative resistance characteristic. Therefore the characteristic curves are continued to the right, beyond the dashed line, as horizontal lines. Actually these lines must have a slightly positive slope because as V_D is increased, the point of initial pinch-off moves toward the source, thus shortening the channel and slightly increasing the current.

The drain current-gate voltage transconductance can be calculated by differentiating Eq. (7.60):

$$\frac{dI_D}{dV_G} = \frac{2\pi a_0 V_D}{3\rho V_0 \ln (r_2/r_1)} \left(\frac{V_D - V_G}{V_0}\right)^{1/2}. \tag{7.61}$$

For the active region beyond pinch-off we must evaluate (7.61) at pinch-off, since all the characteristic curves are parallel beyond this point. At pinch-off, $(V_D - V_G)/V_0 = 1$ and $V_D = (V_0 + V_G)$, giving

$$\frac{dI_D}{dV_G} = \frac{2\pi a_0}{3\rho \ln (r_2/r_1)} \left(\frac{V_0 + V_G}{V_0}\right) = G_{FS}. \tag{7.62}$$

Using the same numerical values as before, we find that the transconductance at $V_G = 0$ is $G_{FS} = 785\ \mu\text{mhos}$.

The example of a depletion-mode field-effect transistor (FET) considered here is typical. A wide variety of geometries have been used experimentally. In one extreme a grid of gate regions has been buried in the semiconductor crystal so that the structure directly simulates a vacuum-tube triode having a multitude of parallel channels between the elements of the gate material. In other cases the gate region has been broken up into two or more segments along the sides of a single channel so that the segments near the drain can act as a "screen grid" and the segments near the source can act as a control. In all cases the pinch-off mechanism controls the operation.

***The enhancement type*[4].** In this type of field-effect transistor an insulating layer is interposed between the gate electrode and the channel. Figure 7.9 shows a sectional view of a metal-oxide-silicon transistor (MOST). The body of this device is high-resistivity P-type silicon. Two N-type strips are diffused into one surface through a suitable mask. These are shown as the shaded regions. An SiO_2 layer is grown over the surface of the device by oxidation and then etched away except for a strip overlapping the two N-regions. A metal counterelectrode is now deposited on the oxide layer forming the gate structure. Ohmic contacts to the two N-regions comprise the source and drain terminals (see Fig. 7.9).

Figure 7.10 shows the energy-band diagram of the gate-electrode region illustrating the formation of an induced channel. We will ignore the effects of surface charge for the time being and assume that in the absence of bias across the insulator, the semiconductor band edges are unbent. As a positive voltage is applied to the gate electrode, positive and negative charges appear on opposite sides of the insulating oxide. The negative charge on the semiconductor side is initially composed of the ionized acceptor levels which are exposed as the band edges bend down creating a depletion region near the surface in the semiconductor. As this bias is increased, the Fermi level at the semiconductor-oxide surface approaches the conduction band. Eventually it gets close enough to produce a sizable concentration of free electrons A at this surface in the conduction band. These free electrons now share with the ionized acceptor levels the duty of balancing the metal-gate electrode surface charge B. When the free-electron concentration A becomes comparable to the acceptor density N_A, we say that the surface has become "inverted." This means that a thin layer of material at the surface is now N-type. Referring to Fig. 7.9, we clearly see that the N-type layer now links the source and drain regions and forms a conducting channel between them. In contrast to the depletion-mode device which is, in general, conducting and must be turned off with gate bias, we have here a device which is usually off and is turned on by a gate bias.

As we noted above, there is a threshold gate-bias voltage which must be applied before any conduction takes place. At lower voltages the negative charge consists primarily of the immobile ionized acceptor centers. Since in the depletion-mode device, the pinch-off voltage V_0 was the voltage at which the channel was depleted of carriers, it seems logical in the enhancement-mode device, also to call the threshold of emergence from depletion the pinch-off voltage. Here V_0 is the voltage which, when applied to the gate electrode, creates a barrier ϕ_0 within the semiconductor just sufficient to render the free-electron distribution A comparable to the acceptor density N_A.

We will now find an expression for the characteristics of the enhancement-mode device. Let C_G be the capacity of the insulated gate electrode. The free-electron charge induced in the semiconductor can be written

$$q \, \Delta n(x) = (C_G/WL)\{[V_G - V(x)] - V_0\}, \tag{7.63}$$

where the dimensions W and L are shown in Fig. 7.9, and the voltage $V(x)$ is the voltage along the channel as electrons flow from source to drain creating an IR-drop; $q \, \Delta n(x)$ is the charge per square centimeter of gate-electrode surface. A length dx of the channel has conductivity

$$\sigma(x) = q \, \Delta n(x)\mu W/dx.$$

We can then write the drain current:

$$I_D = \sigma(x) \, dV = (\mu C_G/L)\{[V_G - V(x)] - V_0\}(dV/dx), \tag{7.64}$$

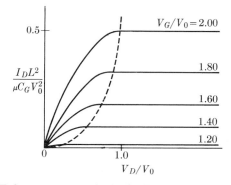

Fig. 7.11. Enhancement-mode field-effect transistor characteristics.

where we have substituted Eq. (7.63). Integrating (7.64) we find that

$$I_D \int_0^L dx = (\mu C_G/L) \int_0^{V_D} (V_G - V_0) \, dV - (\mu C_G/L) \int_0^{V_D} V \, dV,$$

(7.65)

where we are assuming a grounded source and negligible source and drain series resistances. The integral (7.65) leads to

$$I_D = \frac{\mu C_G}{L^2} \left[(V_G - V_0) - \frac{V_D}{2} \right] V_D.$$

(7.66)

Here, the drain current remains substantially zero until V_G rises to V_0. Equation (7.66) is then valid only for $V_G \geq V_0$. Also, as in the case of the depletion type of field-effect transistor, the device saturates at the maximum value of I_D, limiting the range of V_D to $0 \leq V_D \leq (V_G - V_0)$. Physically this means that the current saturates when the voltage across the gate capacitor at the drain end of the channel is sufficient only to create a depletion region and not sufficient to provide any extra mobile carriers. The characteristic curves are continued to the right as horizontal lines from this point. Typical characteristics are shown in Fig. 7.11. We may obtain the transconductance from differentiation of Eq. (7.66), remembering that the saturation value of I_D occurs for $V_D = (V_G - V_0)$:

$$G_{FS} = \frac{dI_D}{dV_G} = \frac{\mu C_G}{L^2} V_D = \frac{\mu C_G}{L^2} (V_G - V_0).$$

(7.67)

Evaluating for a typical set of parameters, we let

$$L = 10 \, \mu, \qquad C_G = 3 \text{ pf}, \qquad \mu = 600 \text{ cm/sec/v/cm}, \qquad V_0 = 2 \text{ v},$$

and obtain a transconductance $G_{FS} = 1800 \, \mu$mhos (for $V_G = 3$ v).

Actually, observed transconductances are about a factor of two smaller than this value. There are several reasons for this. First, the channel is so thin that the effective mobility may be lower due to scattering of current carriers from the oxide surface. In addition, the source- and drain-region series resistances may be comparable to the "on" channel resistance so that an appreciable portion of the applied drain voltage is found across these unmodulated resistances. The gate voltage will then modulate only a fraction of the resistance limiting the drain current.

It should be noted that the time constant $R_{FS}C_G$ can be found from Eq. (7.67):

$$R_{FS}C_G = (C_G/G_{FS}) = L^2/\mu(V_G - V_0) = \tau_{SD}, \qquad (7.68)$$

where τ_{SD} is the majority-carrier transit time along the channel between the source and drain, and the average field in the channel is $(V_G - V_0)/L$.

At the beginning of this section we assumed the absence of surface states. If such states do exist, it means that there will be *a priori* curvature of the semiconductor band edges at the surface of the oxide with zero gate bias. If these states are positively charged, there will already be a partial inversion of the surface and V_0 will be quite low or even negative. In this last case the device is a depletion-mode device with negative V_G required to produce pinch-off. The characteristic curves of such a device would be similar to those shown in Fig. 7.11 except that the parameter V_G/V_0 would exhibit a zero part way up in the active region. The curve nearest the axis would show a negative value of V_G/V_0 and the top curve would show a positive value.

Before ending our discussion of the enhancement-mode device it should be pointed out that V_0 bears a simple relation to the doping of the material in the absence of surface states. If we assume that the semiconductor depletion region is small compared to the oxide thickness, we may consider the depletion-region charge as charge on the inner surface of the oxide. This charge can then be written

$$q\,\Delta N_A = C_G V_0/WL = qN_A WL x_P \qquad (7.69)$$

for the gate voltage required for pinch-off. As previously noted, the band edges will bend down an amount ϕ_0 such that the free-electron distribution A is comparable to the depletion-region charge density N_A. From Eq. (4.18) we may express x_P, the depletion-layer thickness, in terms of ϕ_0:

$$x_P = (2\epsilon\phi_0/qN_A)^{1/2}. \qquad (7.70)$$

If $A \simeq N_A$ at the oxide surface, ϕ_0 must be just the magnitude of the separation of the valence band from the Fermi level in the bulk P-type material (assuming $N_v \simeq N_c$). We may then write ϕ_0 as

$$\phi_0 = (kT/q) \ln (N_v/N_A). \qquad (7.71)$$

Finally, substituting (7.71) and (7.70) into (7.69), we find the voltage V_0 required for pinch-off in the absence of surface states to be

$$V_0 = [W^2L^2/C_G][(2\epsilon kTN_A) \ln (N_v/N_A)]^{1/2}. \qquad (7.72)$$

Enhancement-mode devices have been made from thin films of evaporated semiconductors [5]. In this case, the thin film channel material is usually of the same type as the induced channel. Very high-energy gap material such as CdS is used so that the normally present majority carriers in very pure material will not give too high a drain current leakage. Characteristics of such thin film devices are difficult to control and as yet are inferior to the metal-oxide–silicon single-crystal devices. Their characteristic curves are similar to those described above and usually show a pinch-off voltage different from zero. The fact that their pinch-off voltage is not zero is usually attributed to surface trapping levels.

7.3   PNP Hook Devices

If we consider the normal junction transistor, as described in Chapter 6, without a base connection, the floating N-region can serve as a giant trap for electrons reaching it from either of the flanking P-regions. Excess electrons in the floating N-region will charge it up and raise its level sufficiently to allow a considerable current of holes to flow beneath it if there is a voltage applied across the device. An example of this effect was given in Eq. (6.95), where the normal collector leakage current of a transistor, I_{C0}, was amplified by the factor $1/(1 - \alpha_{FB})$ when the base was allowed to float ($I_B = 0$). Since $\alpha_{FB} \simeq 0.99$, this amplification factor can easily be two orders of magnitude. Such a structure involving a floating region flanked by two regions of conductivity type opposite to that of the floating region is called a *hook* structure.

The hook-collector transistor [5]. This structure, while not widely used as a transistor as such, is used in several devices of interest and is best considered in its simple form first. Figure 7.12 shows the energy-band diagram of such a structure. The hook comprises the entire collector region of the transistor. A typical physical structure and an expanded view of its doping profile are also shown. The structure illustrated is fabricated by a process known as postalloy diffusion. On the emitter side, the original P-type wafer is alloyed with an N-type impurity-bearing pellet, and on the collector side it is alloyed with a pellet containing both N- and P-type impurities. The collector pellet contains an excess of P-type impurity so that the collector recrystallized region will be P-type. Moreover, its minority N-type impurity is selected to be of a rapidly diffusing material so that if the assembly is allowed to soak at the alloying temperature, this

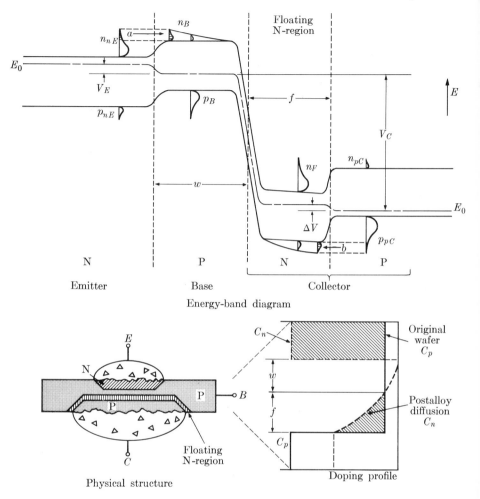

Fig. 7.12. NPNP hook-collector transistor.

impurity will diffuse ahead of the solution region into the undissolved semiconductor crystal creating the floating N-region shown.

Turning now to the energy-band diagram, we will describe the operation of the device in more detail. Following the Fermi level, E_0, we see that the emitter is forward-biased, injecting the electron density, a, into the P-type base region. The junction between the base and the floating region is seen to be reverse-biased so that electrons which traverse the base region fall into the floating region. These electrons tend to charge the floating N-region negatively, thus forward-biasing it relative to the collector contact P-region. If the collector P-region is much more heavily doped than the floating N-region, this forward bias will inject far more holes into the float-

ing region than electrons into the collector contact region. These injected
holes b will then traverse the floating region and fall into the base, ampli-
fying the originally injected electron current by $1/(1 - \alpha_F)$, where α_F
is the current transfer ratio for the floating N-region when the collector
P-region is considered to be an emitter. Defining

ρ_C = resistivity of the collector contact region,

ρ_F = resistivity of the collector floating region,

L_C = diffusion length for electrons in the collector contact region,

we may write the α^* of this device as

$$\alpha^* = \frac{\partial I_C}{\partial I_{nC}} = \frac{\partial(I_{nC} + I_{pC})}{\partial I_{nC}} = 1 + \frac{\partial I_{pC}}{\partial I_{nC}} \tag{7.73}$$

(neglecting multiplication in the reverse-biased junction). If we further
assume that the transport efficiency of holes across the floating region is
unity, we may evaluate $\partial I_{pC}/\partial I_{nC}$ in terms of the injection efficiency of
the junction between the floating region and the collector contact region,
γ_{CF}. By definition,

$$\gamma_{CF}\beta_F \simeq \gamma_{CF} = \frac{\partial I_{pC}}{\partial I_C} \quad \text{or} \quad \frac{1}{\gamma_{CF}} = 1 + \frac{\partial I_{nC}}{\partial I_{pC}}. \tag{7.74}$$

Solving for $(\partial I_{pC}/\partial I_{nC})$ and substituting in Eq. (7.73), we find

$$\alpha^* = 1 + \frac{\gamma_{CF}}{1 - \gamma_{CF}} = \frac{1}{1 - \gamma_{CF}} = 1 + \frac{\rho_F L_C}{\rho_C f}, \tag{7.75}$$

where $\gamma_{CF} = (1 + \rho_C f/\rho_F L_C)^{-1}$ from Eq. (6.14). If the floating region
has an appreciable drift field due to its formation by a diffusion process,
we must use the drift γ to compute α^*:

$$\alpha^* = 1 + \frac{\rho_F \mu_n \mathcal{E}_F L_C}{\rho_C D_n}. \tag{7.76}$$

This analysis is for low injection levels where the injected densities are
small compared to the majority-carrier densities in all regions of the device.
All analysis thus far is based on this limitation except for the section on
the generalized transistor equations, since that section is completely
phenomenological.

All other factors in α_{FB} for this device are the same as derived for the
simple transistor in Chapter 6. The remaining dc parameter I_{C0} is different because the leakage electron current crossing the base and falling
into the collector floating region is also amplified by α^*. By definition
$I_{C0} = I_{nC} + I_{pC}$, for $I_E = 0$. Here we have two sources of I_{nC}, the

electron current crossing the base and the electron current regenerated in the depletion region of the reverse-biased junction. (We will ignore avalanche multiplication on the assumption of a relatively low collector voltage.) Writing the total electron current subject to α^*-amplification we have

$$I_{nC} = qA \left\{ \frac{D_n n_{pB}}{w} (1 - \gamma) + \frac{n_i}{\tau} [2\epsilon(\phi - V_C)(\mu_p \rho_B + \mu_n \rho_F)]^{1/2} \right\}, \quad (7.77)$$

where the first term comes from the electron current diffusing across the base region and is analogous to the last term of Eq. (6.14) and the second term represents the regeneration current of electrons in the depletion region and comes from Eq. (5.22) with the hole component neglected and the resistivities substituted for the majority-carrier densities. The hole contribution I_{pC} is essentially I_{nC} amplified by α^*, giving I_{C0} as

$$I_{C0} = I_{nC}(1 + \alpha^*). \quad (7.78)$$

Equation (7.78) may be evaluated from Eqs. (7.77) and (7.75).

From the preceding discussion it should be clear that the α^* of a hook-collector transistor can easily be equal to $1/(1 - \alpha_{FB})$ for a single collector-region transistor. This means that the α_{FB} for the hook-collector device can be made of the order of 100, with an attendant increase of two orders of magnitude in I_{C0}.

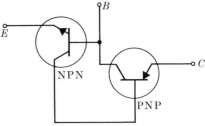

Fig. 7.13.   Hook-collector transistor equivalent.

It might also be pointed out that this device represents the effective integration of two regular transistors connected as shown in Fig. 7.13. Here, the reverse bias is seen to exist across both collectors in parallel. The characteristics of a hook-collector device can be described phenomenologically by using the generalized transistor equations for each of the two component devices connected as shown.

The phototransistor [6]. In Section 4.3 we considered an unbiased PN-junction under the stimulus of photon produced electron-hole pairs. Only the open circuit photovoltage was calculated. Usually, however, a PN-junction used as a photocell is reverse-biased. In this situation with uniform illumination throughout the volume of the junction and its adjacent P- and N-regions for a distance of several diffusion lengths, we may write the photocurrent

$$I = I_n + I_p = qA\left[\frac{D_n(\Delta n + n_p)}{L_n} + \frac{D_p(\Delta p + p_n)}{L_p}\right], \qquad (7.79)$$

where we use the symbolism of Fig. 4.7 and Section 4.3. From Eq. (4.24) we may write (7.79) in terms of the intensity of illumination I_L and the lifetimes:

$$I = qA\eta I_L\left[\frac{D_n\tau_n}{L_n} + \frac{D_p\tau_p}{L_n}\right] + qA\left[\frac{D_n n_p}{L_n} + \frac{D_p p_n}{L_p}\right], \qquad (7.80)$$

or

$$I = qA\eta I_L(L_n + L_p) + I_0,$$

where η is the efficiency of the light in electron-hole pairs per second per cubic centimeter per unit of light intensity. If the photodiode is connected in series with a load resistor, R_L, and a voltage source, V_{DD}, the voltage across the load is $V_L = IR_L$, and the voltage sensitivity would be

$$\frac{dV_L}{dI_L} = qA\eta(L_n + L_p)R_L, \qquad (7.81)$$

where the optimum R_C would match the dynamic slope of the photodiode characteristic which would be of the order of 1 megohm for a germanium junction and 100 megohms for a silicon junction. (Both are operated at relatively low voltage so that avalanche multiplication is negligible.) It should be remembered that the I_0 of Eq. (7.80) will always include the regeneration current of the depletion region of the junction as given in Eq. (5.22). For a silicon device this component is usually not negligible.

From Eq. (7.81) it is clear that the best sensitivity is found for very long-lifetime material, where L_n and L_p are a maximum. From (7.80) we also see that this same condition gives us the lowest dark current I_0. This sensitivity is achieved at the expense of response time. If the photodiode is used as a switch where sufficient light is always present to drive the load, we may define the rise time of the device as simply the average lifetime of the material, τ (assuming that $\tau_n \simeq \tau_p$). This follows from the fact that the photocurrent is proportional to the density of excess carriers which approaches its saturation value with a time constant τ under constant illumination. Since $L^2 = D\tau$, we see that

$$\frac{dV_L/dI_L}{\sqrt{\tau}} = qA\eta R_L(\sqrt{D_n} + \sqrt{D_p}), \qquad (7.82)$$

which is a constant depending on the material used for the photodiode. Here, it can be seen that a high-mobility material is of value (other things being equal), since D is proportional to μ through the Einstein relation.

This sensitivity can be greatly increased if a hook structure is used. Such a structure is often called a phototransistor, since it contains two junctions. Optical injection of carriers replaces the normal emitter, and the hook amplifies the photo-current. Figure 7.14 shows the structure of such a device. The energy-band diagram of this device is identical to that of Fig. 7.12 with the emitter portion omitted. The electron-hole pairs produced by the

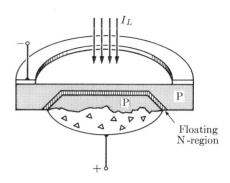

FIG. 7.14. Hook phototransistor.

illumination of the upper P-region (here called the base region) result in electron diffusion current to the brink of the reverse junction. Here, we can no longer work with the concept of an equilibrium, Δn, remote from the junction determined by $\tau_n \eta I_L$. Rather, we assume that the electronic current reaching the reverse-biased junction is determined by equating the sum of the surface recombination current (at the illuminated surface), the bulk recombination in the base region, and the diffusion current to the junction to the generation current $qAw\eta I_L$. We assume that the light is not appreciably absorbed in a thickness $(w + f)$, (as we assumed before, for the thickness of the entire photodiode).

Letting s be the surface recombination velocity, we find that the surface recombination current is $qAns$, where n is the excess density of electrons just beneath the illuminated surface. When we let L_B be the diffusion length for electrons in the base region, the bulk recombination current is $qAwn/2\tau_B$ in the base region of thickness w. We now may write the current balance as

$$qAw\eta I_L = qAns + qAwnD_n/2L_B^2 + qAnD_n/w, \qquad (7.83)$$

giving $n = w\eta I_L/(s + wD_n/2L_B^2 + D_n/w)$, and the electronic current reaching the junction is

$$I_n = \frac{qAnD_n}{w} = \frac{qAw\eta I_L D_n}{ws + (w^2 D_n/2L_B^2) + D_n}. \qquad (7.84)$$

The current must be multiplied by the α^* of the hook to give its true contribution to the current of the device. If the floating region has appreciable bulk recombination losses, we must define α^* as $1/(1 - \gamma_{CF}\beta_F)$, where β_F is the transport efficiency of the floating region. We have $\gamma_{CF}\beta_F = \alpha_F$, which is the α_{FB} of the effective transistor of the collector region, considering the collector contact region as emitter and the floating region as base.

There is another contribution to the electronic current of the floating region due to the light absorbed in this region. The current of electrons introduced into the floating region by light absorption is $qAf\eta I_L$. This must be added to the current of Eq. (7.79) to give the total current acted upon by α^*. We are now able to write the photocurrent as

$$I = qA\eta I_L \left[f + \frac{wD_n}{sw + (w^2 D_n/2L_B^2) + D_n} \right] \alpha^*. \qquad (7.85)$$

In view of the fact that we have a built-in field, $\mathcal{E}_F$, in the floating region, we must use the drift transistors γ and β to compute the α^* of this collector. The basic equations are (7.19) and (7.16), giving

$$\gamma_{CF} = (1 + \rho_C D_n/\rho_F \mu_n \mathcal{E}_F L_C)^{-1},$$

$$\beta_F = (1 + fD_p/\mu_p \mathcal{E}_F L_F^2)^{-1}. \qquad (7.86)$$

Here, we may not assume that γ_{CF} and β_F are very near unity if we intend to thicken the floating region to absorb as many photons as possible. The final form of the photocurrent is then rather complex:

$$I = \frac{qA\eta I_L f \left[1 + \dfrac{w}{f(1 + sw/D_n + w^2/2L_B^2)} \right]}{1 - \left(1 + \dfrac{\rho_C D_n}{\rho_F \mu_n \mathcal{E}_F L_C} + \dfrac{fD_p}{\mu_p \mathcal{E}_F L_F^2} + \dfrac{\rho_C fD_n D_p}{\rho_F \mu_n \mu_p \mathcal{E}_F^2 L_C L_F^2} \right)^{-1}}. \qquad (7.87)$$

In this expression the rise time depends on the charging time of the base and floating regions, rather than on the lifetime of the material. This time can be calculated by the methods of Chapter 6 and the computation will not be repeated here. The sensitivity can be optimized in several ways by using the parameters w, f, $\mathcal{E}_F$, τ_B, and τ_F. When this is done, one will still find that a compromise between sensitivity and response time is necessary.

Comparing Eqs. (7.87) and (7.80) is difficult, but if we assume that $f \simeq L_F$ and $w \simeq L_B$, we see that the total electronic current is of the same order as the sum of the hole and electron currents of the simple photodiode. In the phototransistor the hole current is this electron current amplified by α^*, which may be of the order of 100. The hook phototransistor can then show a current sensitivity two orders of magnitude greater than that of a simple photodiode. The voltage sensitivity will not be increased by this same factor because the impedance of the characteristic will be reduced by about the same factor $(1/\alpha^*)$.

Finally, we may calculate the dark current of a hook phototransistor by calculating the I_{B0} of the effective collector-region transistor mentioned above. Since there is a field in the floating region, this may be calculated from Eqs. (7.77) and (7.78) with suitable modifications. Here, $\alpha^* = 1/(1 - \gamma_{CF}\beta_F)$, giving

$$I_0 = I_{nC}(1 + \alpha^*) = I_{nC}(2 - \gamma_{CF}\beta_F)/(1 - \gamma_{CF}\beta_F). \quad (7.88)$$

In the special case where a normal hook-collector transistor structure is used for a phototransistor, Eqs. (7.87) and (7.88) reduce to simplified forms, since we may assume that $\beta_F = 1$ and γ_{CF} is nearly unity:

$$I = qA\eta I_L f\left[1 + \frac{w}{f(1 + sw/D_n + w^2/2L_B^2)}\right]\frac{\rho_F\mu_n\mathcal{E}_F L_C}{\rho_C D_n}, \quad (7.89)$$

$$I_0 = qA\left\{\frac{D_n n_B}{w}(1 - \gamma) + \frac{n_i}{\tau}[2\epsilon(\phi - V_C)(\mu_p\rho_B + \mu_n\rho_F)]^{1/2}\right\}$$
$$\times\left(\frac{\rho_F\mu_n\mathcal{E}_F L_C}{\rho_C D_n}\right), \quad (7.90)$$

where I_{nC} is given by Eq. (7.77).

The thyratron transistor. Any transistor with α_{FB} greater than unity can be made to show a thyratron-like characteristic. Often the criterion of $\alpha_{FB} > 1$ is achieved by obtaining an appreciable M-factor in the collector-barrier region (an avalanche transistor). One of the easiest ways of obtaining such an α_{FB} is by using a hook collector to give a large α^*.

If we consider the structure shown in Fig. 7.12, together with our previous discussion we realize that whenever the emitter is forward-biased ever so slightly, the device will show $\alpha_{FB} > 1$ because of the built-in $\alpha^* > 1$. This means that if we let the base float and apply a voltage between emitter and collector of such a polarity as to reverse-bias the base-to-floating-region junction, the emitter junction will be slightly forward-biased and the entire device will show a low-resistance characteristic. This is the "on" characteristic of Fig. 7.15.

If we maintain a negative current into the base rather than let it float, we will bias both the emitter-base junction and the floating region-base junction in the reverse polarity. Most of the current will flow through the collector because it represents an ordinary transistor with a floating base region and will then have the normal leakage current multiplied by the factor $1/(1 - \alpha_{FB})$ for that transistor ($\alpha_{FB} = \gamma_{CF}\beta_F$ since the collector contact region acts as an emitter). The emitter-base junction will carry only its normal leakage current, which is low because it is heavily doped on one side. The base voltage will be determined by the I_{B0}-curve of the effective collector-region transistor.

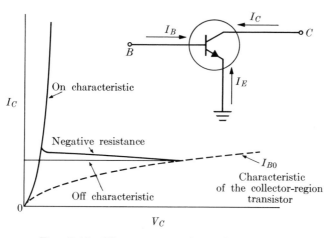

FIG. 7.15. Thyratron transistor characteristic.

If we maintain this current and increase the collector-emitter voltage in the normal polarity, the voltage across the base-floating region junction will remain substantially constant as determined by the I_{B0}-curve mentioned above. When the collector-emitter voltage reaches the full value required to maintain the base current drive, the base will be at ground potential. Any further voltage increase will forward-bias the emitter and the device will "fire," making a rapid transition to the "on" state.

The off-characteristic shown in Fig. 7.15 is traversed while the collector voltage is rising to the firing level and the base voltage is simultaneously falling to zero. The slope of this part of the characteristic is substantially determined by the reverse characteristic of the emitter, since it is supplying the only variation in current.

It is clear that different firing voltages may be set at different points on the I_{B0} curve of the collector-region transistor by setting different negative base currents. The larger the fixed base current, the larger is the firing voltage up to the breakdown voltage of the collector. The device may be reset by turning off the collector voltage momentarily until the stored charge disappears.

The controlled rectifier [7]. The controlled rectifier is a four-layer NPNP-device which operates on a somewhat different principle from the hook-collector thyratron transistor considered above. We have kept the same general nomenclature and symbolism for the controlled rectifier structure and characteristic shown in Fig. 7.16. The subscripts denote emitter, base, floating region, and collector, respectively, reading from left to right. The base connection in a controlled rectifier is usually called the gate, both end regions are often called emitters, and both center regions

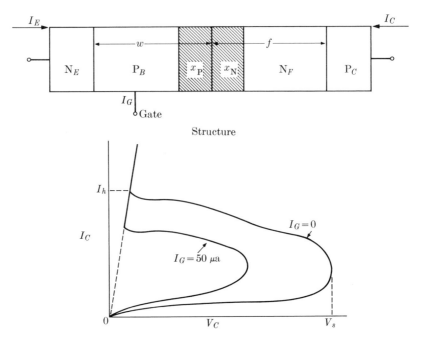

Structure

Characteristic

FIG. 7.16. Controlled rectifier.

are called bases. This nomenclature stems from the fact that it is customary to treat this device as though it consisted of two transistors as shown in Fig. 7.13.

In terms of this phenomenological model we designate the α_{FB} of the NPN-transistor as α_N, and the α_{FB} of the PNP-transistor as α_P. The emitter current of the NPN-transistor is I_E, and the emitter current of the PNP-transistor is I_C. The collector current of the NPN-device is the base current of the PNP, and vice versa. With this in mind we may write, for $I_G = 0$,

$$-\alpha_N I_E + M_n I_{C0}/2 = (1 - \alpha_P)I_C - M_p I_{C0}/2, \qquad (7.91)$$

where the M's are the avalanche multiplication factors of the central junction. The quantity $M_n I_{C0}/2$ on the left-hand side represents the electronic part of I_{C0} falling into the floating region, while the same term on the right represents the hole current part of I_{C0} falling into the base. Letting $M_n = M_p$ for simplicity, and solving for I_C we get

$$I_C = \frac{-\alpha_N I_E + M I_{C0}}{(1 - \alpha_P)}. \qquad (7.92)$$

This is just the result of (7.75) except that there α_P was represented by γ_{CF}.

If we are dealing with diode operation of the controlled rectifier structure (gate open), we must set $I_C = -I_E$, and (7.92) becomes

$$I_C = \frac{MI_{C0}}{1 - (\alpha_N + \alpha_P)}. \tag{7.93}$$

Here, it is clear that I_C will increase without bound as $(\alpha_N + \alpha_P) \to 1$. If there is a gate current, we must set

$$I_C = -(I_E + I_G),$$

obtaining

$$I_C = \frac{\alpha_N I_G + MI_{C0}}{1 - (\alpha_N + \alpha_P)}. \tag{7.94}$$

We can now appreciate the significant difference between the hook-collector thyratron transistor described before and the controlled rectifier. In the hook-collector thyratron device, the alpha sum $(\alpha_N + \alpha_P)$ was always nearly 2, except in saturation, so that the diode response of such a device is a very high current characteristic requiring sufficient saturation of both base regions to degrade their alphas until their sum is slightly less than unity, which gives a high, stable current. In the controlled rectifier the alpha sum, at low currents, is less than unity, and a low current characteristic results until the sum reaches unity, where a breakdown occurs. The hook thyratron had to be held off by negative base current. The controlled rectifier must be triggered on by positive gate current.

The physical mechanism of this type of device can be understood by considering the factors involved in α_{FB}. From Eq. (6.1) we find the factors

$$\alpha_{FB} = \gamma\beta\alpha^*M. \tag{7.95}$$

Of these factors, only γ and β can be less than unity; therefore a low initial α_{FB} must depend on a low initial γ, or β, or both. Moreover, since M is only a function of V_C, and α^* is only a very slowly varying function of current, we must still depend on γ or β to implement the gate current control of the device (M may still supply the current to augment I_{C0} in the diode version).

The current dependence of γ has two effects. First, at very low currents the recombination in the forward-biased emitter-junction depletion region may exceed the injection current, giving $\gamma < 0.5$. Second, at very high levels of current, $\gamma \to 0.5$ from either above or below, depending upon the initial doping ratio of the two sides of the junction. Since we are dealing with very low triggering currents, we may only use the first effect. In this case the junction would be heavily doped on the emitter side to give large

γ at normal currents, and we would hope that up to currents of several times I_{C0} γ would be less than 0.5.

For β we could imagine that w and f are slightly larger than L_B and L_F, respectively, so that the transport efficiencies of the base and floating regions would be less than 0.5 at low currents. As the currents increase, the traps become saturated, giving an increase in lifetime and in L_B and L_F, allowing the transport efficiencies to exceed 0.5. Here again, this effect would occur at currents too high to give the low triggering currents usually observed.

The operation of the typical device is then as follows. For $I_G = 0$, the $V_C I_C$-characteristic starts out as the leakage characteristic of the center junction, since γ_N and γ_P are so low that they essentially supply majority current only. (We assume β_N and β_P to be nearly unity.) As V_C increases, M increases the leakage current of the center junction forcing more current to flow through the emitters and thereby forward-biasing them to the point where their individual γ-values approach 0.5. At $V_C = V_S$, the overall $(\alpha_N + \alpha_P)$ sum reaches unity and the device fires. For a fixed value of I_G, we need less augmentation by avalanching (a smaller M-value), and hence the device fires at a lower voltage.

In the high current "on" state, the overall current transfer ratio of the device must be unity, since the current is determined solely by the load and after the gate trigger is off it is a two-terminal device. This relation is $\alpha_N/(1 - \alpha_P) = 1$, or the familiar $\alpha_N + \alpha_P = 1$. Contrasting this condition for the switching point (I_s, V_s) and the hold point (I_h, V_h) and assuming that $\alpha^* = 1.0$, we have

$$\text{At} \quad (I_s, V_s): \qquad \gamma_{Ns}\beta_{Ns}M_n + \gamma_{Ps}\beta_{Ps}M_p = 1, \qquad (7.96)$$

$$\text{At} \quad (I_h, V_h): \qquad \gamma_{Nh}\beta_{Nh} + \gamma_{Ph}\beta_{Ph} = 1. \qquad (7.97)$$

For simplicity let $\beta_{Ns}M_n = \beta_s M$ and $\beta_{Nh} = \beta_{Ph} = \beta_h$. We then obtain

$$\text{At} \quad (I_s, V_s): \qquad (\gamma_{Ns} + \gamma_{Ps}) = 1/\beta_s M, \qquad (7.98)$$

$$\text{At} \quad (I_h, V_h): \qquad (\gamma_{Nh} + \gamma_{Ph}) = 1/\beta_h. \qquad (7.99)$$

At the switching point, β_s is determined by a minimum base-region thickness because the junction depletion region is a maximum. This gives a maximum β. At the hold point, β_h is determined by a full base width and may be significantly less than β_s. If, for example, $w = L_B$ and $f = L_F$ and if at V_s, the base widths are reduced by 50%, $\beta_s = 1.33\beta_h$. Also M may easily be as great as 2 or 3 at V_s so that it is clear that $(\gamma_{Ns} + \gamma_{Ps})$ may be less than $(\gamma_{Nh} + \gamma_{Ph})$ by a considerable factor, thus requiring I_h to be greater than I_s by a comparable factor. Experimentally I_h is usually two to four times I_s.

7.4   Numerical Example

For this example a thyratron transistor has been chosen because it combines many of the concepts developed up to this point. Given a germanium thyratron transistor with an $N_E P_B NP_C$-structure specified as follows.

	Emitter	Base
Doping level	$N_D = 10^{17}/cc$	$N_A = 10^{15}/cm^3$
Thickness	5×10^{-3} cm	1×10^{-3} cm
Lifetime	$\tau_p = 10^{-8}$ sec	$\tau_n = 10^{-6}$ sec
Diffusion constant	$D_p = 20$ cm^2/sec	$D_n = 100$ cm^2/sec
	Floating region	Collector
Doping level	$N_D = 10^{15}/cm^3$	$N_A = 10^{17}/cm^3$
Thickness	1×10^{-3} cm	5×10^{-3} cm
Lifetime	$\tau_p = 10^{-5}$ sec	$\tau_n = 10^{-7}$ sec
Diffusion constant	$D_p = 50$ cm^2/sec	$D_n = 30$ cm^2/sec

Assuming that the area of all the junctions is the same, 10^{-3} cm^2, that all junctions are abrupt, and that there are no doping gradients in any of the four regions of the device, calculate the leakage current in the "off" condition for $V_C = 10$ v when the device is set to fire at $V_C = 20$ v.

In Fig. 7.17 is shown an energy-band diagram of a thyratron transistor in the bias condition specified in this problem. There is a negative current into the base which divides and flows partly into the emitter region and partly into the floating region. This current consists of the flow of the electron distribution (b) over the two reverse-biased barriers on either side of the base. (It is the base drive I_B which causes both base junctions to be reverse-biased.) The value of I_B is determined by the requirement that the firing voltage be $V_C = 20$ v. At the verge of firing there is no current through the emitter junction and the 20 v appears entirely across the base-floating region junction, except for a very slight forward bias of the collector-region junction. As soon as the collector voltage increases by an infinitesimal amount, there will be some electronic current flowing into the base from the emitter and, because of the large forward current transfer ratio, the device will fire.

From the above considerations we see that we may calculate the I_B necessary to set the device for 20-v firing by calculating the leakage current of the device with the emitter open circuited and 20 v across the center junction. This amounts to calculating the I_{B0} of the collector-region PNP-transistor under the special condition that its collector region (the

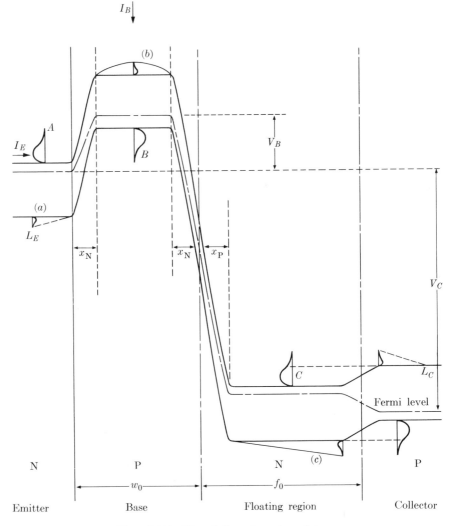

FIG. 7.17. Biased thyratron transistor.

base region of the entire device) is only w_0 in thickness and has no current through its surface opposite the reverse-biased junction.   Under these conditions the leakage current will consist of the following components:

Electronic current

(1) The electron density (*b*), determined by the zero emitter-current requirement, diffusing into the floating region (see the I_{C0} calcula-tion in Section 6.1)

(2) The regeneration electron current from the base region

(3) The regeneration electron current in the depletion region of the center junction

Hole current

(4) The diffusion of the hole density (c) across the floating region. This is equal to the above electronic current multiplied by the α^* of the entire device.

Following the I_{C0} calculation of Section 6.1, we may evaluate the electronic-current component (1) as

$$I_{n1} = qAD_B n_{pB}(1 - \gamma_E)/(w_0 - x_P). \qquad (7.100)$$

Here, the thermodynamic-equilibrium minority hole density in the base, n_{pB}, is diminished by the factor $(1 - \gamma_E)$ by the reverse emitter bias necessary to give a net zero current through the emitter junction. At the emitter side of the base, this density $n_{pB}(1 - \gamma_E)$ is clamped by the tail of the majority electron density distribution in the emitter region.

Since $(1 - \gamma_E)$ is of the order of 10^{-2}, we may calculate the regeneration current in the base region as though the deficient carrier density were the full n_{pB}. This gives the electronic current component (2) as

$$I_{n2} = qAn_{pB}(w_0 - x_P)/\tau_B. \qquad (7.101)$$

The regeneration current in the depletion region of the center junction is given by

$$I_{n3} = qAn_i(x_N + x_P)/\tau, \qquad (7.102)$$

where τ is the effective lifetime in the junction region and is at least as large as the larger of the two neighboring region lifetimes (τ_F here).

The entire electronic current $(I_{n1} + I_{n2} + I_{n3})$ flows into the floating base of the PNP-transistor producing a hole diffusion current component (4):

$$\alpha^* I_n = I_n/(1 - \alpha_P) = I_n/(1 - \gamma_C \beta_F), \qquad (7.103)$$

where

$$1 - \gamma_C \beta_F = \frac{\rho_C(f_0 - x_N)}{\rho_F L_C} + \frac{(f_0 - x_N)^2}{2L_F^2}. \qquad (7.104)$$

Combining Eqs. (7.100) through (7.104), we may write the entire leakage current as the I_{B0} of the PNP-transistor:

$$I_{B0} = I_n(1 + \alpha^*)$$

$$= qA\left[\frac{D_B n_{pB}(1 - \gamma_E)}{w_0 - x_P} + \frac{n_{pB}(w_0 - x_P)}{\tau_B} + \frac{n_i(x_N + x_P)}{\tau_F}\right]$$

$$\times \left\{1 + \left[\frac{\rho_C(f_0 - x_N)}{\rho_F L_C} + \frac{(f_0 - x_N)^2}{2L_F^2}\right]^{-1}\right\}. \qquad (7.105)$$

This current will be the electronic current which must be supplied to the base to set the device to fire at 20 v, where we use 20 v to calculate x_N and x_P. It is also the I_C at the switching or firing point.

Evaluating (7.105) at $V_C = 20$ v and for the parameters specified in this example we have:

$$q = 1.6 \times 10^{-19} \text{ coul},$$
$$A = 10^{-3} \text{ cm},$$
$$D_B = 100 \text{ cm}^2/\text{sec},$$
$$n_{pB} = n_i^2/N_{AB} = 6.25 \times 10^{11}/\text{cm}^3,$$
$$x_N = x_P = (\epsilon V/qN_{DF})^{1/2} = 4.2 \times 10^{-4} \text{ cm},$$
$$\text{where } \epsilon = 1.44 \text{ pf/cm},$$
$$L_E = (D_E\tau_E)^{1/2} = 4.5 \times 10^{-4} \text{ cm},$$
$$(1 - \gamma_E) = \rho_E(w_0 - x_P)/\rho_B L_E = 0.0026,$$
$$n_i = 2.5 \times 10^{13}/\text{cm}^3,$$
$$L_C = (D_C\tau_C)^{1/2} = 1.7 \times 10^{-3} \text{ cm},$$
$$L_E = (D_F\tau_F)^{1/2} = 2.2 \times 10^{-2} \text{ cm}.$$

Now substituting in Eq. (7.105) gives

$$I_{B0} = 1.6 \times 10^{-22}(2.8 \times 10^{14} + 3.6 \times 10^{14} + 21 \times 10^{14})$$
$$\times [1 + (20.540^{-4} + 3.5 \times 10^{-4})^{-1}] = 183 \ \mu a. \qquad (7.106)$$

When we reduce the voltage to $V_C = 10$ v, under the condition that $I_B = -183 \ \mu a$, we shall assume that the 20-v drop across the center junction remains substantially constant. (After we determine the resulting magnitude of emitter leakage, we can go back and correct the center junction voltage and leakage if necessary.)

As can be seen in Fig. 7.17, the reduction of V_C from 20 to 10 v while maintaining the center junction voltage at 20 v serves to reverse-bias the emitter-base junction by -10 v (shown as V_B in the figure). All the voltages are measured with reference to a common emitter. The required leakage current at $V_C = 10$ v will then be just the 20-v leakage current of Eq. (7.106), diminished by the reverse-biased emitter junction current. We now proceed to calculate the emitter-junction leakage current at 10 v reverse bias.

Because of the heavy doping of the emitter region, the depletion region of the emitter junction will be substantially all in the base region and will have the same value x_P calculated above, since the same voltage is involved. The emitter-junction leakage current will consist of the following components:

Electronic current

(5) One-half the base-region regeneration current (shown in Fig. 7.17 as the density (b) flowing in two directions

(6) The regeneration current in the depletion region of the emitter junction

Hole current

(7) The minority hole density in the emitter region, p_{nE}, diffusing into the base region

To calculate electronic current component (5) we must find the thickness of the base region remaining after we subtract the junction depletion region encroachment. This is $(w_0 - 2x_P)$ and half of the base-region regeneration current is

$$I_{n5} = qAn_{pB}(w_0 - 2x_P)/2\tau_B. \tag{7.107}$$

The depletion-region regeneration component is

$$I_{n6} = qAn_i x_P/\tau_B, \tag{7.108}$$

where we have used the longer of the base or emitter-region lifetime as the effective τ in the depletion region. That is, τ_B was not used just because the depletion region occurs in the base material. The minority hole diffusion current is given by

$$I_{p7} = qAD_E p_{nE}/L_E. \tag{7.109}$$

The total leakage current is the sum of these three components:

$$I_0 = qA\{[n_{pB}(w_0 - 2x_P)/2 + n_i x_P]/\tau_B + D_E p_{nE}/L_E\}. \tag{7.110}$$

Evaluating under the $V_B = -10$ v condition and the specifications of this example gives

$$I_0 = 1.6 \times 10^{-22}\{[0.5 \times 10^8 + 10^5 \times 10^8]/10^{-6} + 2.8 \times 10^{14}\}$$
$$= 1.73\ \mu a. \tag{7.111}$$

From this calculation we see that this emitter-junction leakage current is dominated by the depletion-region regeneration term to an even greater extent than was the central-junction electronic leakage current.

The required current is then given by $I_{B0} - I_0 = 181\ \mu a$ at $V_C = 10$ v. Since I_0 is very small compared to I_{B0}, we see that our assumption of the constancy of the voltage across the central junction was justified. This calculation shows that the dynamic impedance of the "off" characteristic is very high, being approximately $10/I_0 = 6$ megohms. Since the leakage currents involved are dominated by depletion-region regeneration terms, it is clear that they will be quite temperature sensitive having the activation energy of n_i, which is $\Delta E/2$. The firing voltage will in turn show a high temperature sensitivity, since it is set by the I_{B0} leakage current.

Problems

7.1 Given a drift transistor with a dc $\alpha_{FB} = 0.99$. Assume that this is all accounted for by the transport efficiency β_F. Calculate the reverse transport efficiency, β_R, under the assumption that $A_E \simeq A_C$ and that the doping density ratio of $[N(0)/N(w)] = 10^3$. Also, assume that the average effective base-region lifetime is the same regardless of the direction of current flow.

7.2 Calculate the gate leakage current just at pinch-off for a silicon depletion field-effect transistor with the geometry illustrated in Fig. 7.7. Assume that the minority-carrier lifetime τ is constant throughout the device, and that the P-regions of the gate are very heavily doped compared to the N-region of the channel. Evaluate your resulting formula for the following parameters (be sure to include regeneration current):

$$r_1 = 0.05 \text{ cm}, \qquad r_2 = 0.15 \text{ cm},$$
$$a_0 = 0.005 \text{ cm}, \qquad N_D = 10^{13} \text{ impurities/cm}^3,$$
$$N_A = 10^{15} \text{ impurities/cm}^3, \qquad \tau_n = \tau_p = 10^{-7} \text{ sec},$$
$$\text{thickness of the entire device} = 0.025 \text{ cm},$$
$$V_D = V_0/2, \quad \text{and} \quad V_G = -V_0/2, \qquad D_p = 10 \text{ cm}^2/\text{sec}.$$

7.3 In a $N_E P_B N P_C$ hook-collector transistor (the subscripts indicate the emitter, base, and collector contacts) the electronic current flowing from the emitter and across the base must charge up the floating N-region before the final collector α^* computed in the text takes effect. Find an expression for this charging time on the assumption that the current level of the collector is not limited by a load resistance.

7.4 Given a PNP germanium drift transistor with a dc $\alpha_{FB} = 0.99$, an $\alpha_{RB} = 0.3$, and $A_C = A_E = 10^{-3} \text{ cm}^2$. Calculate the voltage across the collector junction if $I_E = 2$ ma and $I_B = -1$ ma. Assume that D_n in the base region is 20 cm^2/sec, $w = 10^{-4}$ cm, the doping ratio = 10^3, and $\rho_B = 5$ ohms-cm at the collector side.

7.5 In an enhancement mode silicon field-effect transistor of the NPN-type (N-type source and drain regions set in a high-resistivity P-type matrix), the separation of source and drain is 25 μ; C_G measures 20 pf and the transconductance, G_{FS}, measures 10,000 μmhos at $V_G = V_D = 10$ v. If V_0 is -4 v, calculate and plot the drain characteristic curve for $V_G = 0$ v. What is the effective mobility in the channel?

Bibliography

1. H. KRÖMER, "Zur Theorie des Diffusions- und des Drifttransistor I, II, III," *Arch. Elect. Übertragung* **8,** 223, 363, 499 (1954).
2. M. B. DAS and A. R. BOOTHROYD, "Determination of Physical Parameters of Diffusion and Drift Transistors," *IRE Trans. Electron Devices* **ED-8,** 15–30 (1961).
3. W. SHOCKLEY, "A Unipolar Field Effect Transistor," *Proc. IRE* **40,** 1365–1376 (1952).
4. S. R. HOFSTEIN and F. P. HEIMAN, "The Silicon Insulated-Gate Field Effect Transistor," *Proc. IEEE* **51,** 1190–1202 (1963).

5. S. L. MILLER, *Handbook of Semiconductor Electronics*, edited by L. P. Hunter, 2nd ed., McGraw-Hill, New York, 1962, Chapter 4.

6. J. N. SHIVE, "The Properties of Germanium Phototransistors," *J. Opt. Soc. Am.* **43,** 239–244 (1953).

7. D. R. MUSS and C. GOLDBERG, "Switching Mechanism in the NPNP Silicon Controlled Rectifier," *Inst. Elec. Electron Engrs. Trans. Electron Devices,* **ED-10,** 113 (1963).

CHAPTER 8

TWO-TERMINAL DEVICES

The simple PN-junction diode described in Chapter 5 used as it is for switching and clamping is by far the most frequently encountered two-terminal semiconductor device. Modifications and adaptations of this basic structure are employed for a variety of other applications. Varactor diodes are used as variable and nonlinear capacitances. Here, the simple junction structure is modified to enhance the effect of the voltage variation of the junction depletion capacitance. Mixer and detector diodes are adapted to enhance the nonlinear resistance characteristic of the junction.

A more extreme modification is represented by the Esaki tunnel diode. This diode is formed by a PN-junction between two degenerate regions and involves the phenomenon of quantum-mechanical "tunneling" in its mechanism of operation. The tunnel-diode characteristic shows a negative resistance region and a very fast switching response. It is closely related to the Zener diode used for voltage regulation. Because of the interest in the characteristics of the tunnel diode and because it represents a new phenomenon in the operation of a PN-junction, we will begin our discussion of two-terminal devices with a brief intuitive discussion of tunneling.

8.1 The Tunneling Phenomenon

Up to this point we have treated a PN-junction barrier as though it were impenetrable to free carriers with insufficient energy to surmount it. In actual fact this is not strictly true for very thin barriers. In Section 1.1 a quantum-mechanical example was given in which the allowed states of an electron in a square potential well were determined. There it was assumed that the potential energy inside the well was zero and outside the well it was infinite. We then assumed that the wave function representing the electron was completely reflected at the walls of the well. If the potential outside the well is not infinite and if the walls of the well are not too thick, this last assumption of complete reflection is not valid. Following the elementary approach of LeCroissette [1], we will proceed to solve Eq. (1.14) for the three regions illustrated in Fig. 8.1.

In region 1, to the left of $x = 0$, we have zero potential energy so that Eq. (1.14) for $V = 0$ becomes

$$\frac{d^2\psi_1}{dx^2} = -\frac{2mE}{\hbar^2}. \qquad (8.1)$$

The general equation for a one-dimensional wave can be written

$$\psi_1 = (A_1 e^{ja_1x} + B_1 e^{-ja_1x})e^{-j\omega t}, \qquad (8.2)$$

where the first term represents a wave moving to the right and the second term represents a wave moving to the left. Since Eq. (8.1) is independent of time only, the space-dependent quantity in parentheses is a solution of (8.1) with $a_1^2 = 2mE/\hbar_i^2$.

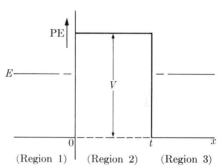

(Region 1) (Region 2) (Region 3)

FIG. 8.1.   One-dimensional potential barrier.

In region 2, the region of the potential-energy barrier, Eq. (1.14) becomes

$$\frac{d^2\psi_2}{dx^2} = \frac{2m(V - E)}{\hbar^2}, \qquad (8.3)$$

with the time-independent solution

$$\psi_2 = A_2 e^{a_2x} + B_2 e^{-a_2x}, \qquad (8.4)$$

where $a_2^2 = 2m(V - E)/\hbar^2$. Here, it is seen that because the right-hand side of (8.3) is positive, the space solution is nonoscillatory consisting of simple exponentials with real arguments. This is a direct consequence of the fact that the barrier height is greater than the energy of the particle. The characteristic length of this exponential is inversely proportional to $(V - E)$ so that we see that the penetration of a ψ-function into a barrier drops off exponentially as the barrier height increases.

In region 3, to the right of the barrier, we find Eq. (8.1) again with the solution

$$\psi_3 = (A_3 e^{ja_3x} + B_3 e^{-ja_3x})e^{-j\omega t}, \qquad (8.5)$$

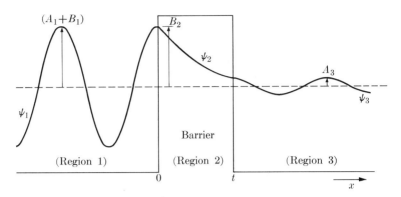

FIG. 8.2. The relationship of the wave-function amplitudes in the barrier tunneling process [1].

where $a_3 = a_1 = 2mE/\hbar^2$. The ψ-functions and their derivatives must be continuous at the surfaces of the barrier. Also B_3 must be zero, since there is no reflection for a wave in region 3 traveling to the right. We are then left with five constants and four conditions. We will proceed to eliminate B_1, A_2, and B_2 and find the ratio $|A_3/A_1|^2$, which can be interpreted as the square of the amplitude ratio of the transmitted to the incident wave. We can then also interpret this quantity as the ratio of the probability of finding a particle to the right of the barrier to the probability of its initial presence to the left of the barrier. In terms of large numbers of particles this is simply the ratio of the number transmitted to the number incident on the barrier.

Much of the algebra involved in applying the boundary conditions can be avoided by making some simplifying assumptions. First, we note that if the barrier is very thick, $A_2 \to 0$, since for $t \to \infty$, we have $\psi_2 \to 0$. Therefore for our finite barrier we will assume $A_2 \ll B_2$ and neglect the A_2-term of ψ_2. Next, we note that the particles must be conserved. All particles incident on the barrier are either reflected or they tunnel through.

Figure 8.2 shows a schematic representation of the amplitudes involved. Here, the barrier is seen to act as an attenuator of the ψ_1-wave. It should be noted that there is no change in energy so that there is no change in wavelength, only a reduction of amplitude, which represents the lower probability of finding the particle on the other side of the barrier.

If we assume that only a very small percentage tunnel through, we may let $A_1 \simeq B_1$. We now have at the $x = 0$ boundary:

$$\psi_1(0) = \psi_2(0), \quad \text{giving} \quad 2A_1 = B_2, \tag{8.6a}$$

and at the $x = t$ boundary:

$$\psi_2(t) = \psi_3(t), \quad \text{giving} \quad B_2 e^{-a_2 t} = A_3 e^{j a_1 t}. \tag{8.6b}$$

Eliminating B_2 we find

$$|A_3/A_1|^2 = 4e^{-2a_2 t}. \tag{8.7}$$

Equation (8.7) gives the first-order transmission coefficient of the barrier. Exact solution of the boundary conditions yields

$$\left|\frac{A_3}{A_1}\right|^2 = \frac{4e^{-2a_2 t}}{1 + (a_2/a_1 - a_1/a_2)^2/4}. \tag{8.8}$$

The Esaki tunnel diode. The previous discussion of the phenomenon of tunneling will allow us to understand the operation of the tunnel diode in a qualitative way.

Figure 8.3 shows a PN-junction with degenerate doping on both sides. In this case the Fermi level is inside the conduction band on the N-side and inside the valence band on the P-side. Here, it is seen that there are free electrons, A, at the same energy as vacant levels (holes), B. These are separated by a barrier consisting of the forbidden energy gap between a and b. At the Fermi level, E_0, the thickness of this barrier is t. At higher energies the thickness decreases until at point c the top of the barrier is reached. The barrier then is shown as the triangle abc. For the case of zero bias shown, no electrons of the distribution A can tunnel into the P-region if they are above the top of the valence band in the P-region. However, if t is small enough, the lower part of the distribution A is free to tunnel through the barrier. Similarly, the top electrons in the valence band of the P-region can tunnel through to vacant energy levels in the N-region. For a very thin barrier it is possible to find a virtual short circuit at the origin of the characteristic of such a degenerate PN-junction.

When this junction is forward-biased by a very small amount, V_a, as shown in Fig. 8.4(a), two things happen. First, as the electronic distribution A is raised relative to the hole distribution B, the fraction of the filled levels in the conduction band of the N-region will exceed by a wide margin

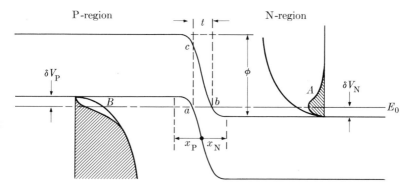

Fig. 8.3. Degenerate PN-junction.

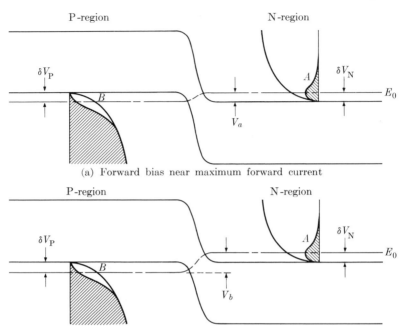

(a) Forward bias near maximum forward current

(b) Forward bias near minimum forward current

FIG. 8.4. Relative positions of the carrier distributions for a forward-biased tunnel diode.

the fraction of filled levels at the same energy in the valence band of the P-region. This means that the number of electrons impinging on the barrier from the right will exceed the number of those impinging from the left. A tunnel current of electrons will then flow steadily from right to left so long as the bias is maintained. The second effect of forward bias is the normal reduction of barrier height so that the normal forward diffusion current of holes and electrons will begin to flow over the top of the barrier. This normal forward diode current is usually quite negligible compared to the tunnel current for thin barriers and low forward bias.

Figure 8.5 shows a typical volt-ampere characteristic for a tunnel diode. The bias voltages V_a and V_b are those illustrated in Fig. 8.4. In Fig. 8.4(a) the bias V_a is just sufficient to bring the bulk of A and B to the same energy level. This means that the tunnel current will be near its maximum, since the number of carriers available for tunneling is at its maximum. In Fig. 8.4(b) the bias V_b is just sufficient to lift the entire electron distribution A above the top of the valence band on the P-side. This means that there are no holes or electrons at the same energy level and therefore the tunneling current ceases. The only remaining current is the normal diffusion current over the barrier.

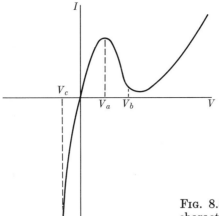

FIG. 8.5. Esaki tunnel diode characteristic.

Actually the minimum current shown to the right of V_b in Fig. 8.5 is usually observed to be much greater than one would calculate for the normal forward diffusion current at that voltage. There has been considerable speculation about the possible origin of this "excess" current. The most probable source seems to be the tunneling which is still possible above V_b when the energy levels introduced by the very heavy concentration of donor and acceptor impurities effectively extend the conduction and valence bands into the normal energy gap, thus reducing the gap width and providing additional band overlap.

When reverse bias is applied, the situation shown in Fig. 8.6 is found. Here, it is seen that a high density of vacant levels in the conduction band is brought to the same energy as a high density of occupied levels in the valence band. There will now be a massive tunneling of electrons from the valence band into the conduction band, giving a very low impedance for the reverse-biased device.

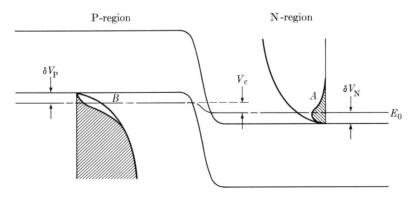

FIG. 8.6. Reverse bias on a tunnel junction.

The voltage of the maximum current point is determined by the band overlap ($\delta V_N + \delta V_P$). This can be understood when one remembers that at a forward bias of ($\delta V_N + \delta V_P$) the tunneling current must have gone through its maximum and returned to zero. The peak current should therefore be near a voltage of ($\delta V_N + \delta V_P$)/2. The current of the maximum point is determined by the area of the junction and the barrier thickness. Doping to the limit of solid solubility on both sides of the junction will give the maximum band overlap and the thinnest barrier if the junction is an abrupt junction. Even for maximum doping a slight amount of grading can render a junction too thick for tunneling. Assuming a perfectly abrupt discontinuity of doping species at the metallurgical junction, we can calculate the barrier thickness, using the results of Chapter 4.

We will first calculate the degeneracy of each side of the junction for maximum doping. In terms of Fig. 8.3 we define the degeneracy as the energy difference between the band edge and the Fermi level when the Fermi level lies inside the band. For the N-region conduction band, this is δV_N and for the P-region valence band, it is δV_P. Assuming a simple case for illustrative purposes, we let the donor level be coincident with the conduction band edge ($E_D = E_c$) in the N-region, and the acceptor level be coincident with the valence band edge ($E_A = E_v$) in the P-region. Now we know that the vacant donor level density must equal the free-electron density in the conduction band of the N-region, and the filled acceptor level density must equal the free-hole density in the valence band of the P-region. These conditions may be written

$$[1 - f(E_c)]N_D = N_c f(E_c), \qquad f(E_v)N_A = [1 - f(E_v)]N_v, \quad (8.9)$$

where the Fermi functions $f(E_c)$ and $f(E_v)$ are given by Eq. (2.14), with E_c and E_v substituted for E_i. Here N_c and N_v are the effective density-of-states constants for parabolic bands defined by the amplitude constants of Eqs. (2.21) and (2.22). A word must be said about the propriety of using these effective density-of-states constants when we are dealing with a degenerate case.

In integrating Eq. (2.21), we replaced the Fermi function by the Boltzmann function when the 1 in the denominator was neglected. This is equivalent to assuming that E_0 is more than $1kT$ below the band edge E_c. However, in equations (8.9) the full Fermi function should be used to get a rigorously correct result. Our approach in equations (8.9) is to use the N_c- and N_v-constants derived with a Boltzmann function, but to multiply them by the full Fermi functions $f(E_c)$ and $f(E_v)$. To check on the error introduced by this approximation, we note that for E_0 more than $1kT$ into the conduction band, we can closely approximate the free-electron density by just integrating the $g_c(E)\,dE$ function from E_c to E_0.

The result of this integration can be written $N_c(4/3\sqrt{\pi})[(E_0 - E_c)/kT]^{3/2}$. Comparing $f(E_c)$ with $(4/3\sqrt{\pi})[(E_0 - E_c)/kT]^{3/2}$ for E_0 $1kT$ into the band gives 0.72 against 0.75, or only a 3% difference in the right-hand side of the first equation of (8.9). For E_0 $2kT$ into the band there is only a 50% difference. From this check we conclude that the use of the simple N_c and N_v effective density-of-states constants is a reasonable approximation at least up to a degeneracy of about $2kT$.

The argument of the N-region Fermi function is $(E_c - E_0)/kT$, which is just $-q\, \delta V_N/kT$ if we express δV_N in electron volts. In the P-region we have the similar relation $(E_v - E_0)/kT = +q\, \delta V_P/kT$. Substituting these relations in the equations (8.9) and solving for δV_N and δV_P yields

$$\delta V_N = (kT/q) \ln (N_D/N_c), \qquad \delta V_P = (kT/q) \ln (N_A/N_v). \qquad (8.10)$$

These equations give a reasonable approximation to the position of E_0 as a function of doping up to about $2kT$ within the band. If a greater degeneracy is found, we can still use equations (8.10) by substituting N_c' and N_v' for N_c and N_v, where the primed constants are simply the unprimed constants multiplied by $(4/3\sqrt{\pi})(q\, \delta V/kT)^{3/2}$.

If we consider ^oN_D and ^oN_A to be the limits of solid solubility in the N- and P-regions, respectively, we may calculate the width of the depletion layer $(^ox_N + {}^ox_P)$ for a perfectly abrupt junction with this doping.

Referring to Fig. 8.3 we see that the barrier thickness t is appreciably less than $(^ox_N + {}^ox_P)$, since it is measured at some distance from each band edge. From Eq. (4.16) we may write

$$V_N(x) = (q^oN_D/2\epsilon)(2^ox_N x - x^2), \qquad V_P(x) = (q^oN_A/2\epsilon)(2^ox_P x - x^2). \qquad (8.11)$$

By definition we let $\delta V_N = V_N(x_N) - V_N(t_N)$ and $\delta V_P = V_P(x_P) - V_P(t_P)$, where $t = t_N + t_P$. Evaluating δV_N and δV_P from Eq. (8.11) we find

$$\delta V_N = (q^oN_D/2\epsilon)(^ox_N - t_N)^2, \qquad \delta V_P = (q^oN_A/2\epsilon)(^ox_P - t_P)^2. \qquad (8.12)$$

From equations (8.12) we may solve for t_N and t_P and find the barrier thickness at the position of the Fermi level:

$$t = t_N + t_P = {}^ox_N - \left(\frac{2\epsilon\, \delta V_N}{q^oN_D}\right)^{1/2} + {}^ox_P - \left(\frac{2\epsilon\, \delta V_P}{q^oN_A}\right)^{1/2}. \qquad (8.13)$$

We are now ready to deduce the doping dependence of the peak current and voltage of the tunnel diode characteristic (Fig. 8.5). The current at any point of the peak characteristic is proportional to the excess density of electrons on one side of the junction, multiplied by the tunneling probability. The excess carrier density will vary nearly linearly with doping level.   The tunneling probability, however, is a very rapidly varying function of the doping density. We will now estimate this latter dependence using the simplified probability given in Eq. (8.7).

If one substitutes Eq. (8.10) into Eq. (8.13) and then substitutes the result in Eq. (8.7) to find the dependence of the tunneling probability on the doping levels, one obtains a very complex expression which is hard to interpret.   Instead, we will assume a factor of 100 in the tunneling probability and trace out the doping variation required to produce it.

We must first evaluate the constant a_2 in the tunneling probability equation (8.7).   The constant a_2^2 is defined as $2m(V - E)/\hbar^2$.   Here, the height of the barrier above the energy of the particles involved in the tunneling process is shown as the line ac in Fig. 8.3.   This is just the energy gap ΔE.   Therefore $(V - E) = \Delta E$.   The effective mass of the electrons involved is m, and here we will let m be the geometric average of the electron and hole effective masses.   Using germanium values we find that $a_2 \simeq 4 \times 10^7/$cm.   For a factor of 100 in the tunneling probability, the argument of the exponential must change by 4.6, which gives $2a_2 \Delta t = 4.6$, or $\Delta t = 0.58 \times 10^{-7}$ cm.   For the first iteration we will assume that δV_N and δV_P are unchanged and calculate the change in doping level required to give this Δt.

For simplicity we will reduce Eq. (8.13) by letting $N_D = N_A$ and $\delta V_N = \delta V_P$, obtaining

$$t = 2t_N = 2[\phi^{1/2} - (2 \, \delta V_N)^{1/2}](\epsilon/q N_D)^{1/2}. \qquad (8.14)$$

Differentiating with respect to N_D gives

$$\frac{\Delta N_D}{N_D} = \frac{(q N_D/\epsilon)^{1/2} \, \Delta t}{2[(2 \, \delta V_N)^{1/2} - \phi^{1/2}]}. \qquad (8.15)$$

From Eq. (8.15) we see that the percentage change in doping level required to yield a fixed Δt increases as $N_D^{1/2}$. At the limit of solid solubility we will have the worst case.   Continuing to evaluate numerically for germanium we let $\phi = \Delta E + 2 \, \delta V_N$ with $\delta V_N = 0.05$ ev.   The value of δV_N is chosen as the typically measured voltage of the current peak in a germanium tunnel diode.   For most N-type impurities in germanium, ^0N_D is about $10^{20}/$cm^3 or less.   Substituting these numbers in Eq. (8.15) we see that $\Delta N_D/N_D = 0.17$ for a factor of 100 in the tunneling probability.

Referring to Eq. (8.10) we can check our assumption that δV_N remained constant for such a doping level change.   Differentiating the top equation in (8.10), we get

$$\frac{\Delta(\delta V_N)}{\delta V_N} = \frac{\Delta N_D}{N_D}\left[1/\ln\left(\frac{N_D}{N_c}\right)\right]. \qquad (8.16)$$

We know that N_D must be considerably greater than N_c for the N-region material to be degenerate. In our simplified case we may use the observed $\delta V_N \simeq 0.05$ ev to calculate this logarithm. From Eq. (8.10) we get the value $\ln (N_D/N_c) = 40 \times 0.05 = 2$, showing that a 17% change in N_D makes only an 8% change in δV_N. For the doping levels discussed here we can consider our assumption of constant δV_N justified.

Several conclusions can be drawn from the above discussion. First, it is clear that the tunneling probability is a much more sensitive function of doping level than is the band overlap. This means that slight variations in doping level may completely wipe out the current peak without shifting the voltage at which it appears. This is observed in practice.

A second observation is that if one plots the measured tunnel diode characteristics using a normalized voltage consisting of the observed voltage divided by the voltage of the energy gap of the material from which the diode is made, one finds that the characteristics of the various diodes nearly coincide. This effect is illustrated for a germanium and a GaAs tunnel diode in Fig. 8.7. Focusing our attention on the peak voltage $(\simeq \delta V_N)$, we find that our simplified approach will account for this dependence on energy gap. The agreement is probably purely fortuitous, since our consideration is based on parabolic bands with nearly the same N_c and N_v for the various materials in question.

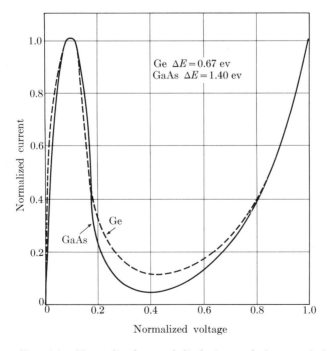

FIG. 8.7. Normalized tunnel diode forward characteristics.

We will assume that the tunneling probability must reach a threshold level for diodes of all materials in order to exhibit the current peak at all. The definition of a_2 in the argument of the exponential shows that it is proportional to the square root of the barrier height, which is the energy gap. For the probability to be constant the product a_2t must be constant. Therefore t must vary as $1/\Delta E^{1/2}$ as we go from material to material. Equation (8.14) shows that $t \sim (\epsilon \Delta E/qN_D)^{1/2}$ (since the barrier height $\phi \simeq \Delta E$ and dominates the first bracket). If t is to vary as $1/\Delta E^{1/2}$, it is clear that N_D must vary as ΔE. Finally, from Eq. (8.16) we see that δV_N varies directly as N_D (or therefore as ΔE). So long as the logarithm is near unity the energy gap can be used directly as a normalizing factor.

Since most tunnel diodes are specified by peak current and since the peak-current density is such a sensitive function of doping level, production diodes are individually etched to adjust the junction area to give the specified current.

The backward diode. If the doping levels are adjusted so that the bands are just on the threshold of overlap at zero bias voltage, there will be tunneling for reverse bias but essentially normal forward diffusion current. The barrier thickness must be the same as that for a tunnel diode, since we want a very low impedance reverse characteristic. Figure 8.8 shows a typical "backward" diode characteristic. Here, as before, the voltage of the P-region is measured with respect to the N-region. This diode is then the same as a tunnel diode except that there is no forward tunnel current and therefore no negative resistance region. The scale of the positive quadrant characteristic is identical to the normal PN-

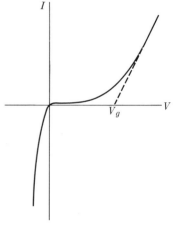

Fig. 8.8. Backward diode characteristic.

junction diode forward characteristic except that the impedance at positive voltages near the origin is much higher.

As Fig. 8.8 shows, the rectification ratio at low voltages is very much greater than for an ordinary diode. The point marked V_g on the voltage axis is essentially the energy gap voltage of the semiconductor material in question. This indicates that the useful range of the device is less than one volt.

Because of the close connection between band overlap and barrier thickness through the junction doping levels, it is probable that the proper technique for achieving a backward diode characteristic involves the adjustment of the tunneling probability threshold to coincide with zero bias. If the doping levels are adjusted to give a barrier thickness which achieves this, it can be seen that a forward bias will have no current peak, since the effective t is monotonically increased with forward bias. Thus no significant tunneling will occur in the forward characteristic even if there is some band overlap. In the reverse-bias condition the effective t is reduced well below threshold so that massive tunneling occurs and a very low resistance characteristic results.

Because of the high doping level, both the backward diode and the tunnel diode have very high junction capacities. Equations (8.10) may be modified to facilitate the calculation of the doping levels N_A and N_B. From Eq. (2.23) we may write

$$n_i^2 = N_c N_v e^{-\Delta E/kT}, \tag{8.17}$$

where $N_c N_v$ can be written as $N_c^2 (m_p/m_n)^{3/2}$ or $N_v^2 (m_n/m_p)^{3/2}$. Solving (8.17) for N_c or N_v and substituting in (8.10) we find that

$$\delta V_N = \frac{kT}{q} \ln \left[\frac{N_D}{n_i} \left(\frac{m_p}{m_n} \right)^{3/4} \right] - \frac{\Delta E}{2},$$

$$\delta V_P = \frac{kT}{q} \ln \left[\frac{N_A}{n_i} \left(\frac{m_n}{m_p} \right)^{3/4} \right] - \frac{\Delta E}{2}. \tag{8.18}$$

The minimum doping that we could possibly have for a backward diode would be for $\delta V_P = \delta V_N = 0$. Any lower doping would not start band overlap at zero bias. Evaluating equations (8.18) for zero degeneracy gives

$$N_D = (m_n/m_p)^{3/4} n_i e^{q\Delta E/2kT}, \qquad N_A = (m_p/m_n)^{3/4} n_i e^{q\Delta E/2kT}, \tag{8.19}$$

where ΔE is given in electron volts. Substituting in the abrupt junction capacitance formula (4.22) evaluated for zero degeneracy ($\phi = \Delta E$), we find

$$C = \left[\frac{q \epsilon n_i e^{q\Delta E/2kT}}{2 \Delta E (m_n/m_p)^{3/4} + (m_p/m_n)^{3/4}} \right]^{1/2}. \tag{8.20}$$

Evaluating Eq. (8.20) for germanium, we use

$$\epsilon = 1.4 \times 10^{-12} \text{ farad/cm}^2, \qquad \Delta E = 0.67 \text{ ev},$$
$$n_i = 2.5 \times 10^{13}/\text{cm}^3, \qquad m_n/m_p = (\mu_p/\mu_n)^{3/2} = 0.33.$$

From the above we calculate a capacity of $0.83 \ \mu f/cm^2$. This compares with about $0.026 \ \mu f/cm^2$ for a normal germanium diode with a doping of 5×10^{15} impurities/cm^3 on each side.

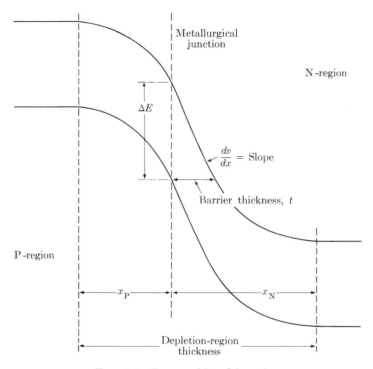

FIG. 8.9. Reverse-biased junction.

The Zener diode. This is a voltage-regulator diode with a sharp break-down voltage. If a PN-junction is doped nearly to degeneracy on both sides but the junction thickness is large enough to prevent appreciable tunneling at zero bias, negative bias will cause the thickness of the barrier to decrease. This is not to be confused with the total thickness of the depletion region.) Figure 8.9 presents a diagram of a reverse-biased junction showing the barrier thickness in relation to the depletion-layer thickness.

If the doping level is significantly less on the N-type side (even though both sides are degenerate), most of the depletion region will fall in the N-region, and we may calculate the field in the barrier region (dv/dx) from Eq. (4.14), which can be written

$$\frac{dv}{dx} = \frac{qN_D}{\epsilon}(x_N - x),\tag{8.21}$$

where the origin of x is at the metallurgical junction. Since the barrier field can also be expressed as $\Delta E/t$ (see Fig. 8.9), to a first approximation, we may find the barrier thickness, t, by evaluating (8.21) at $x = 0$:

$$t = \frac{\Delta E}{\dfrac{dv}{dx}(0)} = \frac{\epsilon\,\Delta E}{qN_D x_N}. \tag{8.22}$$

Substituting Eq. (4.21), we get

$$t = \Delta E \left[\frac{\epsilon(N_D + N_A)}{2qN_D N_A(\phi - V)} \right]^{1/2}, \tag{8.23}$$

and if we again let $\phi \simeq \Delta E$ and $N_D = N_A = N$ (but not the N required for degeneracy), we have

$$t = \Delta E \left[\frac{\epsilon}{qN(\Delta E - V)} \right]^{1/2}. \tag{8.24}$$

When Eq. (8.24) is substituted into (8.7), we see that the onset of a tunnel breakdown can be very abrupt. This model of dielectric breakdown was first proposed by Zener in the early 1930's and semiconductor diodes with very abrupt low-voltage breakdowns have been given his name. A typical Zener diode characteristic is shown in Fig. 8.10.

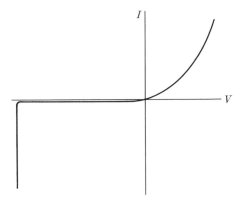

FIG. 8.10. A typical Zener diode characteristic.

When the field at the center of the junction becomes large enough to give an electron several electron volts of kinetic energy between scattering collisions, the breakdown will occur by an avalanching process. It is very difficult to distinguish the tunnel breakdown from the avalanche breakdown experimentally. It is quite likely that most Zener diodes with breakdown voltages in excess of 5 v are really avalanching rather than tunneling.

8.2   Varactor or Variable Capacitance Diodes [2]

Semiconductor variable capacitance diodes are characterized by a low series resistance, a low shunt conductance, and a nonlinear depletion capacitance. Perhaps the simplest example is the abrupt PN-junction diode. In such a diode we know that the depletion capacitance is given by Eq. (4.22) as

$$C(V) = A\left[\frac{\epsilon q N_A N_D}{2(\phi - V)(N_A + N_D)}\right]^{1/2}. \qquad (8.25)$$

In order to maintain a reasonable Q in the device, we must operate the diode in the reverse-bias polarity. This then limits the applied voltage to the range $0 > V > V_B$, where V_B is the breakdown voltage of the diode. The maximum value of C is found for $V = 0$ and the minimum value of C is found for $V = V_B$ (where V is negative reverse bias).

To minimize the series resistance, we would dope both sides of the junction heavily and limit the total thickness to the thickness of the depletion region when the breakdown voltage is just attained. As we have seen from our previous discussion of Zener diodes, the heavy doping results in a low breakdown voltage. There is, therefore, a trade-off between the range of capacitance variation and the series resistance and, hence, the maximum Q of the device.

Most varactors are used at high frequency in parametric applications. It has become customary to rate them by the frequency at which the Q for zero bias drops to unity. The zero bias Q_0 is given by

$$Q_0 = 1/2\pi f C_0 R_s. \qquad (8.26)$$

Setting $Q_0 = 1$ and solving for f, we get

$$f(\text{cutoff}) = 1/2\pi C_0 R_s. \qquad (8.27)$$

Above this frequency the device is predominantly resistive. To evaluate (8.27) for the case of a simple abrupt junction, let us assume that one side of the junction is doped very heavily and does not contribute appreciably to R_s. The other side will contain essentially all of the depletion region and determine both the breakdown voltage and R_s. We will choose the heavily doped side to be the P-side so that we will take advantage of the electron mobility to minimize the R now determined by the N-side. Furthermore, we will let only the thickness of the N-side equal the thickness of the depletion region just at breakdown. Under these circumstances we find that

$$C(V) = \epsilon A/x_N(V) \qquad \text{and} \qquad C_0 = \epsilon A/x_N(\phi), \qquad (8.28)$$

$$R_s = \rho_N[x_N(V_B) - x_N(\phi)]/A. \qquad (8.29)$$

Substituting in Eq. (8.27) gives

$$f(\text{cutoff}) = \left[2\pi\epsilon\rho_N\left(\frac{x_N(V_B)}{x_N(\phi)} - 1\right)\right]^{-1}. \tag{8.30}$$

From Eq. (4.21) we see that the square-root dependence of x_N on V allows us to write the ratio $x_N(V_B)/x_N(\phi)$ as $(1 - V_B/\phi)^{1/2}$, where ϕ is the barrier height, giving

$$f(\text{cutoff}) = [2\pi\epsilon\rho_N\{(1 - V_B/\phi)^{1/2} - 1\}]^{-1}. \tag{8.31}$$

Evaluating (8.31) for germanium, we use

$$\epsilon = 1.4 \text{ pf/cm}^2, \qquad V_B = 87(\rho_N)^{0.72} \quad \text{(empirical relation)}.$$

The results of this evaluation are summarized in Table 8.1 where cutoff frequency is tabulated against breakdown voltage. The last column of this table shows the ratio of the zero bias capacity C_0 to the minimum capacity C_B found at the breakdown voltage. This ratio indicates the range of capacity variation available.

TABLE 8.1

Calculated Germanium Abrupt-Junction Varactor
Cutoff Frequency

ρ_N	V_B, v	ϕ, ev	f (cutoff) kmc	C_0/C_B
0.05	10.0	0.57	690	4.2
0.10	16.5	0.53	244	5.6
0.20	27	0.51	90	7.3
0.40	44	0.49	33	9.5
1.00	87	0.47	9	13.2

In actual practice the measured values of cutoff frequency seldom approach the theoretical values given in Table 8.1 because of the great difficulty in reducing R_s to the value calculated. The addition of ohmic contacts and the difficulty of limiting the thickness of the N-region of the diode to exactly $x_N(V_B)$ all tend to increase R_s. Good techniques can usually achieve about one-half of the theoretical value of $f(\text{cutoff})$.

It should be pointed out that if the device is to be used in a resonant circuit where Q is important, the actual operating frequency will be limited by the minimum Q allowable. For example, the 10-v diode given in the first row of the table can operate only up to about 7 kmc if a Q of 100 is required by the circuit.

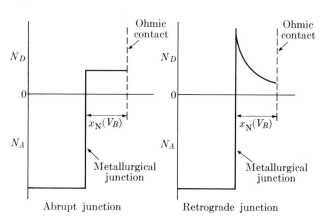

Fig. 8.11. Varactor doping profiles.

Retrograde junction varactors. It is possible to fabricate a varactor diode which shows a variation of C which is nearly proportional to $1/V$ rather than to $(1/V)^{1/2}$. The doping profile of such a diode is shown in Fig. 8.11, and may be compared with the doping profile of the abrupt junction already discussed. The retrograde junction is also often called a "hyperabrupt" junction.

It can be shown that to get $C \sim (1/V)$, we must have $\rho_N(x) \sim x$ to the right of the metallurgical junction. Such a resistivity variation can only be approximated, since we must have a $\rho_N(0)$ which is finite at the junction. In practice, however, a reasonably good $(1/V)$ response can be achieved with a carefully grown epitaxial N-type layer. The overall cutoff frequency is not improved with such a structure because the rapid increase in $\rho_N(x)$ as we move away from the metallurgical junction gives a rapidly increasing R_s which more than offsets the drop in $C(V)$ for a given breakdown voltage.

8.3   The Injection Laser [3]

In Section 3.4 it was pointed out that light of energy equal to the energy-band gap of a semiconductor could be amplified in intensity while traversing the semiconductor crystal, provided that there was an "inverted" electron-population distribution. An inverted population was defined as one in which the pn-product found under conditions of dynamic excitation of electrons from the valence to the conduction band exceeded the carrier-deficiency product $(N_v - p)(N_c - n)$, where N_v and N_c are the effective band-edge densities of states for the valence and conduction bands, respectively. This inversion condition is clearly related to the stimulated emission gain, since the stimulated recombination probability must be proportional to the carrier-density product, and the competing electron-hole pair production probability is proportional to the carrier-deficiency

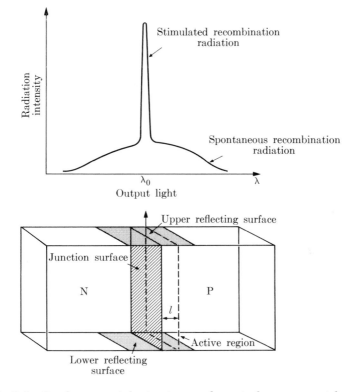

Fig. 8.12. Injection laser crystal, structure and spectral response, at low temperatures.

product. (The transition probability itself is the same for either direction of transition so that only the densities of the initial and final states determine the overall probability.)

Figure 8.12 shows a diagram of an injection laser crystal, together with a typical low-temperature spectral response curve. The narrowness of the stimulated emission peak is due to the natural resonance of the cavity formed by the two mirror surfaces shown. In other words, an integral number of standing waves of the stimulated light are found between the mirrors.

In this injection laser the input power consists of the power required to maintain a forward current sufficient to inject enough minority electrons from the N-region into the P-region that there is an inverted population next to the PN-junction in the P-region. The thickness of material in which this population inversion is maintained is shown as l, and the region of thickness l is called the active region. In this active region, band-edge radiation ($h\nu_0 = \Delta E$) is multiply reflected between the mirror surfaces, shown on the top and bottom of the crystal. To avoid loss, these surfaces must be plane and parallel, and usually represent cleavage planes of the single crystal from which the diode is made. As the band-edge radiation traverses the active region, it stimulates radiative recombination in the inverted population and is thus amplified. Power is extracted through the reflecting surfaces.

There are two criteria for laser action in such a device. First, it is necessary to set up an inverted population, and second, the stimulated emission gain must exceed the various radiation losses from the active region (including the output power). We will now concern ourselves with the criterion for an inverted population.

Population inversion. Making use of the concept of a quasi-Fermi level as introduced in Section 4.3, we define the quasi-Fermi level for electrons, E_{qn}, as the position of the half-probability point of the Fermi occupation-probability function required to give the dynamic equilibrium density of electrons found in the conduction band under conditions of continuous excitation. In the example of Section 4.3, we were continuously exciting electrons from the valence to the conduction band by means of photon absorption. These excess electrons returned to the valence band by normal recombination. When the recombination rate and the excitation rate were equal, a dynamic equilibrium density of excess electrons was established so that a quasi-Fermi level could be defined. The quasi-Fermi level for holes can be defined similarly. In terms of the effective density of states of the conduction and valence bands, N_c and N_v, we may write the dynamic equilibrium carrier densities at the edges of the two bands as

$$n = N_c/[e^{(E_c - E_{qn})/kT} + 1], \qquad p = N_v/[e^{(E_{qp} - E_v)/kT} + 1]. \quad (8.32)$$

Here, it is assumed that the quasi-Fermi levels E_{qn} and E_{qp} never penetrate their respective bands more than $1kT$ or $2kT$ so that the simple approximation using the N_c and N_v effective density-of-states constants is still reasonable. [See the discussion of Eq. (8.9).]

The carrier deficiency densities can be written in the same manner as the products of the Fermi functions and the effective densities of states,

$$(N_c - n) = N_c/[e^{(E_{qn} - E_c)/kT} + 1], \qquad (N_v - p) = N_v/[e^{(E_v - E_{qp})/kT} + 1]. \quad (8.33)$$

It must be remembered that N_c and N_v are considered to be the effective densities of levels in the conduction and valence band edges lumped at the edge energies E_c and E_v, so that when one is multiplied by the appropriate value of the Fermi occupation-probability function for the energy E_c or E_v, it will give the same density of free carriers that is found by integrating the product of the Fermi function and the true density-of-states function over the entire band.

Substituting Eqs. (8.32) and (8.33) into our inversion criterion $np >$ $(N_v - p)(N_c - n)$, we find that the inversion criterion reduces to

$$\frac{e^{(E_{qn}-E_c)/kT} + 1}{e^{(E_c-E_{qn})/kT} + 1} > \frac{e^{(E_{qp}-E_v)/kT} + 1}{e^{(E_v-E_{qp})/kT} + 1}.$$

By inspection it is clear that if the quantity $(E_{qn} - E_c)$ is positive, the left-hand side of the inequality will be greater than 1 and will increase monotonically as $(E_{qn} - E_c)$ increases. The same may be said for the right-hand side of the inequality relative to the quantity $(E_{qp} - E_v)$. From this it is clear that the condition can be reduced to $(E_{qn} - E_c) >$ $(E_{qp} - E_v)$, which yields

$$(E_{qn} - E_{qp}) > (E_c - E_v). \tag{8.34}$$

Here, we note that $(E_c - E_v) = \Delta E$, the energy-band gap, which is the energy of the light involved in the amplification process. In general, we may express the necessary inversion criterion in a semiconductor as

$$(E_{qn} - E_{qp}) > h\nu_0, \tag{8.35}$$

where ν_0 is the frequency of the light involved in the stimulated emission process. This relation is true even if we are working between two sets of levels inside the energy-band gap. We will realize that this statement is true if we remember that we derived (8.35) by representing the two bands as though they were two sets of energy levels lumped at E_c and E_v.

Inversion by injection[4]. The next step in the consideration of an injection laser is to show that the inversion criterion can be met by the minority-carrier injection process in a forward-biased PN-junction. We must estimate the forward-bias current required for inversion.

Figure 8.12 shows the physical arrangement under consideration. For the active region to be fully effective, we must maintain an inverted population throughout the thickness l. Referring to Fig. 8.13, we recognize the familiar minority-carrier diffusion distribution. For $n(l) = n_I$, the minority electron density required for inversion, we may write the electron density at the junction surface from Eq. (6.13):

$$n(0) = n_I e^{l/L_n}, \tag{8.36}$$

where we are neglecting n_p compared to n_I. The diffusion current density can be expressed in the usual way:

$$J_n = qD_n^* n(0)/\eta L_n = (qD_n^* n_I/\eta L_n)e^{l/L_n}, \tag{8.37}$$

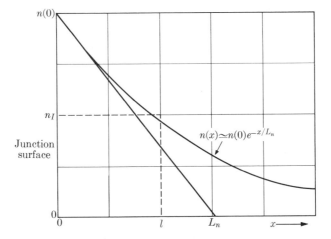

FIG. 8.13.　The minority-electron distribution in the P-region of the junction.

where η is the quantum efficiency of the electrons in the $n(0)$-density in the radiative recombination process. (If all recombinations are radiative, $\eta = 1$.) The quantity D_n^* is the effective electronic diffusion constant as modified by high-level injection (see Section 6.6) and by carrier-carrier scattering. In order to find J_n, we must estimate n_I, l, D_n^*, and τ_n (where $L_n = \sqrt{D_n \tau_n}$).

First, considering n_I, we will assume that detailed balance of space-charge neutrality holds in the P-region so that if n_I minority electrons are injected, there must be $p_p + n_I$ holes present at the same point. We now write the carrier densities at $x = l$, the limit of the active region, as

$$n = n_I, \qquad p = f_p N_A + n_I, \tag{8.38}$$

where f_p is the Fermi occupation probability in the P-region. The carrier-deficiency densities are

$$(N_c - n) = N_c - n_I, \qquad (N_v - p) = N_v - (f_p N_A + n_I). \tag{8.39}$$

Again forming the inversion criterion, we find that

$$n_I > \frac{N_c(N_v - f_p N_A)}{N_c + N_v}. \tag{8.40}$$

At the threshold of inversion, the inequality (8.40) is an equation. For a nondegenerate P-region, $f_p N_A$ may be neglected compared to N_v, since at the threshold of degeneracy, $N_A \simeq N_v$ if $E_A - E_v < kT$. From

Eq. (2.23) we have the relation

$$n_i^2 = N_v N_c e^{-\Delta E/kT}. \tag{8.41}$$

From the definition of N_v and N_c and Eq. (8.41), we can write

$$N_c = N_v (m_n/m_p)^{3/2} = n_i (m_n/m_p)^{3/4} e^{\Delta E/2kT}. \tag{8.42}$$

Substituting (8.41) and (8.42) into (8.40) and neglecting $f_p N_A$, we obtain, at the inversion threshold:

$$n_I = \frac{n_i e^{\Delta E/2kT}}{(m_n/m_p)^{3/4} + (m_p/m_n)^{3/4}}. \tag{8.43}$$

Now substituting (8.43) into (8.37) and noting that $\Delta E = h\nu_0$, we find that the threshold electronic current is

$$J_n = \frac{q D_n^* n_i e^{l/L_n + h\nu_0/2kT}}{\eta L_n [(m_n/m_p)^{3/4} + (m_p/m_n)^{3/4}]}. \tag{8.44}$$

To estimate l, we must consider the radiation losses from the active region. First of all we have the absorption loss due to electron-hole pair production. This is the primary loss associated with the device. We already took this into account when we set up and applied the criterion for inversion, since inversion means that stimulated emission will yield more photons than will be lost in pair production. If we now consider other losses in comparison with this pair-production loss, we can estimate their effect on the threshold current density.

There will be a photon loss at the reflecting surfaces, but we can assume that this loss is small compared with the pair-production loss. Similarly, we will assume that the photon loss due to absorption and scattering by crystalline impurities is small.

Finally, there is a significant diffraction loss of photons. If l is very small, each reflection aperture (the area of the reflecting surface covered by the active region) will be comparable to λ_0 in the x-direction. Such a small reflection aperture will cause a diffraction spreading of the beam into the inactive regions of the crystal. It is clear that l must be large compared to λ_0 in order to prevent this spreading of the laser beam. Lasher [5] finds that a value of $l = 13\lambda_0$ causes the diffraction loss to be about equal to the pair production loss for the most favorable mode.

Next considering D_n^* we will assume that any effect of the carrier-carrier scattering, together with the effect of heavy doping, will reduce the diffusion constant by about an order of magnitude below the room temperature value determined by lattice scattering. Since the injection of n_I electrons will cause $n \simeq p$, the ambipolar diffusion effect considered in Section 6.6 might be thought to increase D_n^* somewhat. It must be remembered, however, that the assumption of Section 6.6 was that the majority electronic diffusion and drift currents completely canceled each other. Here, the majority currents in the valence band of the P-region do not cancel, since the barrier is essentially wiped out by the forward bias necessary to inject the electronic density n_I. The result of all this is to leave D_n^* little changed by the ambipolar effect. It may be slightly reduced if there is a marked difference between D_n and D_p, since at the extreme of $n \simeq p$, it will tend toward an average value.

At the high injection levels required for inversion it is assumed that the injection efficiency is about $\frac{1}{2}$. Therefore we assume that the total diode current density $J \simeq 2J_n$. Letting $l = 20\lambda_0$ to reduce the diffraction loss to negligible proportions and assuming that $\eta = 1$, we may write the diode threshold current density required for the onset of laser action as

$$J \simeq 2J_n = \frac{2qD_n^* n_i \exp\left[20\lambda_0/(D_n^*\tau_n)^{1/2} + h\nu_0/2kT\right]}{(D_n^*\tau_n)^{1/2}[(m_n/m_p)^{3/4} + (m_p/m_n)^{3/4}]}. \tag{8.45}$$

Since n_i, D_n^*, ΔE, and the mass ratio are usually known at or near room temperature, we may either use Eq. (8.45) to determine the effective τ_n from a stimulated emission threshold measurement, or if we can measure the true τ_n for radiative recombination, we can use (8.45) to calculate the threshold current density.

Figure 8.14 shows the temperature dependence of the threshold current as measured for GaAs [3]. The temperature dependence of Eq. (8.45) is a bit uncertain, because it is not known exactly how the high-injection D_n^* varies with temperature. Assuming that D_n^* and the mass ratio are independent of temperature, we consider the temperature dependence of the numerator of Eq. (8.45) by writing it in the form $q(D_n^*\tau_n)^{1/2}N_c e^{l/L_n}$. From the definition of N_c, we see that it has a $T^{3/2}$ temperature dependence. If D_n^* and τ_n have a small temperature dependence, we would expect J to show the $T^{3/2}$ dependence of N_c. However, if the argument of the exponential is large enough, even a small temperature dependence of $L_n = (D_n^*\tau_n)^{1/2}$ might give a significant temperature variation. Using the appropriate constants for GaAs, we may fit the observed threshold current of Fig. 8.14 at room temperature by adjusting L_n. This gives $L_n \simeq 4 \times 10^{-4}$ cm and, for $l = 20\lambda_0$, an argument of 4.6 to the exponential. Such a magnitude would allow even a $T^{-1/2}$ temperature dependence of L_n to match the initial slope of Fig. 8.14.

We discussed the validity of the use of N_c and N_v from the mathematical point of view, but we must also consider the physical implications of the use of a simple parabolic band model. First, it should be pointed out that band-edge emission is a first-order process only in the so-called "direct transition" semiconductors, where the minimum of the conduction-band

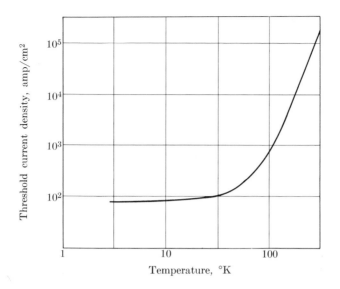

Fɪɢ. 8.14.   Variation of the threshold current in a GaAs PN-junction laser [3].

energy and the maximum of the valence-band energy occur at the origin of momentum space. When this is the case, a recombination transition can conserve momentum directly without involving a lattice phonon. Such bands centered at the origin are much more likely to be well represented by the parabolic model. Second, it should be clear that a first-order edge emission is essential for good laser action.

Doping level requirements.   In the preceding discussion it was assumed that it was possible, by suitable doping of the two sides of the junction, to create a diode capable of injecting an inversion electron density n_I when it was strongly forward-biased. In this section we will examine the doping levels necessary to achieve such injection levels.

Imposing the condition of space-charge neutrality on both sides of the junction, we start with the injection of n_I electrons in the P-region. The carrier densities in the P-region are given by equations (8.38). In the N-region they are given by

$$n = (1 - f_n)N_D + (f_p N_A + n_I)H(\phi - V),$$

$$p = (f_p N_A + n_I)H(\phi - V),$$

(8.46)

where f_n is the Fermi function in the N-region, V is the forward-biasing voltage, and ϕ is the barrier height. We are using $H(\phi - V)$ to express the law of the junction because $q(\phi - V)$ is comparable to kT and the simple $e^{-q(\phi-V)/kT}$ is no longer valid to give the fraction of the majority density injected across the junction into the minority band; $H(\phi - V) \equiv H$ symbolizes this fraction. Equation (8.46) is constructed as follows. The majority hole density of Eq. (8.38) is multiplied by H to give the injected minority hole density in the N-region. This is then added to the density of empty donor levels to give the majority electron density.

Now the majority electron density given in Eq. (8.46) injects the minority density n_I into the P-region, so that we may write

$$n_I = [(1 - f_n)N_D + (f_p N_A + n_I)H]H. \tag{8.47}$$

Solving for n_I gives

$$n_I = \frac{H(1 - f_n)N_D + f_p N_A H^2}{1 - H^2}. \tag{8.48}$$

From Eq. (8.48) it is clear that n_I can be indefinitely large as H approaches unity so long as the doping levels N_A or N_D are finite. This means that it is not necessary to dope either side of the junction to degeneracy in order to achieve a threshold for inversion by injection. It is also clear that it does not matter which side of the junction is more heavily doped.

In the previous section it was assumed that the injection efficiency would be about $\frac{1}{2}$ at threshold levels of injection. If a higher injection efficiency were possible, it would result in the lowering of the threshold current. Examining this point, we write the injection efficiency for electrons as

$$\gamma_n = \frac{D_n^* n_I / L_n}{H D_p^* (f_p N_A + n_I)/L_p + D_n^* n_I / L_n}. \tag{8.49}$$

Here, it is clear that minimizing H will maximize γ_n. We can also let $f_p N_A$ be small compared to n_I. It is likely that $D_p^*/L_p < D_n^*/L_n$: even at high levels of current, so that if H is near unity, γ_n will be greater than $\frac{1}{2}$. Moreover, if we let N_D be large, we can probably minimize D_p^*/L_p further, although this might be upset by a lifetime variation. Investigating H further, we let $f_p N_A$ be negligible in both (8.48) and (8.40), and find the inequality

$$\frac{(1 - f_n)N_D H}{1 - H^2} > \frac{N_c N_v}{N_c + N_v}. \tag{8.50}$$

Substituting (8.42) to eliminate N_v, and (8.9) to eliminate N_D/N_c, we find that

$$f(E_c) > \frac{1 - H^2}{H} \frac{(m_p/m_n)^{3/2}}{1 + (m_p/m_n)^{3/2}}. \tag{8.51}$$

No matter how heavily we dope the N-region, we know that the limit of $f(E_c)$ is unity (the occupation probability at the conduction band edge).

Equation (8.51) then becomes

$$\frac{H}{1 - H^2} > \frac{(m_p/m_n)^{3/2}}{1 + (m_p/m_n)^{3/2}}. \tag{8.52}$$

For GaAs, $(m_p/m_n) = 7$, so that the minimum value of H for this material, injecting n_I into the P-region, is 0.61. This gives a γ_n of only 0.63 if $D_p^*/L_p \simeq D_n^*/L_n$. It is unfortunate that the laser action of this material appears to take place only in the P-region; a much better γ_p could be obtained because of the mass ratio. In a material with a mass ratio of unity, it would be possible to get an $H = 0.42$ and a $\gamma_n = 0.71$ by doping the N-region to degeneracy.

Problems

8.1 Given a GaAs tunnel diode with a peak-current voltage of 0.1 v. Assuming a perfectly abrupt junction and equal doping on the two sides of the junction, calculate N_D using the properties of GaAs given in the Appendix.

8.2 The area of the junction of Problem 8.1 is 10^{-4} cm^2 and the peak current is 10 ma. Find the voltage at which the current is again 10 ma on the other side of the current valley.

8.3 A typical silicon Zener diode breaks down at 6 v reverse bias. Calculate the maximum field in the barrier region at breakdown, given that the doping level on each side of the junction is just at the threshold of degeneracy. (The Fermi level coincides with the band edge on each side.)

8.4 A retrograde junction varactor is made by alloying a P-region into an N-diffused water so that the doping in the N-region can be approximated by $N_D(x) = N_D(0)e^{-x/c}$. Find the voltage dependence of the capacitance ($x = 0$ at the center of the junction and increases into the N-region).

8.5 For a PN-junction injection laser, find an expression for the hole injection efficiency γ_p and evaluate it at the inversion threshold for GaAs for the case where $N_D = N_A$ and the N-region is at the threshold of degeneracy.

Bibliography

1. D. LeCroissette, *Transistors*, Prentice-Hall, Englewood Cliffs, New Jersey, 1963, Chapter 11.
2. J. J. Chang, J. H. Forster, and R. M. Ryder, "Semiconductor Junction Varactors with High Voltage Sensitivity," *Inst. Elec. Electron. Engrs. Trans. Electron Devices* **ED-10**, 281 (1963).
3. G. Burns and M. I. Nathan, "PN Junction Lasers," *Proc. IEEE* **52**, 770–794 (1964).
4. J. L. Moll and J. F. Gibbons, "Threshold Current for PN Junction Lasers," *IBM J. Res. Develop.* **7**, 157–159 (1963).
5. G. J. Lasher, "Threshold Relations and Diffraction Loss for Injection Lasers," *IBM J. Res. Develop.* **7**, 58–61 (1963).

USEFUL CONSTANTS

Constants which may be of use in the problems of the text are given below.

300°K MATERIAL CONSTANTS							
	ΔE ev	n_i^2	m_n/m_p	μ_n	μ_p	ϵ/ϵ_0	Atoms/cm^3
Germanium	0.67	6.3×10^{26}	0.27*	3,900	1900	16	4.43×10^{22}
Silicon	1.11	2.5×10^{20}	0.38*	1,500	480	12	5.02×10^{22}
GaAs	1.40	1×10^{14}	0.143	9,000	400	12.5	4.45×10^{22}
InSb	0.16	–	0.022	78,000	750	17	2.95×10^{22}

* The ratio of the transverse electron mass to the heavy hole mass.

GENERAL CONSTANTS

Free electronic mass	$m_0 = 9 \times 10^{-28}$ gm
Electronic charge	$q = 1.6 \times 10^{-19}$ coul
Planck's constant	$h = 6.6 \times 10^{-27}$ erg·sec
Thermal energy at 300°K	$kT = 0.025$ mev
Permittivity of space	$\epsilon_0 = 0.09$ pf/cm
Boltzmann's constant	$k = 1.37 \times 10^{-16}$ erg/deg
Avogadro's number	$N_0 = 6.06 \times 10^{23}$ molecules/mole
1 electron volt	1 ev $= 1.6 \times 10^{-12}$ erg

Wavelength for $h\nu = 1$ ev is 1.234μ

GLOSSARY

Avalanche breakdown. In a reverse-biased PN-junction, as the voltage across the junction is increased, the field in the depletion region may reach such a value that it will produce internal ionization by collision of the accelerated current carriers falling through the depletion region. In order for this to occur, each current carrier, on the average, must acquire sufficient kinetic energy between scattering collisions so that it is capable of imparting at least enough energy to a valence electron to excite it across the energy gap, ΔE. In Section 3.3 this required kinetic energy was estimated to be of the order of 3 or 4 ΔE. Each new hole-electron pair so created will be accelerated by the field and the process will be repeated creating an avalanche. The empirical equation for the avalanche multiplication factor M is Eq. (6.1). Assuming a field $\mathcal{E} = V/(x_N + x_P)$ and an empirical relation for the ionization coefficient [1], the avalanche breakdown voltage can be expressed as

$$BV = \frac{(x_N + x_P)\beta}{\ln\left[\alpha(x_N + x_P)(\gamma - 1)/\ln \gamma\right]},$$

where α, β, and γ are empirically determined constants. The quantity α represents the saturation ionization coefficient at high fields, γ is the ratio of the hole-to-electron ionization coefficients, and β is a characteristic field producing a factor of e in the ionization coefficient.

Avalanche diode. An avalanche diode is a junction diode in which the abruptness of the junction is adjusted to give an avalanche breakdown at a relatively low voltage. Such devices are used for voltage regulation and are often called Zener diodes, even though their breakdown mechanism is not the tunneling mechanism of the true Zener device.

Avalanche transistor [2]. In Section 6.4 we found that the leakage current for a common emitter transistor with base open-circuited was $I_C = I_{C0}/(1 - \alpha_{FB})$. If the applied collector voltage is increased to the point where avalanche multiplication of carriers in the collector junction causes α_{FB} to reach unity, the collector current will rise very suddenly and will be limited only by the resistance of the external circuit. A transistor operated in this mode is called an *avalanche transistor*. Such a transistor will exhibit a negative resistance if the emitter and base are tied together. At low currents the impedance of the emitter is high, and most of the current flows through the base. When avalanche breakdown occurs, the current flows through the emitter, and the holding voltage is accordingly made lower than the breakdown voltage.

Diffused planar transistor. This structure is illustrated in Fig. 6.3. It is fabricated by a double diffusion process in which the collector junction is first delineated by a masked diffusion of the base region into one surface of the wafer. A second masked diffusion of the emitter region into the previously diffused base region completes the structure. The originally plane surface of the wafer is undisturbed, and the three regions of the transistor (emitter, base, and collector) are all accessible from this one surface.

Double-base diode [3]. This device consists of a PN-junction flanked by two ohmic contacts to one of the regions, called the base region, and a single contact to the other region. For purposes of description we will let the P-region be the base region. If we now ground one end of the P-region and the N-region and apply a negative bias to the other base contact, it is clear that the IR-drop in the base will reverse bias the entire junction. If, on the other hand, we apply a positive bias to this base contact, we will begin to bias the PN-junction in the forward direction at the edge nearest the positive contact. As electrons are injected they will be swept toward the positive contact, reducing the resistivity of the P-material in this region. The bulk of the IR-drop will then shift toward the grounded contact, biasing still more of the junction in the forward direction. This positive feedback process will continue until the entire junction has reached a forward-bias condition and the current between the two base contacts is greatly increased by the injected carriers, even though the voltage has remained constant and equal to the value needed to first bias the edge of the junction to the threshold of injection. The device is thus seen to exhibit a negative resistance between the two base contacts. The firing voltage can be set by applying a positive voltage bias to the N-region.

Electroluminescence. When a PN-junction is forward-biased to inject minority carriers into one or both of the regions of the device, some of these excess carriers recombine by means of radiative transitions. This conversion of part of the electrical energy supplied to the forward-biased junction into light is called electroluminescence. The high gap width compound semiconductors are most efficient in this conversion process.

Epitaxial transistor. The adjective "epitaxial" refers to a method of fabricating one or more regions of the transistor structure. The region in question is grown by depositing the basic semiconductor material from the vapor phase so that it builds on, and extends, the single crystal structure of the semiconductor wafer substrate. Thus it is possible to start with a heavily doped P-type wafer and grow on it a lightly doped N-type epitaxial layer with a good junction between them and independent control of the impurity levels in both regions. Since epitaxial growth can take place at temperatures that are low compared with the temperatures used for solid-state impurity diffusion, it is possible to control impurity profiles during growth. Any type of transistor for which such a fabrication step is used is called an *epitaxial transistor*.

Four-layer diode. This structure is essentially a controlled rectifier with an open base. It exhibits the negative resistance characteristic one would expect for such operation of the controlled rectifier. (See Section 7.3.)

Hall effect [4]. If a semiconductor bar carrying a current density, $\mathbf{J}$, in the x-direction is placed in a magnetic field, $\mathbf{H}$, directed along the positive z-axis, an electric field component, $\mathbf{E_H}$, will appear in the positive y-direction with the value $\mathbf{E_H} = -R(\mathbf{J} \times \mathbf{H})$, where $\mathbf{E_H}$ is called the Hall field and R is called the Hall constant. The constant R has a positive sign if the current carriers are positive, and a negative sign if they are negative. This means that a measurement of the Hall constant will reveal the conductivity type of the material. The magnitude of the Hall constant is determined by the density of current carriers present and is given by,

$$R = \frac{p - b^2 n}{q(p + bn)^2} ,$$

where b is the mobility ratio (μ_n/μ_p) and p and n are the hole and electron densities, respectively.

Hall-effect device. Since the Hall effect is determined by the product of a current and a magnetic field, it lends itself to a number of devices. A magnetometer sets up a calibrated current, and the Hall voltage is directly proportional to the magnetic field in which it is inserted. A watt meter makes the current proportional to the line voltage, and the magnetic field proportional to line current. A modulator sets the current proportional to the dc voltage to be measured and applies a calibrated ac Hall voltage proportional to the dc voltage.

Mesa transistor. This transistor structure is characterized by the delineation of the collector-junction area by etching away all surrounding material. This leaves the base and emitter regions in the form of a raised plateau or mesa, which gives the structure its name.

MOST transistor. This designation stands for Metal-Oxide–Silicon transistor and describes a specific form of field-effect transistor, discussed in Section 7.2.

PIN-diode. This structure comprises an intrinsic region in the junction between the N- and P-regions, which, in effect, makes a very thick junction with a very low capacity and a very high breakdown voltage.

Punch-through voltage. The collector-base voltage at which the depletion region of the collector junction penetrates the base-region thickness and contacts the emitter region is called the *punch-through voltage*. If the base region is uniformly lightly doped and the collector region is heavily doped, the collector-junction depletion region will lie mainly in the base, and the punch-through voltage will be relatively low. This is typical of certain alloy transistors. If the base region is doped heavily enough to require a high punch-through voltage, the avalanche breakdown voltage of the collector junction will be reached first and punch through will not be observed. This is typical of most diffused base transistors

For a PNP alloy transistor the punch-through voltage may be calculated from Eq. (4.21) by letting x_N equal the base width, w, giving $PV = w^2 q N_D / 2\epsilon$, where we have assumed that $\phi \ll PV$ and that the N_A of the collector region is very much greater than the N_D of the base region.

Solar cell. A large-area semiconductor photovoltaic cell designed to extract electric power from solar radiation is called a *solar cell*. Silicon is usually used for such devices.

Surface-barrier transistor. A surface-barrier transistor is a transistor in which the collector and emitter junctions are formed by plated contacts on the opposite surfaces of a web of single-crystal semiconductor material which forms the base region of the transistor. In such a structure, base-width control is usually obtained by jet etching the surface of the wafer, using the same solution which will be used for plating but with a reversed electrical polarity, between the solution and the semiconductor wafer. When the desired thickness is reached, the polarity necessary for the plating process is established, and the etching stops as the plating begins.

Tetrode transistor. A normal transistor in which two contacts are made to opposite sides of the base region, instead of the usual single base-region contact, is called a *tetrode transistor*. By applying a bias between these two contacts, it is possible to confine the emitter injection to a small region near the grounded base contact and thus decrease the effective base resistance, giving a higher frequency performance.

Bibliography

1. J. L. Moll, *Physics of Semiconductors*, McGraw-Hill, New York, 1964, Chapter 11.
2. S. L. Miller and J. J. Ebers, "Alloyed Junction Avalanche Transistors," *BSTJ* **41**, 883–902 (Sept. 1955).
3. J. A. Lesk and V. P. Mathis, "The Double Base Diode," *IRE Intern. Conv. Record.* **6**, 2–8 (1953).
4. L. P. Hunter (ed.), *Handbook of Semiconductor Electronics*, 2nd ed. McGraw-Hill, New York, 1962, Section 20.3.

INDEX